Gabe acco ~~m~~ **n into a vast** ~~e~~ **lavishly laid** ~~rated~~ **with fragrant roses coloured deep crimson.**

'I have seated you next to the Ambassador of Maraban, one of the most influential men in the region,' said the Sultan. 'With my sister on the other side. Her English is excellent and she is eager to meet with you. Ah, here she comes now. Leila!'

But Gabe didn't need to hear his host say her name to know the woman's identity. He knew that from the moment she entered the banqueting hall. Even though Leila's body was swathed in flowing silk, and even though a matching veil of palest silver was covering half her face, there could be no mistaking her. No amount of camouflage could disguise the sexy sway of her body—or maybe it was because in some primeval and physical way he still felt connected to her.

He could still smell her on his skin.

THE DESERT MEN OF QURHAH

Their destiny is the desert!

The heat of the desert is nothing compared to the passion
that burns between the pages of this stunning new trilogy
by Sharon Kendrick!

Defiant in the Desert
December 2013

Oil baron Suleiman Abd al-Aziz has been sent to
retrieve the Sultan of Qurhah's reluctant fiancée—
a woman who's utterly forbidden, but is determined to
escape the confines of her engagement…by seducing him!

Shamed in the Sands
February 2014

The Princess of Qurhah has always wanted
something different from her life. So when sexy
advertising magnate Gabe Steele arrives to work for
her brother, Leila convinces Gabe to give her a job…
but that's not the only thing to cause a royal scandal!

Seduced by the Sultan
April 2014

The Sultan of Qurhah is facing a scandal of
epic proportions. His fiancée has run off,
leaving him with a space in his king-sized bed.
A space once occupied by his mistress Catrin Thomas.
And now he wants her back—at any price!

SHAMED IN THE SANDS

BY
SHARON KENDRICK

Published in Great Britain 2014
by Mills & Boon, an imprint of Harlequin (UK) Limited,
Eton House, 18-24 Paradise Road, Richmond, Surrey, TW9 1SR

© 2014 Sharon Kendrick

ISBN: 978 0 263 90823 7

Harlequin (UK) Limited's policy is to use papers that are natural,
renewable and recyclable products and made from wood grown in
sustainable forests. The logging and manufacturing processes conform
to the legal environmental regulations of the country of origin.

Printed and bound in Spain
by Blackprint CPI, Barcelona

Sharon Kendrick started storytelling at the age of eleven, and has never really stopped. She likes to write fast-paced, feel-good romances with heroes who are so sexy they'll make your toes curl!

Born in west London, she now lives in the beautiful city of Winchester—where she can see the cathedral from her window (but only if she stands on tiptoe!). She has two children, Celia and Patrick, and her passions include music, books, cooking and eating— and drifting off into wonderful daydreams while she works out new plots!

Recent titles by the same author:

DEFIANT IN THE DESERT
  (Desert Men of Qurhah)
THE GREEK'S MARRIAGE BARGAIN
A SCANDAL, A SECRET, A BABY
BACK IN THE HEADLINES
  (Scandal in the Spotlight)

For Olly Wicken, whose imagination and expertise helped bring Gabe to life. Thank you.

CHAPTER ONE

GABE STEEL WAS naked when he heard the sound of knocking.

He picked up a towel and scowled. He wanted peace. No, he *needed* peace. He'd come to this strange city for all kinds of reasons—but none of them included being disturbed when he had just stepped out of the shower.

He thought about the harsh light of spring he'd left behind in England. The way it could still make his heart clench with pain at this time of year. He thought how guilt never really left you, no matter how deeply you tried to bury it. If you scratched beneath the surface you could always bring up stuff you didn't want. Which was why he didn't scratch. Ever.

But sometimes you couldn't escape it, no matter how hard you tried. Hadn't one of the staff sent someone up earlier, asking if he would like any special arrangements made for his birthday? He'd wondered how the hell they had known it was his birthday—until he realised that they had seen his passport when he'd checked in yesterday.

He stood still and listened. The knocking had stopped and everything was quiet again. He started to slide the towel over one hair-roughened thigh when the sound resumed, more urgently this time.

At any other time and in any other place, he would have ignored the unwanted summons and carried on with what he was doing. But Gabe recognised that these were not normal circumstances. This job was a first. He'd never been the guest of a member of a royal family before. Correction. The *head* of a royal family. He'd never worked for a sultan before—a man who ruled over one of the world's wealthiest countries and who had already lavished on Gabe a breathtaking amount of hospitality. And maybe that was what was beginning to irritate him most of all—because he didn't like to be beholden to anyone, no matter how exalted their position.

Uttering a muttered curse beneath his breath, Gabe wrapped the towel around his hips and crossed a room so vast that back home the walk might almost have qualified as a workout. He'd stayed in some amazing places in his time, and his own place in London was pretty mouth-watering. But he had to acknowledge that this penthouse suite in Qurhah's finest hotel took luxury to a whole new level.

The knocking continued. A low drumming sound he found impossible to ignore—and its persistence made his impatience increase. He pulled open the door to find a woman standing there. Or rather, a woman who was doing her best not to look like a woman.

Tall and slim, her body was completely covered and her features were in shadow. She was carrying a briefcase and wearing a trench coat over a pair of jeans, with a fedora hat pulled down low over her face. Her appearance was so androgynous that she could almost have been mistaken for a man. But Gabe could smell a woman's scent in a pitch-black room, even when she wasn't wearing perfume. He could accurately assess the hip-width of a pair of panties from nothing more than a cursory glance. Where the opposite sex was concerned, he was an expert—even if his expertise went no further than the physical.

Because he didn't do *emotional*. He didn't need a woman to unpick his mind at the end of a stressful day, or cry on his shoulder in the mistaken belief that it might make his heart melt. And he certainly didn't want some unknown female turning up today, when his heart was dark and his schedule full.

'Where's the fire?' he demanded.

'Please.' Her voice was low and urgent and very faintly accented. 'Can I come in?'

His lips gave the faintest curve of contempt. 'I think you must have the wrong room, sweetheart,' he said and started to shut the door.

'Please,' she repeated—only this time he could hear panic underpinning her words. 'Men are trying to find me.'

It was a stark appeal and it stopped Gabe in his tracks. It wasn't the kind of thing he heard in the slick, controlled world he called his life. It took him back to a time and a place where threat was a constant. Where fear was never very far away.

He stared down at her face and he could see the wide gleam of alarm in eyes shadowed by the fedora.

'Please,' she said again.

He hesitated for no longer than a heartbeat before something kicked in. Some unwanted protective urge over which he seemed powerless. And he didn't do powerless.

'Come in,' he said abruptly. He caught the drift of her spicy perfume as she hurried past, and the fragrance seemed to cling to his skin as he closed the door and turned to face her. 'So what's the story?'

She was shaking her head and turning to look at the door as if she was petrified somebody was going to burst in behind her.

'Not now,' she said in that soft accent, which was making his senses start to prickle into life. 'There's no time. I'll tell you everything you need to know But only when it's safe. They mustn't find me here. They mustn't.'

She was looking at the far side of the vast room, where the open bedroom door revealed the unmade bed, on which he'd been taking a catnap before his shower. He saw her quickly turn her head away.

'Where can you hide me?' she questioned.

Gabe's eyes narrowed. He thought her attitude was arrogant—almost imperious—considering the way she'd burst in on him like this. He was the one doing *her* a favour—and a little gratitude wouldn't have gone amiss. But maybe now was not the time to give her a lecture on the etiquette of gate-crashing—not when she was looking so jittery.

He thought about where he used to hide whenever the bailiffs bashed on the door. The one room which always seemed safer than any other.

'Go through into the bathroom,' he said, flicking his fingers in the direction of the en-suite. 'Crawl underneath the tub and stay there until I tell you otherwise. And your explanation had better be good enough to warrant this unwanted intrusion into my time.'

But she didn't appear to be listening. She was already moving towards the bathroom with an unconscious sway of her slender bottom before she was lost to view.

And somehow she had managed to transfer her anxiety to Gabe and his body began to react accordingly. He could feel adrenalin coursing through his bloodstream and the sudden pounding of his heart. He wondered whether he should put on some clothes and then realised there was no time, because he could hear the heavy approach of footsteps in the corridor outside.

The rap on the door was loud and he opened it to find two men outside, their eyes as dark and pinched as raisins. Loose suits did little to conceal their burly strength, and Gabe could detect the telltale bulges of gun holsters packed against each of their bodies.

The taller of the two let his gaze flicker to Gabe's still-damp torso and then to the small towel which was knotted at his hip. 'We are sorry to disturb you, Mr Steel.'

'No problem,' said Gabe pleasantly, registering that they knew his name, just as everyone else in the hotel seemed to. And that their accents sounded like a pronounced version of the one used by the mystery woman currently cowering in his bathroom. 'What can I do for you?'

The man's accent was thick. 'We are looking for a woman.'

'Aren't we all?' questioned Gabe conspiratorially, with a silken stab at humour. But neither man took the bait and neither did they respond to the joke. Their faces remained unsmiling as they stared at him.

'Have you seen her?'

'Depends what she looks like,' said Gabe.

'Tall. Early twenties. Dark hair,' said the smaller of the two men. 'A very…striking woman.'

Gabe gestured towards the tiny towel at his hips and rubbed his hands over his upper arms, miming a chill which wasn't quite fictitious, since the icy kick of the air-conditioning was giving him goose-bumps. 'As you can see—I've been taking a shower. And I can assure you that nobody was keeping me company at the time—more's the pity.' He glanced over his shoulder towards the room before turning back to them, his forced smile hinting at a growing irritation. 'Of course, you're perfectly at liberty to look for yourselves, but I'd appreciate it if you could do it swiftly. I still have to get dressed and shaved—and I'm due to dine with the Sultan in a couple of hours.'

It worked. The mere mention of the Sultan's name produced the reaction he'd hoped for. Gabe thought it almost comical as he watched both men take a step back in perfect unison.

'Of course. Forgive us for interrupting you. We will take up no more of your time, Mr Steel. Thank you for your help.'

'My pleasure,' said Gabe, and closed the door softly behind them.

His footsteps across the carpet were equally soft, and when he opened the bathroom door, the woman was just slithering out from under the bathtub like some kind of sexy serpent. He felt the instant rush of heat to his groin as she scrambled to her feet and began brushing her hands over her body.

The fedora had fallen off and as she raised her face and he got a proper look at her for the first time he felt awareness icing his skin. Because suddenly he was looking at the most arresting woman he had ever seen. His mouth dried with lust. She looked like a fantasy come to life. Like a character from the *Arabian Nights* who had wandered into his hotel bathroom by mistake.

Her olive skin was luminous and her dark-fringed eyes were a bright shade of blue. A ponytail of black hair hung almost to her waist—hair so shiny that it looked as if she might have spent the morning polishing it. Despite the silky trench coat, he could see that her breasts were neat and her legs so long that she would have been at home on any international catwalk.

Her face remained impassive as he looked her over, as if she was no stranger to submission. Only the faintest flush of pink in her cheeks gave any indication that she might be finding his attention unsettling. But what did she expect? If you burst into a strange man's bedroom and demanded refuge, then surely the normal rules of conduct flew right out of the window.

'They've gone,' he said shortly.

'So I heard.' She hesitated. 'Thank you.'

He noticed the way her gaze kept flickering towards his bare torso and then away again. As if she knew she shouldn't stare at him but couldn't help herself. He gave a grim kind of smile. It wasn't the first time he had encountered such a problem.

'I think you owe me an explanation,' he said. 'Don't you?'

'Sure.' She bent to pick up her briefcase, and as she

straightened up she did that not-quite-looking thing at his chest again. 'Just not…not in here.'

Was the intimacy of the setting too much for her? he wondered. Was she aware that beneath the tiny towel his body was beginning to respond to her in a way which might make itself embarrassingly obvious if he wasn't careful? He could feel the hot pump of arousal at his groin and suddenly he felt curiously vulnerable.

'Go through there,' he said abruptly. 'While I get dressed.'

The stir of his erection had subsided by the time he'd pulled on some jeans and a T-shirt and walked through to the sitting room to see her standing with her back to him. She was staring out of the panoramic windows which overlooked the city of Simdahab, where golden minarets and towers gleamed in the rich light of the late afternoon sun. But Gabe barely noticed the magnificent view—his attention remained captivated by the mystery stranger.

She had removed her trench coat and had slung it over the back of one of the sofas—was she planning on staying?—and suddenly there were no more concealing folds to hide her from his eyes. His gaze travelled to where denim clung to the high curves of her bottom, to where her dark ponytail hung down her back like a dark stream of satin.

She must have sensed that he was in the room because she turned round—the ponytail swinging in slow motion—and from this angle he thought the view was even better. She looked at him with those clear blue eyes, and suddenly all he could see was temptation.

He wondered if she had been sent to him by the

Sultan—a delicious package for him to open and enjoy at his leisure. Another lavish gift, just like the others which had been arriving at his hotel suite all morning. It was said that, despite his relative youth, the Sultan was an old-fashioned man and this might be a very old-fashioned gesture on his part. Mightn't the powerful potentate have decided to sweeten up Gabe with a woman? A submissive and beautiful woman who would cater to his every whim…

'Who are you?' he questioned coolly. 'A hooker?'

Her face showed no reaction to his crude question, but it seemed to take for ever before she spoke.

'No, I'm not a hooker. My name is Leila,' she said, and now her blue eyes were watchful.

'Pretty name, but I'm still no wiser.'

'Mr Steel—'

Gabe shook his head in faint disbelief. 'How come everyone in this city knows my name?'

The woman smiled—her lips softening into cushioned and rosy curves. And even though he had never paid for sex in his life, in that moment he almost wished she *were* a hooker. What would he get her to do first? he wondered. Unzip him and take him in her delicious mouth, and suck him until he came? Or lower those narrow hips and bounce around on him until he cried out with pleasure?

'People know who you are because you are the guest of the Sultan,' she was saying. 'Your name is Gabe Steel and you are an advertising genius who has come to Qurhah to improve our global image.'

'That's a very flattering summary,' offered Gabe drily. 'But I'm afraid that unsolicited flattery doesn't really do it for me and it still doesn't explain why you're here. Why you burst into my hotel room unin-vited and hid in my bathroom…*Leila*.'

For a moment there was silence.

Leila's heart pounded against her ribcage as she heard the blatant challenge in his voice, which coun-tered the silky way he emphasised her name. Her mind was in a muddle and her senses felt raw and exposed. She had taken a risk and she needed to fol-low it through, but it was proving more difficult than she'd anticipated. Everything so far was going accord-ing to plan but suddenly she was filled with a power-ful rush of nerves. She wondered how she could have been so stupid. How she could have failed to take into account Gabe Steel himself and the effect he would have on her.

She looked into his grey eyes. Strange, quicksilver eyes, which seemed to pierce her skin and see straight through to the bones beneath. She tried to find the right words to put her case to him, but everything she'd been planning to say flew clean out of her mind.

She wasn't used to being alone with strange men and she certainly wasn't used to being in a hotel room with a foreigner. Especially one who looked like this.

He was gorgeous.

Unbelievably gorgeous.

She'd read up about him on the internet, of course. She'd made it her business to do so once she'd discov-ered that her brother was going to employ him. She'd found out all the external things about Gabe Steel. She knew he owned Zeitgeist—one of the world's biggest advertising agencies. That he'd been a millionaire by the age of twenty-four and had made it into multi-millions by the time he reached thirty. At thirty-five, he remained unmarried—though not for the lack of women trying to get a wedding ring on their finger. Or at least, not according to reports from the rather more downmarket sources.

She'd seen images of him, too. Crystal-clear images, which she'd gazed at with something approaching wonder as they'd flashed up onto her computer screen. Because Gabe Steel seemed to have it all—certainly in the physical sense. His golden-dark hair gave him the appearance of an ancient god, and his muscular body would have rivalled that of any Olympian athlete.

She'd seen photos of him collecting awards, dressed in an immaculate tuxedo. There had been a snatched shot of him—paparazzi, she assumed—wearing faded jeans and an open shirt as he straddled a huge motorbike, minus a helmet. On one level she had known that he was the type of man who would take your breath away when you met him for real. And she hadn't been wrong.

She just hadn't expected him to be so…charismatic.

Leila was used to powerful men. She had grown up surrounded by them. All her life, she'd been bossed around and told to show respect towards them. Told that men knew best. She gave a wry smile because she had witnessed how cruel and cold they could be. She'd seen them treat women as if they didn't matter. As if their opinions were simply to be tolerated rather than taken seriously. Which was one of the reasons why, deep down, she didn't actually *like* the opposite sex.

Oh, she deferred to them, as she had been taught, because that was the hand which fate had dealt her.

To be born a princess into a fiercely male-dominated society didn't leave you with much choice other than to defer. There hadn't been a single major decision in her life which had been hers and hers alone. Her schooling had been decided without any consultation; her friends had been carefully picked. She had learnt to smile and accept—because she had also learnt that resistance was futile. People knew what was 'best' for her—and she had no alternative but to accept their judgement.

Materially, of course, she had been spoiled. When you were the only sister of one of the richest men in the world, that was inevitable. Diamonds and pearls, rubies and emeralds lay heaped in jewellery boxes in her bedroom at the palace. Her late mother's tiaras lay locked behind glass for Leila to wear whenever the mood took her.

But Leila knew that all the riches in the world couldn't make you feel good about yourself. Expensive jewels didn't compensate for the limitations of your lifestyle, nor protect you from a future you viewed with apprehension.

Within the confines of her palace home she usually dressed in traditional robes and veils, but today she was looking defiantly Western. She had never worn *quite* such figure-hugging jeans before and it was only by covering them up with her raincoat that she would have dared. She was aware of the way the thick seam of material rubbed between her legs. The way that the silky shirt felt oddly decadent as it brushed against her breasts. She felt *liberated* in these clothes, and while it was a good feeling, it was a little scary too—

especially as Gabe Steel was looking at her in a way which was curiously...*distracting*.

But her clothes were as irrelevant as his reaction to them. She had worn them in order to look modern and for no other reason. The most important thing to remember was that this man held the key to a different kind of future. And she was going to make him turn that key—whether he wanted to or not.

Fighting another wave of anxiety, she opened the briefcase she'd been holding and pulled out a clutch of carefully chosen contents.

'I'd like you to have a look at these,' she said.

He raised his eyebrows. 'What are they?'

She walked over towards a beautiful table and spread out the pictures on the gleaming inlaid surface. 'Have a look for yourself.'

He walked over to stand beside her, his dark shadow falling over her. She could detect the tang of lime and soap combined with the much more potent scent of masculinity. She remembered him wearing nothing but that tiny white towel and suddenly her mouth grew as dry as dust.

'Photographs,' he observed.

Leila licked her lips. 'That's right.'

She watched him study them and prayed he would like them because she had been taking photos for as long as she could remember. It had been her passion and escape—the one thing at which she'd shown real flair. But perhaps her position as princess meant that she was ideally placed to take photos, for her essentially lonely role meant that she was always on the outside looking in.

Ever since she'd been given her very first camera,

Leila had captured the images which surrounded her. The palace gardens and the beautiful horses which her brother kept in his stables had given way to candid shots of the servants and portraits of their children.

But most of the photos she'd brought to show Gabe Steel were of the desert. Stark images of a landscape she doubted he would have seen anywhere else and, since few people had been given access to the sacred and secret sites of Qurhah, they were also unique. And she suspected that a man like Gabe Steel would have seen enough in his privileged life to value something which was unique.

He was studying one in particular and she watched as his eyes narrowed in appreciation.

'Who took these?' he questioned, raising his head at last and capturing her in that cool grey gaze. 'You?'

She nodded. 'Yes.'

There was a pause. 'You're good,' he said slowly. 'Very good.'

His praise felt like a caress. Like the most wonderful compliment she had ever received. Leila glowed with a fierce kind of pride. 'Thank you.'

'Where is this place?'

'It's in the desert, close to the Sultan's summer palace. An area of outstanding natural beauty known as the Mekathasinian Sands,' she said, aware that his unsettling gaze was now drifting over her rather than the photo he was holding. He was close enough for her to be able to touch him, and she found herself wanting to do just that. She wanted to tangle her fingers in the thick, molten gold of his hair and then run them down over that hard, lean body. *And how crazy was that?*

With an effort, she tried to focus her attention on the photo and not on the symmetry of his chiselled features.

'I took this after one of the rare downpours of rain and subsequent flooding, which occur maybe once in twenty years, if you're lucky.' She smiled. 'They call it the desert miracle. Flower seeds lie dormant in the sands for decades and when the floods recede, they suddenly germinate—and flower. So that millions of blooms provide a carpet of colour which is truly magical—though it only lasts a couple of weeks.'

'It's an extraordinary picture. I've never seen anything like it.'

She could hear the sense of wonder in his voice and she felt another swell of pride. But suddenly, her work didn't seem as important as his unsettling proximity. She should have been daunted by that and she couldn't work out why she wasn't. She was alone in a hotel room with the playboy Gabe Steel and all she was aware of was a growing sense of excitement.

With an effort, she forced her attention back to the photo. 'If…if you look closely, you can see the palace in the distance.'

'Where?'

'Right over there.' The urge to touch him was overwhelming. It was the strongest impulse she'd ever felt, and suddenly Leila found herself unable to resist it. Leaning forward so that her arm brushed almost imperceptibly against his, she pointed out the glimmering golden palace. She felt his body stiffen as she made that barely there contact. She thought she could hear his breath catch in his throat. Was his heart hammering as hers was hammering? Was he too filled with an inexplicable sense of breathless wonder?

But he had stepped away from her, and his cool eyes were still curious. 'Why did you bring these photos here today, Leila? And more importantly, why were those men pursuing you?'

She hesitated. The truth was on her lips but she didn't dare say it. Because once he knew—he would change. People always did. He would stop treating her like an ordinary woman and start eyeing her warily—as if she were a strange creature he had never encountered before. And she was enjoying herself far too much to want him to do that.

So why not tell him part of the truth? The only part which was really important.

'I want to work for you,' she said boldly. 'I want to help you with your campaign.'

He raised his eyebrows in arrogant query. 'I don't recall advertising for any new staff,' he said drily.

'I realise that—but can't you see that it would make perfect sense?' Leaning forward, Leila injected real passion into her voice. 'I know Qurhah in a way you never can, because I grew up here and the desert is in my blood. I can point you in the direction of the best locations to show the world that our country is a particular kind of paradise. I've done plenty of research on what a campaign like yours would involve and I know there's room on this project for someone like me.'

She stared at him hopefully.

There was silence for a moment and then he gave a short laugh. 'You think I'd hire some unknown for a major and very lucrative campaign, just on the strength of a pretty face?'

Leila felt the sharp stab of injustice. 'But surely my "pretty face" has nothing to do with the quality of my work?'

'You don't think so?' He shot her a sardonic look. 'Well, I hate to disillusion you, sweetheart—but without the raven hair and killer figure I'd have kicked you out of here just as soon as those goons had gone.'

Leila tried to keep the sulk from her voice, because this was not what was supposed to happen. *She couldn't let it happen.* She narrowed her eyes in a way which would have made her servants grow wary if they had seen her. 'So you won't even consider me?'

'I won't consider anything until you satisfy my curiosity, and I am growing bored by your evasion. I'm still waiting for you to tell me who those men were.'

'My bodyguards,' she said reluctantly.

'Your *bodyguards*?'

She had surprised him now. She could see it in his face. She wondered how he would react if she told him the whole truth. That she had been born to be guarded. That people were always watching her. Stifling her. Making it impossible for her to breathe.

'I'm rich,' she said, by way of an explanation. 'In fact, I'm very rich.'

His grey eyes were speculative. 'So you don't *need* the work?'

'What kind of a question is that?' she questioned heatedly. 'I *want* to work! There's a difference, you know. I thought a man like you would appreciate that.'

Gabe acknowledged the reprimand in her voice. Yes, he knew there was a difference—it was just one which had never applied to him because he had always needed to work. There had been no wealth or legacy for him. No cushion waiting to bolster him if ever he fell. He had known only hunger and poverty. He had known what it was like to live beneath the radar and have your life subsumed by fear. He had needed to work for reasons of survival and for the peace of mind which always seemed determined to elude him. Even now.

'Oh, I appreciate it all right,' he agreed slowly.

'So you'll think about it? About hiring me?'

He looked down into her beautiful eyes and felt his heart twist with something like regret. He saw hope written in their azure depths—just as he saw all kinds of passionate possibilities written in her sensual lips. What would happen if he kissed this beautiful little rich girl who had marched into his hotel suite with such a sense of entitlement? Would she taste as good as she looked? He could feel the savage ache at his groin as he realised how badly he *wanted* to kiss her and for a moment temptation washed over him again.

But his innate cool professionalism reasserted itself and, regretfully, he shook his head. 'I'm sorry. I don't work that way. I run my organisation on rather more formal lines. If you really want to work for me, then I suggest you apply to my London office in the usual way. But I suspect that you've blown your chances anyway.' His eyes sent out a mocking challenge. 'You see, a long time ago I made a decision never to mix business with pleasure.'

She was staring at him, her nose wrinkling as if she was perplexed by his words. 'I don't understand.'

'Don't you?' He gave an unconvincing replica of a smile. 'Are you trying to tell me you haven't noticed the chemistry between us?'

'I—'

'Look, just take your photos and go,' he interrupted roughly. 'Before I do something I might live to regret.'

Leila heard his impatient words and some deep-rooted instinct urged her to heed them. To make her escape back to the palace while she still could and forget all about this crazy rebellion. Forget the fairy-tale ending of a legitimate job with the hotshot English tycoon. Forget the film-script scenario and get real. She needed to accept her life the way it was and accept that she couldn't just break out and change her entire existence.

But her thoughts were being confused by the powerful signals her body was sending out. She could feel the honeyed rush of heat between her thighs, where the thick seam of her jeans was rubbing against the most secret place of her body. She wanted to wrap her arms around her chest to try to quell the terrible aching in her breasts, yet she knew that would only draw attention to them.

Leila had read plenty of books and seen most of the current crop of films which had got past the palace censors. She might have been sheltered, but she wasn't stupid. This was sexual attraction she was experiencing for the first time and she knew it was *wrong*. Yet even as she silently urged herself to get out before she made even more of a fool of herself, those rebellious thoughts came back to plague her.

She thought about how her brother behaved. How

her own father had behaved. She'd heard the rumours about their sexual conquests often enough. She knew that men often acted on the kind of attraction she was experiencing right now, if the circumstances were right. People sometimes got intimate after nothing more than a short acquaintanceship, and nobody thought the worst of them for doing so. Because physical love wasn't a *crime*, was it?

Was it?

'What might you regret?' she asked, but she knew the answer to her question as soon as the words had left her lips. Because you wouldn't need to be experienced to realise why Gabe Steel's face had darkened like that. Or why he was staring at her with a hot, hard look which was making her feel weak.

'Does your mother know you're out?' he questioned roughly.

She shook her head. 'I don't have a mother. Or a father.' She kept her voice light, the way she'd learned to do. 'I'm just an orphan girl.'

His eyes narrowed. Darkened. He winced, as if she'd said something which had caused *him* pain.

'I'm sorry,' he said softly and reached out to brush the tip of his thumb over her lips. 'So sorry.'

The weirdest thing was that Leila wasn't sure if he was talking to her, or talking to himself. But suddenly she didn't care because it was happening—just like in all the films she'd seen. He was reaching out and pulling her into his arms and she could feel the heat of his body as he moulded it against her. He framed her face with the palms of his hands and now his mouth was coming down towards hers. He seemed to be moving in slow motion, and Leila felt weak with excitement as her lips parted eagerly to meet his.

Because for the first time in her life, a man was going to kiss her.

CHAPTER TWO

GABE FELT THE thunder of his heart as their mouths made that first contact. The warmth of her flesh collided with his and her skin smelt of flowers and spice. Desire flooded through him like fire but his hot lust was tempered by the cool voice of reason.

This was insane.

Insane.

He thought about the way she'd burst into his suite and the surly-faced bodyguards who might return at any time. It was obvious she shouldn't be here—and he was in danger of jeopardising a deal. A very important deal. He was here on business and due to dine at the Sultan's palace in a little under two hours. There wasn't time to make love to her properly—no matter how gloriously accessible she appeared to be.

So for God's sake, get rid of her!

But the moment he chose to push her away was the moment she chose to wind her arms around his neck and to move her body against his and to whisper something breathless in a language he didn't understand. The breath died in his throat as heat pooled in his groin and he was helpless to do anything other than deepen the kiss. He could feel the mound of her pubic bone pressing against his growing arousal—making his erection exquisitely hard and almost painful. Her tiny breasts were flattening themselves against his chest and, for the first time all day, his body felt warm instead of filled with the cold and aching memories of the past.

Tearing his mouth away, he stared down into her face, trying to ignore the provocative trembling of her lips. 'That was a mistake,' he said unsteadily. 'And I think you'd better get out of here before I make another one.'

'But what if I want you to?' she questioned breathlessly. 'What then?'

He felt another fierce stab of arousal as she looked at him. Her eyes were wide. Wide and bright. Shining as brightly as the aquamarine studs at her ears. He could feel his senses warring with his moral compass. *Send her away before it's too late.* But he couldn't stop looking at her or wanting her. Her lips were soft and gleaming. They looked as if they had been specially constructed to accommodate his erection and to suck him dry.

He thought about the dull pain nailed deep into his heart and how her soft body could alleviate it— even for an hour. Because sex could obliterate pain, couldn't it? He could feel his resolve slipping away from him, like sand through his fingers, and wondered if there was a man on earth who could have resisted what was being offered to him now.

'I'm giving you one last chance to get out of here,' he said unevenly. 'And I'd advise you to take it and go.'

'But I don't want to go anywhere,' she whispered. 'I want to stay right here.'

'Then I make no apologies for doing this,' he said. 'Which I have been wanting to do ever since you first walked in.'

He started to unbutton her shirt, exposing the silken flesh beneath, and another fierce jerk of desire shot through him. She was perfect, he thought. Just perfect. Her olive skin was dark against a brassiere so white that it looked as if she'd put it on new that morning. He drifted his fingertips over the gentle swell of her breast. 'So what have you got to say about that, *Leila*?'

Beneath the tantalising touch of his fingers, Leila grew weaker still. Where were the nerves she should be feeling? And why did it feel so natural? As if she had been waiting all her life for Gabe Steel to touch her like this?

'I think it's gorgeous,' she said, praying he wouldn't stop.

'I want to kiss your breasts,' he vowed unsteadily. 'Each beautiful breast which is peaking towards me, just waiting to be kissed.'

A pulse was hammering at his temple and Leila jerked with pleasure as he lowered his mouth to one tightening nipple. His dark blond head contrasted against the snowy silk of her bra, and she could feel the fabric growing moist as he sucked her. She squirmed in time to each provocative lick of his tongue, as helpless then as she could ever remember feeling. And suddenly she understood what all the fuss was about. Why sex was so powerful. Why people did such crazy things to get it.

'G-Gabe,' she gasped, the word stumbling over itself in disbelieving pleasure.

He lifted his head to stare at her, and suddenly his grey eyes were not so cold. They seemed bright with pewter fire.

'I think we're going to have to skip the next few stages,' he said. 'In fact, if I don't get you horizontal in the next couple of minutes, I think I'm going to go out of my mind.'

He caught hold of her fingers and led her straight into the bedroom she'd seen earlier—the bed still in rumpled disarray.

Now slightly disorientated, Leila looked around in faint bewilderment because she had never seen a room in such a state before. In her ordered and en-closed world, a servant would have attended to it while she'd been in the shower—making the bed all neat and pristine again and tidying away her discarded clothes.

She had never been lowered down onto untidy sheets which were still rich with the scent of the man who had slept in them. Nor towered over by someone whose mouth was tight as he continued to undress her. She stared up at him but he wasn't staring back. He was too busy removing her trainers and then unzip-ping her jeans as if he'd removed countless pairs of women's jeans in his life.

He probably had.

Of *course* he had.

Leila remembered what she'd read about him on the internet. Fragments of information about all the beautiful models and actresses he'd dated came drift-ing back. Women infinitely more experienced than she was.

She felt the cold shiver of insecurity reminding her to face facts and not be swept away by fantasy. She

knew what men were like. How they were guided by
the heat in their loins or the weight of their own ambition. She knew that they viewed women simply as
possessions or as adornments—or as vessels to carry
children.

She must not forget that.

This might feel as if she were living out a scene
from a film, but it wasn't a film. This was real life and
Gabe Steel wasn't suddenly going to turn into some
fantasy hero and fall madly in love with her.

She didn't believe in that kind of love.

Her head fell back against the pillow as she felt the
slide of his fingertips brushing over her thigh and suddenly it was difficult to think about anything, other
than how good it felt.

He tugged the jeans down over her knees and she
could hear the soft rustle as they fell to the floor.

'Nice knickers,' he murmured before deftly removing her bra and shirt.

Leila blushed at his words, telling herself this was
normal. This was *natural*. 'Thanks,' she said, as if
men complimented her on her choice of underwear
every day of the week.

He tugged off his T-shirt and stood up to unbutton his jeans, and Leila was mesmerised as he peeled
them off. Her heart began to pound with excitement
as his body was revealed to her, for she had only ever
seen a horse from the royal stables in such a state of
arousal before.

Yet he seemed proud and unashamed of his na-
kedness as he walked across the room and retrieved
something from his suitcase. Leila saw the glint of

foil and the reality of what she was about to do suddenly hit her.

Because that was a condom; she was certain of it. She might never have encountered one before, but what else could it be?

She felt the icy clamp of sweat on her forehead as reality suddenly broke into her erotic thoughts. Did all women feel this sudden sense of panic the first time? The fear that she might disappoint him?

He was putting the item on the table beside the bed, and while she knew that she should be grateful to him for being pragmatic, it destroyed the mood a little. Why was real life so messy? she wondered bitterly. In films, you never saw any of *this*. Couples seemed to find themselves in bed together almost by magic and then the scene cut to them giggling as they ran down a street, usually in Paris. Not that she and Gabe Steel would be running anywhere here in Simdahab—at least not without the Sultan's guards giving chase. And if he didn't come back here and kiss her soon, she was going to get cold feet.

But almost as if he'd read her mind, he came back and lay down beside her. His body was warm, but his face was sombre as he traced a thoughtful line around her lips.

'Suddenly so serious,' he said, his grey eyes narrowing. 'As if you've started having regrets. Have you, Leila? Because we can stop this right now if that's what you want.'

Leila closed her eyes as she felt the brush of his finger over her lips. And wouldn't that be best? To put her clothes back on and get out of here as quickly as possible. She would feel embarrassed, and he might be angry with her for having led him on, but no real harm would have been done. She could slip away and act as if nothing had happened—because nothing had.

But then she thought about what awaited her back at the palace. She thought about all the inevitable restrictions and rules which had governed her life so far. All the things she wasn't allowed to do and never would be able to do *just because she was a woman and a princess*. She thought about the royal prince her brother would probably arrange for her to one day marry. The watchful eyes of both nations as they waited for her to produce an heir, before her husband thankfully sought refuge in the pleasures of his harem, just as her own father had done.

And suddenly she thought why *shouldn't* she experience this—as millions of other women had done? The way that men did *almost every day of their lives. Why shouldn't she have this one brief interlude of pleasure before she took up the duties which lay ahead of her?*

She wrapped her arms around his neck. 'Kiss me,' she whispered. 'Kiss me. Please.'

He smiled as his mouth came down to cover hers, and suddenly it *did* feel like a fairy tale. As if her senses had been fine-tuned. As if she were capable of anything. *Anything.*

'Oh,' she said, her eyes fluttering to a close as he drifted his mouth to her neck to kiss it over and over. 'Oh.'

Now his lips had found her breast and she could feel a thousand tiny sparks of pleasure as his tongue flicked against her puckered skin. She splayed her hands over his chest, where his heart pounded so strongly. She felt the coarse whorls of hair which grew there and she tugged at them—as playfully as a puppy with a new toy. His groan of delight filled her with confidence and she let her fingers drift downwards to explore the muscular flat of his belly and another helpless groan made her feel invincible. As if she could do anything or be anyone.

Anyone but herself.

He kissed her until she thought she would go out of her mind with longing. Until her heart was full of him. And suddenly, she wanted more. She could feel the restless movements of her body, orchestrated by a desire which seemed outside her understanding. Her fingers were kneading at his broad shoulders and she could hear him give a low laugh—as if her hunger pleased him. She could feel him tense as he began to nudge her legs apart with one insistent knee.

Her breath caught in her throat as he slid his hand between her thighs, and she cried out as he touched her where no man had ever touched her before.

'God, you're wet,' he groaned.

'Am I?' she questioned almost shyly.

'Mmm,' he affirmed as his finger began to strum against her, moving against her heated flesh in a light and silken rhythm.

Against his shoulder, Leila closed her eyes and felt as if she might melt beneath his touch. It felt gorgeous. He felt gorgeous. Gorgeous Gabe Steel who had stopped touching her and was now tearing at the little packet of foil he'd left beside the bed.

His face was formidable as he moved over her again and suddenly it was happening, almost without warning. He was lifting up her hips and making one deep, long thrust inside her, and she was crying out—only this time her cry sounded different, because the pain was very real. She felt him grow still and her heart plummeted as she saw the new expression on his face. The intense pleasure had changed into an expression of disbelief as he stared down at her.

'No,' he said, shaking his head. 'No.'

'What?' she gasped, because he was deep inside her and now that her body had adjusted to accommodate him, it felt amazing.

'You're a virgin?'

She sensed that he was about to pull out of her, but she had come this far and she couldn't bear him to stop. Some deep instinct was governing her now, and she prevented his withdrawal by the simply expedient of tightening her body around him. She saw his eyes grow at first angry and then smoky as tentatively she moved her hips upwards so that he was deeper still.

'So what if I am?' she whispered. 'Somebody's got to be the first and that somebody happens to be you. Please, Gabe. I want to experience pleasure the way that other women do. I want you to show me how. I know you can show me how.'

Gabe shook his head as he felt her slick heat yielding to his helpless thrust. The potent combination of her innocence and tightness and the erotic words she was whispering was making him harder than he could ever remember feeling before. But she was a virgin, he reminded himself. *Unbelievably, she was a virgin.* She had come to his room—this complete stranger—and given herself to him without any kind of ceremony. What kind of woman did that? He felt perplexed and resentful at having been lured into a situation which wasn't what it seemed.

So call a halt to it right now.

He swallowed. 'This is—'

'Heaven,' she said, her voice an irresistible murmur. 'You know it is. Don't stop, Gabe. Please don't stop.'

Her heartfelt plea was his final undoing. His anger evaporated and Gabe gave a groan of submission. Why fight it when she didn't want him to stop and... oh, God, neither did he? Pushing himself up on his elbows, he stared down at her beautiful face as he began to move inside her.

Her eyes were closed and he was glad about that. He didn't want to have to *look* at her; he just wanted to feel. He pushed deeper into her moist heat and groaned again, because she felt so good. She felt unbelievable. Was this why men spoke wonderingly about virgins, because they were so tight? Or because it gave a man a sense of power to know that he was the first?

But in the midst of all his macho triumph, he fought another wave of helplessness which was unfamiliar to him. Gone was the slick and seasoned Gabe who could last all night. He felt like a teenager who wanted instantly to explode inside her. But he mustn't. This had to be nothing less than amazing, because it was her first time. He *had* to take it slowly.

Yet it wasn't easy. He found himself stunned by the intense pleasure which was radiating through every pore of his body and not just because she was so tight. He realised how liberating it was not to have any emotional expectations hovering over him like a dark cloud. This really *was* sex without strings. Sex without the fear that she would fall in love with him and want more than he was ever prepared to give.

His thumb on her clitoris, he tilted her back against the pillows, listening to the rising volume of her cries. He watched as she began to move inexorably towards orgasm. Suddenly, she opened her eyes, and he met a clear flash of startled blue. As if she couldn't quite believe what was happening to her.

'Gabe?' she whispered, her accented voice unsteady.

'Relax.' He gave another deep thrust. 'Just. Let. Go.'

He saw her lips frame something which was destined never to be said as her eyelashes flew down to shutter out the blue. And then her body started to quiver helplessly around him and her back began to arch. He heard the words she said as she convulsed around him, although she spoke them in a language he didn't understand. He kissed away the muffled little cries which followed and tried to ignore her fingernails, which were now digging painfully into his back. He waited until her body was almost still before he let go himself, spilling out his seed in great wrenching bursts he never wanted to end.

For a moment he felt so dazed that it was almost as if he'd been drugged. Today, of all days—his body was warm and pulsing with life, instead of feeling empty and cold or deliberately anaesthetised. From between slitted eyes, he surveyed her. Her glossy black hair was tumbling down over her breasts and her perfect olive skin was flushed.

He lifted his hand to her cheek and felt her shiver beneath that light touch. 'Who are you?' he questioned, but she leaned over him and kissed his lips into silence.

'Shh,' she said, and her voice was very gentle. 'You look weary. Go to sleep, Gabe. Just go to sleep.'

CHAPTER THREE

'HAVE YOU BEEN listening to a word I've been saying, Leila?'

Leila gave a start as her brother's impatient question cut through the confusion of her thoughts. In the air-conditioned cool of the palace, she wondered if the hectic colour had faded from her cheeks and for once she gave thanks to the veil which concealed them from the Sultan. But there were other signs, too. She knew that. The mirror had told her so when she'd looked in it a short while ago.

Had the telltale glitter disappeared from her eyes? She prayed it had. Because if her clever and dictatorial brother Murat ever guessed how she had spent that particular afternoon...

If he had any idea that she had given her virginity to a man who had been a stranger to her.

She shivered.

He would kill her.

'Of course I was listening,' she defended.

His black eyes narrowed. 'So I was saying...what?'

Leila swallowed as she searched around in the fog of her memory for something to remind her. 'Something about the banquet you're holding tonight.'

'Very good, Leila.' He nodded. 'It seems you were paying attention, after all. A banquet in honour of my English guest, Gabe Steel.'

The sudden tremble of her knees at the mention of his name made Leila glad that she was sitting down. 'Gabe Steel?' she echoed and his name tasted nearly as sweet on her lips as his kisses had done.

Murat gave an impatient click of his tongue. 'He is coming here tonight. You *knew* that, Leila.'

Leila forced a smile, acknowledging the power of the human mind to deny something which made you feel uncomfortable. It was the same as going for a ride in the desert—you knew that in the sand lurked snakes and scorpions, but if you thought about them for too long you'd never get on a horse again.

Of course she had known that Gabe was coming here tonight but—as with all the Sultan's formal banquets—she hadn't been invited. If she had, then there would have been no need to have gone to the advertising executive's room in secret to make her doomed job application. And then to have acted like some kind of…

Briefly, she closed her eyes. She mustn't think about him. She mustn't.

Yet try as she might, it was impossible to stem the flashbacks which plagued her, as if someone were playing a forbidden and erotic movie inside her head on an endless loop. She couldn't seem to stop remembering the way he'd made love to her and the way he had made her feel.

She knew that what she had done today had been wrong. It had flown in the face of everything she had been brought up to believe in. In Qurhah, women who were 'good' saved themselves until marriage. Especially royal princesses. There was simply no other option and up until today she had never questioned it. Yet she had seized the opportunity to let the powerful tycoon take her to his bed without a second thought. She had wanted him with a hunger which had taken her by surprise, and he had wanted her just as much, it seemed. For the first time in her life, she had behaved in a way which was truly liberated.

She remembered the gleam of his dark golden hair against the white of the pillow after he'd made that strange low cry and shuddered deep inside her. The way he had fallen asleep almost immediately—a sleep so deep that for a moment she'd had to check he was still breathing. He hadn't even stirred when she'd slipped from the bed—her body still warm and aching and her skin suffused with a soft, warm glow.

Silently, she had crept around the hotel suite—gathering up her discarded clothes, which she'd put on in the bathroom with trembling fingers, terrified that he would hear. And she hadn't wanted him to hear. She had known that her only option was to slip away before he awoke because she couldn't face saying goodbye, Not when she was feeling in such a volatile emotional state and she wanted nothing more than to snuggle into his warm embrace and kiss those sensual lips of his again.

Because that was simply not on the cards. There was no future for them. She knew that. Not now and not ever—and she sensed that in her vulnerable post-orgasm state she might have been tempted to overlook that simple fact.

She sucked in a deep breath, telling herself that

what was done was done and she wasn't going to feel ashamed about something she had enjoyed so much. Not when for the first time in her life she had behaved like a free-thinking woman instead of a puppet whose strings were constantly being pulled by her powerful brother, the Sultan.

But she could also see now that her thinking had been skewed. She had been foolishly naive to approach the Englishman in the first place. Had she really imagined that Gabe Steel—no matter how powerful he was in his own country—could persuade her brother to let her work with him? Did she really think she could go from pampered princess to Westerner's aide in one easy transition?

She could feel Murat's eyes on her and knew he was waiting for some kind of response. He might be her brother, but he was first and foremost the Sultan—and, as such, the world always revolved around Murat.

'There is no need for me to express my hope that your banquet will be successful, Murat,' she said formally. 'For that is a given.'

There was a pause as he inclined his head, silently acknowledging her praise.

'I thought you might wish to attend,' he said.

For the second time, Leila was glad she was sitting down. She narrowed her eyes, thinking she must have misheard him. 'The banquet?'

The Sultan shrugged his shoulders. 'Why not?'

'Why not?' She laughed. 'Is that a serious question? Because it's "business" and these affairs are traditionally men only.'

Murat gave a little shake of his shoulders and Leila thought he seemed a little *unsettled* tonight. Which wasn't like her brother at all. Maybe the cancellation of his arranged marriage had affected him more than it had appeared to do at the time.

'Then perhaps it is time that Qurhah embraced the untraditional for a change,' he said.

Leila stared at him in growing disbelief. 'What on earth has brought all this on?'

Murat glowered. 'Does there have to be a reason for everything? You have harangued me for many years for a more inclusive role in state affairs, Leila—'

'And you always ignore everything I say!'

'And now that I am actually proposing a break in tradition,' he continued implacably, 'I am being subjected to some sort of inquisition!'

Leila didn't answer because her heart had grown disconcertingly light. She tried to ignore the flutter in her stomach and the rush of blood to her cheeks, but she couldn't ignore the glorious words which were circling round and round in her mind. She had been invited to the banquet! She was going to see Gabe again!

Her heart pounded. How would it feel to face him again at a formal palace dinner? And how would he react to seeing her in the last place he would ever expect to see her?

She felt the sudden rush of nerves and sternly she told herself not to get carried away. It didn't matter how he reacted because that was irrelevant. Yes, he had been the kind of lover that every woman dreamt of, but Gabe was just a man. And she knew about men. She knew about the pain and heartbreak they caused women. The muffled sound of her mother's tears had characterised her childhood and she reminded herself not to weave any foolish dreams about Gabe Steel.

'You are very quiet, Leila,' observed the Sultan softly. 'I had imagined you would be delighted to meet my Western guest.'

Leila gave a cautious smile. 'Forgive me for my somewhat muted response,' she said. 'For I was a little taken off-guard by your unexpected generosity. Naturally, I shall be delighted to meet Mr Steel.'

'Good. And you will wear the veil, of course. I like the thought of our Western visitor observing the quiet decorum of the traditional Qurhahian woman.' Murat frowned. 'Though I hope you're not coming down with a fever, Leila—for your complexion has suddenly grown very flushed.'

Gabe barely registered the gleaming golden gates which had opened to allow his bulletproof car through. Just as he had failed to register the colourful and bustling streets of Simdahab on his way to the palace. The journey through the city had been slower than he had anticipated—mainly, he suspected, because the car was so heavily armoured. He guessed that was one of the drawbacks to being a fabulously powerful sultan—that the risk of assassination was never far from the surface.

Yet instead of focusing on the task ahead or reflecting on the cultural differences between the two countries, as he usually would have done, he had spent the entire journey thinking about the woman it was probably safer to forget.

Leila.

When he'd woken from a deep sleep in that sex-rumpled bed, he had known a moment of complete and utter peace—before disjointed memories had come flooding back. For a moment he'd thought that he must have dreamt the whole bizarre incident. And then he had seen the faint red spots of blood on the sheet—not knowing if it had sprung from her broken hymen or when her fingernails had clawed deep into the flesh of his shoulders at the moment of orgasm.

He stared out of the car window at the vast splendour of the palace gardens, but this faint feeling of disorientation would not leave him.

He had always been successful with women—and not just because of his hard body and what the press had once described as his 'fallen angel' looks. He had quickly learnt how best to handle the opposite sex, because he could see that it was in his best interests to do so. To take what he wanted without giving any false hope. He'd learnt that guaranteeing pleasure was the most effective way of having someone overlook your shortcomings—the main one being his aversion to emotion. He knew that he couldn't give love—but he could certainly give great orgasms.

He'd seen it all and done it all—or so he'd thought—though he'd avoided any situation involving cameras or threesomes. But he had never had a beautiful, virginal stranger turning up at his hotel room and allowing him to seduce her within minutes of meeting.

He felt his heart miss a beat as he recalled the way she had made him feel. That initial hard thrust against her tight hymen. Who *was* she? And why had she chosen to give her innocence to a man she didn't know?

He thought about the photographs she'd shown him. Nobody could deny that she was talented. Did she think that her sexual generosity would guarantee her the offer of a job? Yet if that was the case, then surely she would have left him her card—or some number scribbled down on a sheet of hotel notepaper, so that he could contact her again. But she hadn't. There had been nothing to mark the fact that she'd been there. Only her very feminine fragrance lingering with the unmistakeable scent of sex when he'd woken to find an empty space beside him and silence in the adjoining suite of rooms.

Gabe shook his head as the limousine drew to a halt and a robed servant opened the door for him. He must put her out of his mind and concentrate on the evening ahead. It didn't matter who his mystery virgin was. It had happened and it was over. He could shut the door on it, just as he did with every other aspect of his past. He was here at the palace to meet formally with the Sultan and none of the other stuff mattered.

Buttoning up the jacket of his suit, he stepped out onto the honey-coloured gravel of the forecourt and in the distance he could see a long line of similar limousines already parked. The turreted palace gleamed red-gold in the light of the setting sun, like something out of an upmarket Disney film. Gabe wondered how long it had taken to build this impressive citadel—an unmistakeable symbol of beauty and power, set in an oasis of formal and surprisingly green gardens.

The evening air was thick with the scent of roses and soft with the sound of running water from the stream which traversed the palace grounds. In the distance, he could see soaring mountain peaks topped with snow and, closer, the circular and steady flight of what looked like a bird of prey.

That was what he should be thinking about, he reminded himself grimly. Not a woman who had made him feel slightly…

He frowned.

Used?

Had she?

'Gabe! Here you are at last. May I welcome you to my home?'

An accented voice broke into his thoughts. Gabe turned to find the Sultan standing on the steps to greet him. A tall and imposing figure, he was framed by the dramatic arches of the palace entrance behind him. His robes and headdress were pure white and the starkness of his appearance was broken only by the luminosity of his olive skin. For a moment, a distant memory floated across Gabe's mind before it disappeared again, like a butterfly on a summer's day.

Gabe smiled. 'Your Most Imperial Highness,' he said. 'I am most honoured to be invited to your palace.'

'The honour is all mine,' said the Sultan, stepping forward to shake him warmly by the hand. 'How was London when you left?'

'Rainy,' said Gabe.

'Of course it was.' The two men exchanged a wry look.

Gabe had first met the Sultan at the marriage of one of his own employees. At the time, Sara Williams had been working as a 'creative' at his advertising agency before she'd ruffled a few feathers by bringing her rather complicated love-life into the office.

During that rather surreal wedding day in the nearby country of Dhi'ban, the Sultan had told Gabe that he knew of his formidable reputation and asked if he would help bring Qurhah into the twenty-first century by helping change its image. Initially, Gabe had been reluctant to accept such a potentially tricky commission, but it had provided a challenge, in a life where fresh challenges were rare.

And he had timed it to coincide with an anniversary which always filled him with guilt and regret.

'You are comfortable at your hotel?' asked the Sultan.

For a moment, Gabe felt erotic recall trickle down his spine. 'It's perfect,' he said. 'One of the most beautiful buildings I've ever stayed in.'

'Thank you. But you will find our royal palace more beautiful still.' The Sultan made a sweeping gesture with his hand. 'Now come inside and let me show you a little Qurhahian hospitality.'

Gabe followed the monarch through the long corridors of the palace, made cool by the soft breeze which floated in from the central courtyard. Past bowing ranks of servants, they walked—overlooked by portraits of hawk-faced kings from ages gone by, all of whom bore a striking resemblance to his host.

It was more than a little dazzling but the room which they entered defied all expectation. Tall and as impressive as a cathedral, the high-ceilinged chamber was vaulted with the soft gleam of gold and the glitter of precious gems. People stood chatting and sipping their drinks, but the moment the Sultan entered everyone grew silent and bowed their heads in homage.

What must it be like to have that kind of power over people? wondered Gabe as he was introduced first to the Sultan's emissary and then to a whole stream of officials—all of them men. Some of them—mainly

the older generation—were clearly suspicious of a
foreigner who had been brought in to tamper with
the image of a country which had always fiercely
prided itself on its national identity. But Gabe knew
that change inevitably brought with it pain, and so he
listened patiently to some of the reservations which
were being voiced before the bell rang for dinner.

He accompanied Sultan into a vast dining room,
where lavishly laid tables were decorated with fragrant roses coloured deep crimson. Inexplicably, he
found his eyes flickering towards their dark petals and
wondering why the sight of them unsettled him so.
Like the blood on his sheets, he thought suddenly—
and a whisper of apprehension iced his skin.

'I have seated you next to the Ambassador of Maraban, who is one of the most influential men in the
region,' said the Sultan. 'With my sister on the other
side. Her English is excellent and she is eager to meet
with you, for she meets few Westerners. Ah, here she
comes now. Leila!'

But Gabe didn't need to hear his host say her name
to know the woman's identity. He knew that from the
moment she entered the banqueting hall. Even though
her body was swathed in flowing silk and even though
a matching veil of palest silver was covering half her
face, there could be no mistaking her. No amount
of camouflage could disguise that sexy sway of her
body—or maybe it was because in some primeval and
physical way, he still felt connected to her.

He could still smell her on his skin.

He could still taste her in his mouth.

He could still remember the exact moment when

he had broken through her tightness and claimed her for his own.

Why the hell had she kept her identity hidden from him?

The Sultan was saying something, and Gabe had to force himself to listen and to pray that the sudden clamour of his senses would settle.

'Leila.' The hawk-faced leader smiled. 'This is Gabe Steel—the advertising genius from London of whom you have heard me speak. Gabe, I'd like you to meet Princess Leila Scheherazade of Qurhah—my only sister.'

For a moment Gabe was so angry he could barely get a word out in response, but he quickly asserted the self-possession which was second nature to him. He had worked all his life in an industry which traded on illusion and knew only too well how to wear whichever mask the occasion demanded. And so he produced the slightly deferential smile he knew was expected of him on meeting the royal princess. He even inclined his head towards her, before catching a peep of a crystal-encrusted sandal which was poking out from beneath the folds of her gown. And the sight of those beautiful toes sent a surge of anger and lust shooting through him.

'I am honoured to meet you, Your Royal Highness,' he said, but as he straightened up he saw the sudden colour which flushed over the upper part of her face. He saw the brief flicker of distress which flared in the depths of her blue eyes. And that distress pleased him. His mouth hardened. It pleased him very much.

'The pleasure is also mine, Mr Steel,' she said softly.

'Leila, please show our guest to his place.' The

Sultan clapped his hands loudly, and once again the room grew silent. 'And let us all be seated.'

Silently, Gabe followed Leila across the dining room and took his place beside her. In the murmured moments as two hundred guests sat down, he seized the opportunity to move his head close to hers. 'So. Are you going to give me some kind of explanation?'

'Not now,' she said calmly.

'I want some sort of explanation, Your Royal *Highness*.'

'Not now,' she repeated, and then she lifted her fingers and began to remove her veil.

And despite the anger still simmering away inside him, Gabe held his breath as her features were slowly revealed to him. Because in a world where nudity was as ubiquitous as the cell phone, this was the most erotic striptease he had ever witnessed.

First he saw the curve of her chin and, above that, those sensual lips, which looked so startlingly pink against her luminous skin. He remembered how those lips had felt beneath the hard crush of his own and he felt himself harden instantly. He tried to tell himself that her nose was too strong and aquiline for conventional beauty and that there were women far more lovely than her. But he was lying—because in that moment she looked like the most exquisite creature he had ever seen.

And she had deceived him. She had lied to him as women always lied.

Taking a long draught of wine in an effort to steady his nerves, somehow he hung on to his temper for as long as it took to charm the ambassador during the first course, which he had no desire to eat.

He wondered if it was rude to completely ignore Leila, but he didn't care—because he still didn't trust himself to speak to her again. It wouldn't look good if he exploded with anger at the exalted banqueting table of the Sultan, would it? Yet he found his gaze drawn inexorably to the way her fingers toyed with the heavy golden cutlery as she pushed food around her plate.

The ambassador had turned away to talk to the person on his left and Gabe took the opportunity to lean towards her, his voice shaking with suppressed rage. 'So is there some kind of power game going on that I should know about, Leila?' he said. 'Some political intrigue which will slowly be revealed to me as the evening progresses?'

Her heavy golden fork clattered to her plate and he saw the apprehension on her face as she turned to face him.

'There's no intrigue,' she answered, her voice as low as his.

'No? Then why all the mystery? Why not just tell your brother that we've already met. Unless he doesn't know, of course.'

'I—'

'Maybe he has no idea that his sister came to my hotel today,' he continued remorselessly. 'And let me—'

'Please.' Her interruption sounded anguished. 'We can't talk here.'

'Then where do you suggest?' he questioned. 'Same time, same place tomorrow? Maybe you'd already planned to return for a repeat performance, wearing a different kind of disguise. Maybe the mas-

querade aspect turns you on. I don't know.' His eyes
bored into her. 'Had you?'

'Mr Steel—'

'It's Gabe,' he said with icy pleasantry. 'You remember how to say my name, don't you, Leila?'

Briefly, Leila closed her eyes. She certainly did.
And she hadn't just *said* it, had she? She'd gasped it
as he had entered her. She had whispered it as he'd
moved deep inside her. She had shuddered it out in a
long, keening moan as her orgasm had taken hold of
her and almost torn her apart with pleasure.

And now all those amazing memories were being
swept away by the angry wash from his eyes.

She wished she could spirit herself away. That she
could excuse herself by saying she felt sick—which
was actually true, because right at that moment she
did feel sick.

But Murat would never forgive her if she interrupted the banquet—why, it might even alert his suspicions if he suspected that she found the Englishman's
presence uncomfortable. He might begin to ask himself why. And surely the man beside her—*the man
who had made such incredible love to her*—couldn't
keep up this simmering hostility for the entire meal?

'Look, I can understand why you're angry,' she
said, trying to keep her tone conciliatory.

'Can you?' His pewter eyes glittered out a hostile
light. 'And why might that be? Because you failed to
reveal your true identity to me?'

'I wasn't—'

'Or because it's only just occurred to you that you
might have compromised my working relationship
with your brother?' His voice was soft but his words

were deadly. 'Because no man likes to discover that his sister has behaved like a whore.'

He leaned back in his chair to study her, as if they were having a perfectly amicable discussion, and Leila thought how looks could deceive. The casual observer would never have noticed that the polite smile on his lips was completely at odds with the angry glitter in his grey eyes.

'I was behaving as other women sometimes behave,' she protested. 'Spontaneously.'

'But most women aren't being pursued by body-guards at the time,' he continued. His voice lowered, and she could hear the angry edge to his words. 'What would have happened if they had burst in and found us in bed together?'

Leila tried desperately to block the image from her mind. 'I don't know.'

'Oh, I think you've got a pretty good idea. What would have happened, Leila?'

She swallowed, knowing that he was far too intelligent to be fobbed off with a vague answer. 'You would have been arrested,' she admitted reluctantly.

'I would have been arrested,' he repeated grimly and nodded his head. 'Destroying my reputation and losing my freedom in the process. Maybe even my head?'

'We are not that barbaric!' she protested, but her words did not carry the ring of conviction.

'It's funny really,' he continued, 'because for the first time in my life I'm feeling like some kind of stud. Wham and bam—but not much in the way of thank you, ma'am.'

'No!' she said. 'It wasn't like that.'

'Really? Then what was it? Love at first sight?'

Leila picked up her goblet of black cherry juice and drank a mouthful, more as a stalling mechanism than because she was thirsty. His words were making her realise just how impulsive she had been and how disastrous it would have been if they'd been caught. But they *hadn't* been caught, had they? Maybe luck—or fate—had been on their side.

And the truth of it was that her heart had leapt with a delicious kind of joy when she'd seen him again tonight, in his charcoal suit and a silver tie the colour of a river fish. She had stared at the richness of his hair and longed to run her fingers through it. Her eyes had drifted hungrily over his hard features and, despite everything she'd vowed not to do, she had wanted to kiss him. She had started concocting unrealistic little fantasies about him, and that was crazy. Just because he had proved to be an exquisite lover, didn't mean that she should fall into that age-old female trap of imagining that he had a heart.

Because no man had a heart, she reminded herself bitterly.

'Love?' She met the challenge in his eyes. 'Why, do you always have to be in love before you can have sex?'

'Me? No. Most emphatically I do not. But women often do, especially when it's their first time. But then I guess most women aren't just spoiled little princesses who see what they want and go out and take it—and to hell with the consequences.'

Leila didn't react to the *spoiled-little-princess* insult. She knew people thought it, though no one had ever actually come out and said it to her face before.

She knew what people thought about families like hers and how they automatically slotted her into a gilded box marked 'pampered'. But what they saw wasn't always the true picture. Unimaginable wealth didn't protect you from the normal everyday stuff. Glittering palace walls didn't work some kind of magic on the people who lived within them. Prick her skin and she would bleed, just like the next woman.

'It was an unconventional introduction, I admit,' she said. 'To bring my work to your hotel room unannounced like that and ask you for a job.'

'Please don't be disingenuous, Leila. That's not what I'm talking about and you know it.' He sounded impatient now. 'Which guide to interview technique did you study before you started removing your clothes and climbing all over me? *The 1960s Guide to Sexual Behaviour*? Or *A Hundred Ways To Make The Casting Couch Work For You*?'

'You didn't seem so averse to the idea at the time!'

'Funny that,' he mused. 'A beautiful woman comes up to my suite, turns her big blue eyes on me and starts coming on to me. She brushes my arm so lightly that I wonder if I'd imagined it, though my senses tell me I hadn't. Then she pirouettes around so that there can be no mistaking the tight cut of her jeans or the cling of her blouse as she shows off her amazing body. She gazes into my eyes as if I am the answer to all her prayers.' *And for one brief moment hadn't he felt as if he could be?*

There was a pause as Leila forced herself to scoop some jewel-coloured rice onto her fork—terrified that someone might notice that she hadn't eaten a thing and start asking themselves why. Had she done everything which Gabe had accused her of? Had she behaved like some kind of *siren*? She lifted her head to look at him. 'You could have stopped me,' she said.

Gabe stilled as he met the challenge sparking from her blue eyes. Because hadn't he been thinking the same thing ever since it had happened? He could have stopped her. He *should* have stopped her. He should have waited until her bodyguards had gone and then told her to get out of his room as quickly as possible. He could have dampened down his desire, using the formidable self-control which had carried him through situations far more taxing than one of sexual frustration. He could have told her that he didn't have a type, but that if he did—she wouldn't be it.

He didn't like women who were *obvious*. Who had persistent exes or *brothers who were sultans*. He had an antenna for women who were trouble and it had never failed him before. He resisted the tricky ones. The neurotic and needy ones.

But something had gone wrong this time.

Because he hadn't resisted Leila, had he? He had broken his own rules and taken her to bed without knowing a single damned thing about her. And he still couldn't work out why. He shook his head slightly. It had been something indefinable. Something in those wide blue eyes which had drawn him in. He had felt like a man whose throat was parched. Who had been shown a pool of water and invited to drink from it. He had felt almost…

His eyes narrowed.

Almost *helpless*.

And that was never going to happen.

Not twice in a lifetime.

'I could have stopped you,' he agreed slowly.

'So why didn't you?'

He didn't answer straight away because it was important to get this right. He wanted to send out a message to her. A very clear message she could not fail to understand. That it had meant nothing to him. That it would be a mistake to fall for him. That he caused women pain. Deep pain.

'Sometimes sex is like an itch,' he said deliberately. 'And you just can't help yourself from scratching it.'

Her face didn't register any of the kind of emotions he might have expected. No indignation or hurt. He suspected that hers was a world where feelings as well as faces were hidden. But he saw her eyes harden, very briefly. As if he had simply confirmed something she had already known.

'I'm sure that the romantic poets need have nothing to fear from your observations,' she said sarcastically.

He picked up his goblet of wine, twirling the long golden stem between his fingers. 'Just so long as we understand each other.'

She leaned forward, and he caught a drift of some faint scent. It made him think of meadow flowers being crushed underfoot. He found it...*distracting*.

'Oh, I get the message loud and clear,' she said. 'So forgive me if I ignore you as much as possible for the rest of the meal. I think we've said everything there is to say to each other, don't you?'

CHAPTER FOUR

LEILA GRIPPED THE side of the washbasin as terror sliced through her like the cold blade of a sword. She wanted to scream. Or to throw back her head and howl like an animal. But she didn't dare. Because her fear of discovery was almost as great as the dark suspicion which had been growing inside her for days.

She stayed perfectly still and listened, her heart thudding painfully in her chest. Had anyone heard her? Had one of the many unseen servants been close enough to the bathroom to catch the sound of her shuddered retching?

She closed her eyes.

Please no.

But when she opened them again, she knew that she could no longer keep pretending. She couldn't keep hoping and praying that this wasn't happening, because it was.

It had started with a missed period. One day late. Two days late—then a full week. Her nerves had been shot. Her heart seemed to have been permanently racing with horror and fear. She was *never* late—her monthly cycle was as reliable as the morning sunrise. And the awful thing was that she'd had to *pretend* that it had arrived. She'd forced herself to wince and to clutch at the lower part of her stomach as if in discomfort, desperate not to alert the suspicions of her female servants. Because in that enclosed, watched world of the palace, nothing went unnoticed—not even the princess's most intimate secrets.

She had told herself that it was just a glitch. That it must be her body behaving in an unusual way because it had been introduced to sex. Then she had tried not thinking about it at all. When that hadn't worked, she'd made silent pleas to Mother Nature, promising that she would be good for the rest of her life, if only she wasn't carrying Gabe Steel's baby.

But her pleas went unanswered. The horror was real. The bare and simple fact wasn't going away, simply because she wanted it to.

She was pregnant.

Her one brief experiment with sex—her one futile attempt to behave with the freedom of a man—had left her with a consequence which was never going to leave her. Pregnant by a man who never wanted to see her again.

She was ruined.

With trembling fingers, she tidied her mussed hair, knowing she couldn't let her standards slip. She had to maintain the regal facade expected of her, because if anyone ever *guessed*...

She thought about the meagre options which lay open to her and each of them filled her with foreboding. She thought what would happen if her brother found out, and a shudder ran down her spine. She gripped the washbasin, and the cold porcelain felt like ice beneath her clammy fingers. Murat must not find out—at least, not yet.

She was going to have to tell Gabe.

But Gabe had gone back to England and there were no plans for her to see him again. He had spent a further fortnight working here in Qurhah without their paths ever crossing. Why would they? He had made it clear that he wanted to forget what had happened and she had convinced herself she felt the same way. She'd found herself reflecting how strange it was that two people who'd been so intimate could afterwards act like strangers.

Even the farewell dinner given in honour of the English tycoon had yielded no moments of closeness. She and Gabe had barely exchanged any words at all, bar a few stilted ones of greeting. During the meal she'd read nothing but cool contempt in his pewter eyes. And that had hurt. She had experienced for the first time the pain of rejection, made worse by the dull ache of longing.

Her mind working overtime, Leila shut the bathroom door behind her and walked slowly back to her private living quarters. Gabe Steel might not be her first port of call in normal circumstances, but right now he was the only person she could turn to.

She had to tell him.

But how?

She looked out over the palace rose gardens where the bright orange bloom which had been named after her in the days following her birth was now in glorious display.

If she phoned him, who wasn't to say that some interfering palace busybody might not be listening in to her call? And phoning him would still leave her here, pregnant and alone and vulnerable to the Sultan's rage if he found out.

But if she left it much longer it was inevitable he would find out anyway.

A sudden knock at the door disturbed her, and her troubled thoughts became magnified when one of her servants informed her that the Sultan wished to see her with immediate effect.

Leila's mouth was dry with fear as she walked silently along the marble corridors towards Murat's own magnificent section of the royal palace. Had he guessed? Was he summoning her to tell her that she had brought shame on the royal house, and that she was to be banished to some isolated region of their vast country to bring up her illegitimate child in solitude?

But when she was ushered into his private sitting room, Murat's demeanour was unusually solicitous, his black eyes narrowed with something almost approaching *concern*.

He began by asking whether she was well.

'Yes, I am very well,' she lied, praying that her horror at this particular question would not show on her face. 'Why...why do you ask?'

Murat shrugged. 'Just that you seem to have been almost invisible lately. You don't seem to have been yourself at all. Is something wrong, Leila?'

He'd *noticed*!

Despite her wild flare of fear, Leila knew that she must not react. She must not give her clever brother any inkling that she was concealing a desperate secret. With a resourcefulness she wasn't aware she possessed—though maybe desperation was in itself an inspiration—Leila shrugged. 'I have been feeling a little discontented of late.'

His eyes narrowed. 'In what way?'

She licked her lips. 'I feel as if I have seen nothing of the world, or of life itself. All I know is Qurhah.'

'That is because you are a princess of Qurhah,' Murat growled. 'And your place is here.'

'I know that,' said Leila, thinking that he made her sound like an ancient piece of furniture which had never been moved from its allocated place on the rug. 'But you travel. You get to visit other countries. And I…I have seen nothing of the world, other than the surrounding lands of the desert region.'

The Sultan's black eyes narrowed. 'And?'

She forced herself to say the words, to make him think that she had accepted the future which had been planned for her. A future which could now never happen, because what prospective royal husband would wish to take a bride who carried another man's child?

'I know that my place is here, Murat,' she said quietly. 'But before I immerse myself in the life which has been mapped out for me—could I not have an overseas trip?'

Beneath his silken headdress, Murat's dark brows knitted together. 'What kind of trip?' he echoed.

Leila could hardly believe she'd got this far and knew she mustn't blow it now. She thought about the tiny, forbidden life growing inside her and she drew in a deep breath. 'You know that Princess Sara has a place in London?'

'So I gather,' said Murat carelessly.

Leila watched her brother's reaction closely, but if

he was hurt to hear the name of the woman he'd once been betrothed to, he didn't show it.

'She often writes to me and tells me all about the fabulous shopping in the city,' Leila continued. 'Many times she has asked me to visit her there. Couldn't I do that, Murat—just for a few days? You know how much I love shopping!'

There was silence for a moment. Had she made her request sound suitably fluffy? If she'd told her brother that she wanted to go and see a photographic exhibition which was being launched, he would never have approved. He was one of those men who believed that shopping kept women subdued. Lavish them with enough *stuff* and it kept them satisfied.

'I suppose that a few days could be arranged,' he said eventually.

Leila gave a little squeal of joy—showing her brother the gratitude she knew would be expected of her—but it was with a heavy heart that she packed for her forthcoming trip. She thought about the terrifying secret she carried. About how humiliating it was to have to seek out a man who did not want her, to tell him something he would be appalled to hear.

Arrangements were made between the palace and Princess Sara, who Leila had known since she'd been a child. Sara had once been promised to Murat himself but was now married to Suleiman, and they had homes all around the world.

With a retinue of bodyguards and servants, Leila flew by private jet to England where they took over the entire top floor of the Granchester Hotel in central London. She was one step closer to Gabe. One step closer to sharing her news—and didn't they say that a problem shared was a problem halved?

But then she remembered his cold face as she'd sat beside him at the banquet. She forced herself to recall the fact that he had never wanted to see her again. There was to be no fairy-tale ending with this man, she reminded herself sombrely. She looked out of the penthouse windows of her hotel suite, across a beautiful park alive with flowers—and a terrible feeling of isolation came over her.

She could see couples openly walking together—their arms looped around each other as they kissed. A young child chased a dog and, behind him, a woman wheeled a pram. Everyone seemed part of the world which lay before her eyes—all except her. And Leila couldn't remember ever feeling quite so alone as she did right then.

Knowing she couldn't keep putting off the dreaded moment much longer, she picked up the hotel phone and dialled Gabe's office, her heart pounding with apprehension. She had to go through two different people before his voice came on the line, and when it did—he sounded distant.

Wary.

Terror gripped her as she realised she was about to drop a live grenade into his perfect life.

'Leila?'

'Yes, it's me. How…how are you, Gabe?'

'I am well.' There was a pause. 'This is a surprise.'

'I imagine it is.' She drew in a deep breath. 'Look, I need to see you.'

'I thought we'd agreed that wasn't such a good idea.

And anyway, I'm back in England now and I'm not planning to return to Qurhah for a while.'

Leila stared out of the window. The child which had been chasing the dog had fallen over and a woman—presumably the child's mother—was picking him up and comforting him. She realised how hopelessly ill-prepared she was to become a mother and her heart clenched. 'I'm in England too,' she said. 'In fact, I'm in London.'

She could hear so much more in that second pause. She imagined his mind working overtime as he tried to figure out what the hell she was doing in England and why she was calling him. And if he asked her outright—would she have the guts to tell him on the phone?

'What are you doing in London?'

For a moment, she didn't answer. He asked the question so casually. Did he think, with the arrogance which seemed to be second nature to all alpha males, that her desire for him was so great that she was pre-pared to trample over her pride in order to seek him out? Didn't he have a *clue* what she might be about to say? That their rash act of passion might have yielded this very result? 'That's what I'd like to talk to you about.'

'Where are you staying?' he asked. 'I'll come over.'

Her gaze drifted down to the traffic which was clogging the park road, knowing it would be much easier if he came here than having to negotiate her way round this strange new city. But if Gabe wanted nothing to do with this new life...then might that not complicate matters further? Why implicate him to her retinue as the father of her baby, unless he was willing to accept that role?'

'I'm at the Granchester. But I don't want you to come here. It's too…public.' She gripped the phone more tightly. 'Can I come to your place?'

At the other end of the line, Gabe listened to her hesitant words, and his eyes narrowed. It was a presumptuous question and one he would usually have deflected. Invitations to his home were rare and *he* was the one who did the inviting. His apartment was his refuge. His sanctuary. It was where he went to escape. If ever he spent the night with someone, he preferred somewhere which provided him with a clearly marked exit route. Where *he* could be the one doing the leaving.

But Leila was different. Her royal status set her apart from other women. It made people break rules for her. Unwillingly, he felt the quickened beat of desire as he remembered her blue eyes and the silky texture of her olive skin. His mouth dried as he recalled her hot, tight body. He leaned back in his chair and stared at the ceiling. Why the hell hadn't she told him who she really was at the time?

'This is all very mysterious,' he said. 'Do you want to tell me what it's all about?'

'I'd rather do it in person.'

Oh, would you, my presumptuous princess? With a flicker of irritation, Gabe waved an impatient hand at Alice, his newly promoted assistant, who had just stuck her head around his office door. 'Very well. I'll send a car for you at seven.'

'No,' answered Leila flatly. 'That won't be possible.'

'Excuse me?'

'My bodyguards will not permit me to visit a man's apartment. It must be done in total secrecy. Will you be there tonight—at two a.m.?'

'Two a.m.?' His deep voice reverberated with incredulity. 'Are you out of your mind? Some of us have work to go to in the morning.'

'I'm afraid that the cover of darkness is the only solution to ensure I won't be seen, and I can't afford to be seen,' she said, a note of determination entering her voice. 'It will be best if you send the car for me then. But I need to know if you'll…if you'll be alone?'

'Yes, I'll be alone,' said Gabe coldly—and gave her the address.

Leila's heart was racing as she replaced the phone, but she couldn't shake off her feeling of apprehension—and hurt—as he cut the connection without even the politeness of a formal goodbye. Was he always this cool towards the women he'd slept with—as if he couldn't wait to put as much distance between them as possible? And how the hell was he going to react when she told him?

She told her retinue that she intended to rest for the remainder of the evening and instructed them to order themselves food from room service. Then she phoned Sara, cutting through the princess's delighted exclamations by telling her that she needed a favour.

'What kind of a favour?' asked Sara.

'Just that if my brother calls and asks if we're having a good time together, you tell him yes.'

'I think it's unlikely that your brother will call me himself,' said Sara drily. 'Is there something going on, Leila? And does that something have to do with a man?'

'How did you guess?'

'Because with most of my girlfriends, it's usually a man,' answered Sara with a wry tone. 'Don't suppose it's anyone I know?'

Leila hesitated. In a way she was wary of saying anything, but part of her wanted to blurt it out. 'Actually, you do. You used to work for him and he came to your wedding.'

There was a long silence. 'I hope you don't mean Gabe Steel?' said Sara, her voice low and disbelieving.

'That's exactly who I mean.' Leila could feel a skitter of panic washing over her skin. 'Why, what's the matter with him?'

'There's nothing the *matter* with him—that's the trouble. Just about every woman in London is or has been in love with him at some point. He's gorgeous, but he's a heartbreaker, Leila—and my advice is to stay away from him.'

It's too late for that now.

'I can't,' said Leila slowly. 'Will you cover for me, Sara?'

Sara's sigh came heaving down the phone. 'Okay, I'll cover for you—just so long as you promise me you won't do anything stupid.'

I already have, thought Leila, but she injected a breezy note into her voice.

'I promise,' she said as she put the phone down.

She could hear the sound of the room-service trolleys being trundled along the corridor towards the rooms of her retinue. Praying that their attention would be occupied by the novelty of eating Western food and that they would eat too much of it, she settled down to wait.

Shortly before ten, she allowed her servants into the room to turn down the bed and generally fuss around while she did a lot of exaggerated yawning.

The next few hours seemed to tick by with agonising slowness but Leila was too strung out to be sleepy, despite her long flight. Just before two o'clock she dressed and slipped on her raincoat and peered outside her room to find the corridor empty. With a surreptitiousness which was becoming second nature, she took the lift down into the empty foyer and walked straight outside to where Gabe's car was waiting.

Her heart was hammering as the plush vehicle whisked her through the darkened streets of London, before coming to a halt outside a looming tower of gleaming glass which overlooked the wide and glittering band of the river Thames.

And there was Gabe, waiting for her.

The pale moonlight illuminated his features, which were unsmiling and tense. As the vehicle drew to a halt she could see that he was wearing faded jeans and a sweater which hugged his honed torso and powerful arms. He looked shockingly sexy in a rock-star kind of way and that only added to Leila's feelings of discomfiture. As he bent to open the car door his eyes looked as forbidding as a frozen lake which had just been classified as unsafe.

Her mouth felt dry. Her legs were unsteady as his narrowed gaze raked over her. How was she going to go through with this?

'Hello, Leila,' he said, almost pleasantly—and she realised he was doing it again, just as he'd done on the night of the banquet. His civilised words were sending out one message while his eyes glittered out something completely different.

'Shall we go inside?'

Glass doors slid silently open to let them inside the apartment block. She was aware of a vast foyer with a jungle of elaborate plants. A man sitting reading by lamplight at a desk seemed to show surprise when he saw her walking in beside the tycoon with the dark golden hair. Or maybe she was imagining that bit.

But she certainly wasn't imagining Gabe's detached manner as they rode in one of the glass elevators towards the top of the tall building. She might as well have been travelling with a statue for all the notice he took of her, but unfortunately she wasn't similarly immune.

She tried to look somewhere—anywhere—but he filled her line of vision in his sexy, off-duty clothes. Her gaze stayed fixed determinedly on his chest for she didn't dare lift it to his face. She tried to concentrate on the steady rise and fall of his breathing instead of giving in to the darkly erotic thoughts which were crowding into her mind. He didn't want her—he couldn't have made that more clear. Yet all she could think about was the way his hands had slid round her waist when he'd still been deep inside her, the spasms dying away as he'd pumped out the last of his seed.

His seed.

The elevator stopped, the doors opened and Leila stepped out—straight into a room which momentarily took her breath away. An entire wall consisted of windows which commanded a breathtaking view of the night-time city, where stars twinkled and skyscrapers gleamed. The floors were polished and the furniture was minimalist and sleek. It was nothing like the ancient palace she called home and she felt as if she had walked into a strange new world.

For a moment she just stood and stared out of the windows. She could see the illuminated dome of St Paul's Cathedral and moonlight glittering on the river Thames. There was the sharp outline of the Shard and the pleasing circle of the London Eye. For years she had longed to come here, but never like this—because now she was seeing the famous city through the distorted lens of fear.

'Can I get you a drink?' he asked.

Leila allowed herself a moment of fantasy that this was a normal date between two people who had been lovers. How would that work? Would he open champagne and let her drink some before taking the glass from her hand and kissing her? Was that how he usually operated? Probably not at two in the morning when his night was being disturbed by a woman he was indifferent to...

For a moment she wondered what she might have done in this situation if she'd been a normal, Western woman—with all the freedoms that those women seemed to take for granted. There would have been no need for her to behave like this. Moving around under cover of darkness. Having to throw herself on the mercy of someone who didn't want her...

'No, I don't want a drink, thanks,' she said. 'That's not why I'm here.'

'Then why don't you sit down,' he suggested, 'and tell me why you are?'

She sank onto a leather sofa which was more comfortable than it looked. 'Look, there's no easy way to say this—and I know it's going to come as a shock, but I think I'm pregnant.'

For a moment Gabe didn't say a word. He couldn't. It was a long time since he had felt fear, but he felt it now. It was there in the hard beat of his heart and the icy prickle of his skin. And along with fear came anger. The sense that something was happening to him which was outside his control—and hadn't he vowed a long time ago never to let that happen to him again?

Yet on some instinctive and fundamental level, her words were not as shocking as she had suggested. Because hadn't he already guessed what she was going to say? Why else would she have pursued him like this across thousands of miles? She was a desert princess and surely someone like her wouldn't normally seek out a man who'd shown her nothing but coldness, no matter how much she had enjoyed the sex.

But none of his thoughts showed in his face. He had been a survivor for too long to react to her dramatic words—at least, not straight away. He had spent his life perfecting this cool and impenetrable mask and now was not the time to let it slip. He studied her shadowed eyes and seized on the words which offered most hope. The only hope.

'You only *think* you're pregnant?'

She nodded. 'Yes, but I'm pretty sure. I've been sick and my...'

Her words tailed off, as if she couldn't quite bring herself to say the next bit, but Gabe was in no mood to help her out—and certainly in no mood to tiptoe around her sensibilities. Because this was the woman who had disguised herself. Who had burst into his suite and come on to him without bothering to tell him who she was. She might have been a virgin but she certainly hadn't acted like one—and he was damned if he was going to let her play the shy and sensitive card now. Not when she was threatening to disrupt the ordered calm of his life. Disrupt it? She was threatening to blow it apart.

He felt a sudden flare of rage. 'Your what?' he prompted icily.

'My period is late!' she burst out, her cheeks suddenly turning red.

'But you haven't done a pregnancy test?'

'Funnily enough, no.' She bit her lip. 'It's not exactly easy for me to slip into a chemist back home to buy myself a kit. Somebody might recognise me.'

He wanted to say, *You should have thought of that before you let me strip you naked and lead you to my bed.* But he was culpable too, wasn't he? He had deflected the advances of women before and it had never been a problem. So why hadn't he sent this one on her way? Why hadn't he read any of the glaring clues which had warned him she was trouble? Had the subterfuge of her disguise and the fact that she was being pursued by bodyguards turned him on? Brought colourful fantasy into a life which was usually so cool and ordered?

'I used a condom,' he bit out.

Like a snake gathering strength before striking again, she drew her shoulders back and glared at him with angry blue eyes. 'Are you seriously suggesting that somebody other than you could be the father, Gabe?'

He remembered the way her trembling hand had circled his erection until he had been forced to push it away, afraid he might come before he was inside her. Had she inflicted some microscopic tear in the condom with those long fingernails of hers? *And had that been deliberate?*

But he pushed those thoughts away, because nothing was certain. And a man could drive himself insane if he started thinking that way.

'I'm not suggesting anything, because at the moment all we have is a hypothetical situation,' he said. 'And we're not doing anything until we have facts. There could be a million reasons why your period is late and I'm not going to waste time thinking about some nightmare scenario which might never happen.'

Nightmare scenario.

Leila flinched as his words cut into her like the nicks of a dozen tiny blades. That was all this was to him. *Remember that. Hold that thought in your mind and never forget it. A nightmare scenario.*

Had she thought that he would make everything all right? That he would sweep her into his arms as men sometimes did in films and stroke her hair, before telling her that she had no need to worry and he would take care of everything?

Maybe she had. Maybe part of her had still bought into that helpless feminine fantasy, despite everything she knew about men and the way they treated women.

'Perhaps you could go and buy a pregnancy test for me,' she suggested, staring out at the dark sky, which was punctured by tiny stars. 'Since I find the thought of braving the London shops a little too much to contemplate at the moment.'

Something small and trembling in her voice made Gabe's eyes narrow in unwilling comprehension. He wasn't used to picturing himself inside the skin of a woman—except in the most erotic sense—but he did so now. He tried to imagine this pampered princess transplanted to a foreign country, bringing with her this terrible secret. How must it feel to give such momentous news to a man who did not want to receive it?

'We're not having some do-it-yourself session,' he said flatly. 'I will make an appointment for you to see someone in Harley Street tomorrow.'

Her eyes were suddenly wide and frightened.

'But somebody might tip off the press if I am seen going to the doctor's. And my brother mustn't find out. At least, not in that way.'

'Haven't you ever heard of the Hippocratic oath?' he questioned impatiently. 'And patient confidentiality?'

Leila almost laughed. She thought that, for a man of the world, he was being remarkably naive. Or maybe he just didn't realise that royal blood always made the stakes impossibly high. It made the onlooking world act like vultures. Didn't he realise that professional codes of conduct could fall by the wayside, when a royal scoop like this offered an unimaginably high purse?

'I'll take your word for it,' she said.

Gabe watched as she reached for her handbag. She was wearing that same damned raincoat, which reminded him uncomfortably of their erotic encounter in Qurhah. For one tempting moment he entertained the thought of having sex with her again. It had been the most amazing sex of his life and he still couldn't work out why.

Because he had been the first?

Or because her touch had felt like fire on a day when his heart had been as cold as ice?

He remembered the way her long legs had parted eagerly beneath the quest of his hungry fingers. The way she had moaned when he had touched her. He could almost feel the eager warmth of her breath on his shoulder as he'd entered her, as no man had done before. Vividly, he recalled the sensation of tightness and the spots of blood on his sheets afterwards. He closed his eyes as he remembered seeing them spattered there like some kind of trophy. It had felt *primitive*, and he didn't do primitive. He did cool and calculated and reasoned because that was the only way he'd been able to survive.

Pain gnawed at his heart as he tried to regain his equilibrium, but still his body was filled with desire. Wasn't it also primitive—and natural—for a man to want to be deep inside a woman when she'd just told him she might be carrying his child?

His mouth tightened. If he pulled her into his arms and started to kiss her, she would not resist. No woman ever did. He imagined himself reacquainting himself with her scented flesh, because wouldn't that help him make some kind of sense of this bizarre situation?

'Leila,' he said, but she had stood up very quickly and was brushing her hand dismissively over the sleeve of her raincoat, in a gesture which seemed more symbolic than necessary.

'I must get back before anyone realises I've gone,' she said.

She walked across to the other side of the room, and Gabe felt the bubble of his erotic fantasy burst as she fixed him with a cool look. For a moment it almost seemed as if she had just rejected his advances—even though he hadn't actually *made* any.

'Phone me at my hotel and tell me where to meet you tomorrow,' she said. 'I will have to use Sara as a decoy again, but I'm sure I can manage it.'

'I'm sure you can,' he said with the grim air of a man whose whole world was about to change, whether he wanted it to or not.

CHAPTER FIVE

'So,' SAID LEILA slowly. The word was tiny and meant nothing at all, but one of them had to say *something*. Something to shatter the tense, taut silence which had descended on them the moment they'd left the consulting room. Something to make Gabe move again instead of sitting there frozen, staring out of the windscreen as if he had just seen some kind of ghost.

He had brought the car to a halt in a wide, tree-lined street, and Leila was glad he'd driven away from the Harley Street clinic which had just delivered the news she had already known.

He hadn't said a thing—not a thing—but she'd noticed the way his hands had tightened around the steering wheel, and the ashen hue which had drained his face of all colour.

She was pregnant.

Very newly pregnant—but pregnant all the same.

A new life growing was beneath a heart now racing as she waited—though she wasn't really sure what she was waiting for.

She remembered Gabe's barely perceptible intake of breath as the expensively dressed consultant had delivered the results of the test. The doctor had looked at them with the benign and faintly indulgent smile he obviously reserved for this kind of situation. Probably imagining they were yet another rich young couple eager to hear what he had to say. Had he noticed the lack of a wedding ring on her finger? Did anyone actually care about that kind of thing these days? She swallowed. They certainly did in Qurhah.

She wondered if the medic had been perceptive enough to read the body language which existed between the prospective parents. Or rather, the lack of it. She and Gabe had sat upright on adjoining antique chairs facing the medic's desk, their shoulders tense. Close, yet completely distant—like two strangers who had been put into a room to hear the most intimate of information.

But that was all they were really, wasn't it?

Two strangers who had created a life out of a moment of passion.

She turned in the low sports car to glance at Gabe. She didn't know what to do. What to say or how to cope. She wanted something to make it better, but she realised that nothing could. Something unplanned and ill-advised had resulted in both their lives being changed—*and neither of them wanted this.*

The sunlight illuminated his chiselled features, casting deep shadows beneath the high slash of his cheekbones. But still he hadn't moved. His profile was utterly motionless, as if it had been carved from a piece of golden dark marble.

She knew she couldn't keep sitting there like some sort of obedient chattel, waiting for his thoughts on what had happened. She wasn't in Qurhah now. No longer did she have to play the role of subservient female. She had always longed for equality—and this was what it was supposed to be about. Taking control of her own destiny. Learning to express her own feelings instead of waiting for guidance and approval from a man.

Knotting her fingers together in a tight fist, she knew something else, too. That she didn't want this icy-eyed Englishman to feel that she had trapped him. What kind of a man was he who could sit there like a statue in the face of such news? Didn't he feel *anything*? 'Whatever happens, I'm not going to ask you for anything,' she said. 'You must understand that.'

Gabe didn't answer straight away—and not just because her accented words sounded as disjointed as if she had been speaking them in her native tongue. He had learnt when to be silent and when to speak. Once—a long time ago—he had given in to the temptation of hot-headedness. But never again. It had been the most brutal lesson and one he had never forgotten. And then, when he'd started out in advertising and was clawing his way up the slippery slope towards success, he had learnt that you should never respond until you were certain you had the right answer.

Except that this time, he couldn't see that there *was* a right answer. Only a swirling selection of options—and none of them were good. The facts were unassailable. A woman with a baby and a man who did not wish to become a father.

Who should never become a father.

He felt a dark dread begin to creep over his heart as he wondered whether history always repeated itself. Whether humans were driven by some biological imperative over which they had no control. Driven to make the same mistakes over and over again.

'Not here,' he said, his voice tight with restraint. 'I don't intend discussing something as important as this in the front seat of a car. Do up your seat belt and let's go.'

But he could see that her hands were trembling as she struggled to perform the simple action. He leaned forward to help her, and her proximity left him momentarily disorientated. The warmth radiating from her body seemed to have intensified the spicy scent of her perfume. The sunlight was bouncing off the ebony gloss of her hair and her lips looked so unbelievably kissable that he was left with the dull ache of longing inside him.

And wanting her would only complicate things. It would cloud his mind and his judgement at a time when he needed to think clearly.

Clipping in the seat belt, he quickly moved away from the temptation she presented and started up the engine.

For a while they were silent as they stop-started through the busy streets, where outside the world carried on as normal. While inside…

He shot her a glance and saw that her face looked as white as chalk and he found himself unexpectedly shocked at the sight of her physical frailty. 'Have you eaten?' he demanded.

She shook her head. 'I'm not hungry.'

'You should be. You haven't had any lunch.' And neither had he. The morning had passed in a dazed kind of blur ever since he'd met Leila at the Harley

Street clinic, where she had been dropped off by Sara, a princess who had once worked for him.

He was still remembering the look on his assistant's face this morning when he'd told her to clear his diary for the rest of the day. Surprise didn't even come close to it. He could just imagine the gossip reverberating around the building as people started second-guessing why Gabe Steel had done the unimaginable and taken an unscheduled day off work.

And when they knew? When they discovered that the man who was famous for never committing was to become a father? What then?

'You need to eat,' he said implacably.

'I don't want anything,' she said. 'I feel sick. I've felt sick for over a month.'

'Is that intended to make me feel guilty, Leila? Because you'd better know that I won't accept all the blame.' He sent out a warning toot on his horn, and the cyclist who had shot out from a side road responded with a rude gesture. 'If you hadn't come on to me in a weak moment, then we wouldn't have found ourselves in this intolerable situation.'

Wondering briefly what the weak moment had been, Leila leaned her head back against the seat as the cool venom of his words washed over her. Yet, she couldn't really condemn him for speaking the truth, could she? It *was* intolerable—and there wasn't a thing that was going to make it better. A wave of panic hit her and the now-familiar refrain echoed around in her head.

She was ruined.

Ruined.

Outside the car window, London passed by but she

barely noticed the brand-new city which should have excited her. She felt like an invisible speck of dust being blown along and she didn't know where she was going to end up. She was with a man who did not want her but was forced to be with her, because she carried his child within her belly.

'Where are you taking me?' she asked.

'To my apartment.'

She shook her head. 'I can't be seen at your apartment. My brother might find out.'

'Your brother is going to have to find out sooner or later—and this isn't about him or his reaction to what's happening. Not any more. This is about you.' *And me*, he thought reluctantly. *Me*.

Without another word he drove to his apartment and parked in the underground garage before they took the elevator to his apartment. The rooms seemed both strange yet familiar and Leila felt disorientated as she walked inside. As if she was a different person from the one who had arrived here in the early hours of this morning.

But she was.

Yesterday nothing had been certain and there had still been an element of hope in her heart, no matter how misplaced. But with the doctor's diagnosis, that hope had gone and nothing would ever be the same. Never again would she simply be Leila, the princess sister of the Sultan. Soon she would be Leila, the mother of an illegitimate child—a baby fathered by the tycoon Gabe Steel.

The man who had never wanted to see her again.

She tried to imagine her brother's fury when she found out but it was hard to picture the full extent of his predictable rage. Would he strip her of her title? Banish her from the only land and home she had ever known? And if he did—what then? She tried to imagine supporting herself and a tiny baby. How would she manage that when she'd never even *held* a baby?

She was so preoccupied with the tumult of her thoughts that it took her a few minutes to realise that Gabe had left her alone in his stark sitting room. He returned a little while later with his suit jacket removed and the sleeves of his shirt rolled up. She noticed his powerful forearms with their smattering of dark golden hair and remembered the way he had slid them around her naked waist. And wasn't that a wildly inappropriate thing to remember at a time like this?

'I've made us something to eat,' he said. 'Come through to the dining room.'

His words made Leila's sense of disorientation increase because she came from a culture where men didn't cook. Where they had nothing to do with the preparation of food—unless you counted hunting it down in the desert and then killing it.

She told herself that he wasn't listening to what she'd said—and she'd said she wasn't hungry. But it seemed rude to sit here on her own while he ate and so she followed him into the dining room.

This was not a comfortable room either. He was clearly a fan of minimalism, and the furniture looked like something you might find in the pages of an architectural magazine. Tea and sandwiches sat on a table constructed from dull metal, around which was a circle of hard, matching chairs. The table sat beneath the harsh glare of the skylight, which made Leila think she was about to be interrogated.

And maybe that wasn't such a bad idea. She certainly had a few questions she needed to put to the man now pushing a plate of food towards her.

She held up the palm of her hand. 'I don't—'

'Just try,' he interrupted. 'Is that too much to ask, Leila?'

The hard timbre of his voice had softened into something which sounded almost gentle and the way he said her name suddenly made her feel horribly vulnerable. Or maybe she was imagining that. Maybe she was looking for crumbs of comfort when all he was doing was being practical. She realised that she felt weak and that if she didn't look after herself she would get weaker still. And she couldn't afford to do that.

So she ate most of the sandwich and drank a cup of jasmine tea before pushing away her plate. Leaning back against the hard iron chair, she crossed her arms defensively over her chest and studied him.

She drew in a deep breath. 'You can rest assured that I don't expect anything from you, Gabe. You've made your feelings absolutely plain. That afternoon was a mistake—we both know that. We were never intended to be together and this…this *baby* doesn't have to change that. I want you to know that you're free to walk away. And that I can manage on my own—'

'What are you planning to do?' The question fired from his mouth like a blistering fusillade of shots. 'To get rid of it?'

The accusation appalled her almost as much as the thought that he should think her capable of such an action, and Leila glared at him. *He doesn't know you*, she realised bitterly. *He doesn't even* like *you*.

'How dare you make a suggestion like that?' she

said, unable to keep the anger from her voice. 'I'm not ready to be a mother. I'm not sure I ever wanted to *be* a mother, but it seems that fate has decided otherwise. And I will accept that fate,' she added fiercely. 'I will have this baby and I will look after him—or her. And nothing and no one will stop me.'

Some of the tension had left him, but his mouth was still unsmiling as his gaze raked over her face. 'And just how are you planning to go about that?' he demanded. 'You who are a protected and pampered princess who can't move around freely unless under cover of darkness. What are you going to tell your brother? And how are you intending to support your-self when the child comes?'

She wished there were some place to look other than at his eyes, because they were distracting her. They were reminding her of how soft and luminous they'd been when he had held her in his arms. They were making her long for things she could never have. Things like love and warmth and closeness. A man to cradle her and tell her that everything was going to be all right.

But she didn't dare shift her gaze away from his, because wouldn't that be a sign of a weakness? A weakness she dared not show. Not to him. Not to her brother. Not to anyone. Because from here on in she must be strong.

Strong.

'I have jewellery I can sell,' she said.

His smile was faint. 'Of course you do.'

She heard the sardonic note in his voice. Another *rich princess* reference, she thought bitterly. 'Things my mother left me,' she added.

'And how do you propose getting your hands on this jewellery?' he questioned. 'Are you planning to take a trip to Qurhah and smuggle it out of the safe? Or perhaps you're thinking of asking your brother to mail it to you?'

'I could probably…I might be able to get one of my servants to get it to me,' she said unconvincingly. 'It would be risky, of course, but I'm sure it could be doable.'

Gabe gave a short laugh. Of all the women who could have ended up carrying his baby, it had to be her. A spoiled little rich girl who just snapped her beautiful fingers and suddenly money appeared. Did she really think it was going to be that easy?

His customary cool composure momentarily deserting him, he leaned across the table towards her. 'Do you really think your brother will be amenable to you taking funds out of the country to support an illegitimate baby?'

Her face seemed to crumple at the word, and Gabe felt a brief twist of regret that he had spoken to her so harshly. But she needed to confront the truth—no matter how unpalatable she found it.

'You have to face facts, Leila,' he said. 'And you're not going to find this easy. At some point you're going to have to tell your brother what's happened.' He saw the way her eyelids slid down to conceal the sudden brightness of her eyes, the thick lashes forming two ebony arcs which feathered against her skin. 'Have you thought about what his reaction might be?'

'I have thought of little else!'

'So what are you planning to tell him?'

The lashes fluttered open and the look in her eyes

was defiant, though the faint tremble of her lips less so. 'Oh, I won't mention your name, if that's what you're worried about.'

'I am not frightened of your brother, Leila. And neither am I denying what happened—no matter how much I might now regret it.' His mouth hardened. 'I'm asking what you are intending to tell Murat.'

She didn't answer for a moment and when she did, her voice was heavy. 'I guess I'm going to have to tell him the truth.'

'Or your unique version of the truth?' he questioned wryly. 'Won't the Sultan think that his sister's innocence has been compromised by a man with enough experience to have known better? It might suit your purpose—and his—to convince him that you were taken advantage of by an Englishman with something of a reputation where the opposite sex is concerned. Mightn't it be more acceptable for him to think of you as a victim rather than a predator?'

'I'm no victim, Gabe!' she flared back. 'And I'm no predator either, no matter how much it suits *you* to think that. I certainly didn't plan to seduce you—I was a virgin, for heaven's sake! I just…just gave into the "chemistry" you were talking about. And you certainly didn't seem to be objecting at the time.'

'No, you're right. I didn't put up much in the way of a fight.' His face tightened—as if her words were taking him some place he didn't want to go. 'But your brother is going to wonder when and where this great love affair of ours took place.'

She flushed. 'Obviously, he doesn't know that I came to your hotel room.'

'Actually, you came *in* my hotel room,' he reminded

her sardonically. 'Don't forget that part of the story, Leila—because it's probably the best part of all.'

Her flush deepened as his words brought back memories of the way it had been that day. The way he had kissed her and told her she was beautiful. In those few brief and glorious moments, she'd thought she'd found her heart's desire. For a short while she had felt as perfect as it was possible to feel.

But those feelings were in the past and they had been nothing but fantasy. All that was left was the brittle reality of the present—so why torture herself by remembering something which had been so fleeting?

'That's irrelevant,' she said. 'And I'm not scared of my brother.' But then some of her bravado left her. Tiredly, she lifted up her hands and buried her face in them as the warm darkness enveloped her like a welcoming cloak.

'Leila?' His voice was suddenly soft. 'Are you *crying*?'

'No, I am *not*!' she said fiercely, but she kept her face hidden all the same.

'Then look at me,' he commanded.

Rebellion flared inside her. She didn't *want* to look at him because, although there were no tears, she was afraid of what he might be able to read in her eyes. She didn't want to expose her sense of deflation and defeat. The liberated woman she'd yearned to be seemed to have slipped away into the shadows and was nowhere to be seen. And she had no one to blame but herself. She had gone to a *known playboy's* bedroom and let him kiss her. Why had she thought that having sex with a total stranger was somehow *empowering*?

'I have a solution,' he said.

His words broke into her thoughts. She lowered her hands but her head remained bent—as if she had found something uniquely fascinating to look at on the dark denim of her jeans. 'You have a magic wand with the power to turn back time, do you?'

'Unfortunately, I'm clean out of magic wands, so it looks like I'll just have to marry you instead.'

At this, her head jerked up, her gaze meeting his in disbelief. 'What?'

'You heard. And you're clever enough to realise it's the only option. I have no choice, other than to make you my wife—because I can see it would be intolerably cruel to let a woman like you face this on your own.' His eyes glittered like ice. 'Because you are not on your own. I share equal responsibility for what has happened, although you are a princess while I am…'

His face grew taut and Leila saw the sudden flare of pain which had darkened his grey eyes.

'You're what?' she prompted breathlessly.

For a moment he said nothing. A sudden darkness passed over his face, but just as quickly it was gone. The billionaire tycoon was back in control.

'It doesn't matter. For obvious reasons, this child cannot be born illegitimate. You will not need to hide your head in shame, Leila. I didn't ever want to be a husband.' His cool eyes flashed silver. 'Or a father. But as you say—fate seems to have decided otherwise. And I will accept that fate. We will be married as soon as possible.'

It should have been the dream solution but to Leila it felt like no such thing. She didn't want to marry a man who looked as if he were destined for a trip to the gallows, or to live with the realisation that she had trapped him into a life he didn't want. She couldn't imagine ever bonding with this icy *stranger*.

'I won't do it,' she said stubbornly. 'I won't tie myself to a man who doesn't want me. And you can't make me marry you.'

'You think not?' The smile he gave did not meet his eyes. 'You'd be surprised what I can do if I set my mind to it—but I'm hoping that we can come to some kind of *amicable* agreement. These are the only terms I am offering and I'd advise you to accept them. Because you're not really in any position to object. Your brother will disown you if you don't and I doubt whether you have a clue how to look after yourself. Not in a strange city without your servants and bodyguards to accede to your every whim. You cannot subject a baby to a life like that and I won't allow you to, because this is my baby too. You will marry me, Leila, because there is no alternative.'

CHAPTER SIX

Leila stared into the full-length mirror at someone who looked just like her. Who moved just like her. A woman who was startlingly familiar yet who seemed like a total stranger.

She was eight weeks pregnant by a man who didn't love her and today was her wedding day.

She glanced around the luxury hotel room to which she would never return. Her suitcases had already been collected by Gabe's driver and taken to his riverside apartment, which was to be her new home after she became his wife. She thought about the bare rooms and the minimalist decor which awaited her. She thought about the harsh, clear light which flooded in from the river. As if such a soulless place as that could ever be described as home!

He had asked her to be his bride, yet he had made her feel as if she was an unwanted piece of baggage he had been forced to carry. She had eventually—and reluctantly—agreed with him that marriage seemed to be the only sensible solution, when his phone had begun to ring. *And he had answered it!* He had left her sitting there as if she'd been invisible while he had conducted a long and boring business call right in front of her. It had not been a good omen—or an encouraging sign about the way he treated women.

Inside she had been seething, but what could she do? She could hardly storm out onto the unknown streets of London—or rush back to the safety of Qurhah, where nobody would want a princess who had brought shame onto her family name. She had felt trapped—and her heart had sunk like a heavy stone which had been dropped into a river. Was she destined to feel trapped for the rest of her days, no matter where in the world she lived?

Her reflected image stared back at her and she regarded it almost objectively. Her bridal dress of cobalt-blue was sleek and concealing and the hotel hairdresser had woven crimson roses into her black hair. She had refused to wear white on principle. It hadn't seemed appropriate in the circumstances. Much too romantic a gesture for such an occasion as this— because what was romantic about an expectant bride being taken reluctantly by a man who had no desire to be married to her?

Yet didn't some stupid part of her wish that it could all be different? Didn't she wish she were floating along on a happy pink cloud, the way brides were *supposed* to do? Maybe all those books and films she'd devoured during her lonely life at the palace had left their mark on her after all. She had no illusions about men or marriage, but that didn't stop her from wanting the dream—like some teenager who still believed that anything was possible.

But at least this was to be a quiet wedding. And a quick wedding—which had presented more of a problem.

The three-week wait required by English law had not been practical for a couple in their situation. As a desert princess, she could not live with Gabe and she had no desire to spend weeks in limbo at the Granchester Hotel, no matter how luxurious her suite there. Short of flying to Vegas, the only alternative was to get married in the Qurhahian Embassy in London—for which she needed her brother's permission. And she hadn't wanted to ask him, because she hadn't wanted to tell him why she needed to marry the Englishman in such a rush.

Yet she'd known she was going to have to break the news to Murat some time, hadn't she? She'd known she was going to have to tell him she was having Gabe's baby—so how could he refuse to grant her use of the embassy? She knew—and he knew—that the niece or nephew of the Sultan could not be born outside wedlock.

It had been the most difficult conversation of her life—not helped by the fact that it had been conducted by telephone. Her nervous stammering had been halted by Gabe taking the phone from her and quietly telling the Sultan that he intended to marry her. She wasn't sure what Murat actually said in response because Gabe had just stood there and listened to what sounded like an angry tirade thundering down the line.

But the Englishman had stood his ground and, after calmly reasserting his determination to take her as his bride, had handed the phone back to Leila.

Beneath Gabe's grey gaze, she had explained to Murat that while she would prefer to do this with his blessing, she was perfectly prepared to do it without.

Such a wait would, of course, mean living with a man who was not her husband.

The Sultan had sounded shocked—as much by her attitude as by her words—for she was aware that few people ever openly defied him. But unexpectedly, his voice had softened and for a moment he had sounded just like the Murat she'd thought no longer existed. The one she'd seen all those years ago, after their mother had died. When for once he had let down his guard and Leila had sobbed in his arms until there were no tears left to cry. And afterwards she'd noticed his own damp cheeks and seen the grief which had ravaged his dark face.

That was the only time in her life she had seen her brother showing emotion until now, when he asked her a question which came out of nowhere.

'And do you love him, Leila?' he had asked her quietly. 'This man Gabe Steel.'

Leila had closed her eyes and walked to the far end of the room, knowing that a lie was the only acceptable answer. A lie would make Murat leave them alone. A lie would confer an odd kind of blessing on this strange marriage.

'Yes,' she had answered in a low voice, glad that Gabe was not within earshot. 'Yes, I love him.'

And that had been that. Blessing conferred. They were given permission to use the embassy although Murat told her he would not be attending the nuptials himself.

In fact, the ceremony was to have only two witnesses—Sara and her husband, Suleiman, who had also known Leila since she had been a child. A relatively informal lunch following the ceremony was to be their only celebration. Time had been too tight to arrange anything else, although Gabe told her that a bigger party for his colleagues and friends could be arranged later, if she was so inclined.

Was she? She didn't know any of his colleagues or friends. She knew hardly anything about him—and in truth he seemed to want it to stay that way. It was as if the man she was marrying was an undiscovered country—one which she had suddenly found herself inhabiting without use of a compass. She was used to men who told women little—or nothing—but this was different. She was having his baby, for heaven's sake—and surely that gave her some sort of *right* to know.

On the eve of their wedding, they had been eating an early dinner in the Granchester's award-winning rooftop restaurant when she'd plucked up enough courage to ask him a few questions.

'You haven't mentioned your parents, Gabe.'

His expression had been as cold as snow. 'That's because they're dead. I'm an orphan, Leila—just like you.'

The cool finality in his tone had been intimidating but she wasn't going to give up that easily. She had put down her glass of fizzy water and looked him squarely in the eyes.

'What about brother or sisters?'

'Sadly, there's none. Just me.' The smile which had followed this statement had been mocking. 'Tell me, did you bring your camera to England with you?'

The change of subject had been so abrupt that Leila had blinked at him in confusion. 'No. I left Qurhah in such a hurry that my camera was the last thing on my mind.'

'Pity. I thought it might have given you something to do.'

'I'm going to buy myself a new one,' she said defensively.

'Good.'

It was only afterwards that she realised he had very effectively managed to halt her line in questioning, with the adroitness of a man who was a master of concealment.

But now was not the moment to dwell on all the things which were missing from their relationship, because Sara had arrived to accompany her to the embassy for the wedding and Leila knew she must push her troubled thoughts aside. She must pin a bright smile to her lips and be prepared to play the part expected of her. Because if Sara guessed at her deep misgivings about the marriage, then mightn't she try to talk her out of it?

They embraced warmly and Sara's smile was soft as she pulled away and studied her. 'You look utterly exquisite, Leila,' she said. 'I hope Gabe knows what a lucky man he is.'

Somehow, Leila produced an answering smile. Lucky? She knew Sara had guessed the truth—that she was newly pregnant with Gabe's baby. But Sara wasn't aware that the thought of having a baby didn't scare her nearly as much as the fact that she was marrying a man who seemed determined to remain a stranger to her. She thought of his shuttered manner. The way he had batted back her questions as if she had no right to ask them. How could she possibly cope with living with such a man?

Yet as she made a final adjustment to her flowered headdress she felt a little stab of determination. Couldn't she break through the emotional barriers which Gabe Steel had erected around his heart? She had come this far—too far—to be dismissed as if what she wanted didn't matter. Because it *did* matter. *She* mattered. And no matter how impossible it seemed, she knew what was top of her wish-list. She wanted Gabe to be close to her and their baby. She'd had enough of families who lived their lives in separate little boxes—she'd done that all her life. Sometimes what you wanted didn't just *happen*—you had to reach out and grab it for yourself. And grab it she would.

'Let's hope he does,' she said with a smile as she picked up her bouquet.

But her new-found determination couldn't quite dampen down her flutter of nerves as the car took her and Sara to Grosvenor Square, where Gabe was standing on the steps waiting for her.

She thought how formidably gorgeous he looked as he came forward to greet her. Toweringly tall in a charcoal suit which contrasted with the dark gold of his hair, he seemed all power and strength. She told herself she wouldn't have been human if her body hadn't begun to tremble with excitement in response to him.

But he was only standing there because he had no choice.

Because she was carrying his baby.

That was all.

'Hello, Leila,' he said.

Her apprehension diminished a little as she saw the momentary darkening of his quicksilver eyes. 'Hello, Gabe,' she answered.

'You look…incredible.'

The compliment took her off-guard and so did the way he said it. Her fingers fluttered upwards to check the positioning of the crimson flowers in her hair. 'Do I?'

Gabe read the uncertainty in her eyes and knew that he could blot it out with a kiss. But he didn't want to kiss her. Not now and not in public. Not with all these damned embassy officials hovering around, giving him those narrow-eyed looks of suspicion, as they'd been doing ever since he'd arrived. He wondered if they resented their beautiful princess marrying a man from outside their own culture. Or whether they guessed this was a marriage born of necessity, rather than of love.

Love.

He hoped his exquisite bride wasn't entertaining any fantasies about love—and maybe he needed to spell that out for her. To start as he meant to go on. With the truth. To tell her that he was incapable of love. That he had ice for a heart and a dark hole for a soul. That he broke women's hearts without meaning to.

His mouth hardened.

Would he break hers, too?

CHAPTER SEVEN

THE MARRIAGE CEREMONY was conducted in both Qurhahian and English, and Gabe reflected more than once that the royal connection might have intimidated many men. But he was not easily intimidated and essentially it was the same as any other wedding he'd ever been to. He and Leila obediently repeated words which had been written by someone else. He slid a gleaming ring onto her finger and they signed a register, although his new wife's signature was embellished with a royal crest stamped into a deep blob of scarlet wax.

She put the pen down and rose gracefully from the seat, but as he took her hand in his he could feel her trembling and he found his fingers tightening around hers to give her an encouraging squeeze.

'You are now man and wife,' said the official, his robed figure outlined against the indigo and golden hues of the Qurhahian flag.

Sara and Suleiman smilingly offered their congratulations as soft sounds of Qurhahian *Takht* music began to play. Servants appeared as if by clockwork, bearing trays of the national drink—a bittersweet combination of pomegranate juice mixed with zest of lime. After this they were all led into a formal dining room, where a wedding breakfast awaited them, served on a table festooned with crimson roses and golden goblets studded with rubies.

Leila found herself feeling disorientated as she sat down opposite Suleiman and began to pick at the familiar Qurhahian food which was presented to her. The enormity of all that had happened to her should have been enough to occupy her thoughts during the meal. But all she could think about was the powerful presence of her new husband and to wonder what kind of future lay ahead.

Who *was* Gabe Steel? she wondered as she stabbed at a sliver of mango with her fork. She listened to him talking to Sara about the world of advertising and then slipping effortlessly into a conversation about oil prices with Suleiman. He was playing his part perfectly, she thought. Nobody would ever have guessed that this was a man who had effectively been shotgunned into marriage.

He must have sensed her watching him, for he suddenly reached out his hand and laid it on top of hers, and Leila couldn't prevent an involuntary shiver of pleasure in response. It had been weeks since he'd touched her, and she revelled in the feeling of his warm flesh against hers—but the gesture felt more dutiful than meaningful. She couldn't stop noticing the way Suleiman and Sara were with each other. The way they hung off the other's every word and finished each other's sentences. She felt a tug of wistfulness in her heart. Their marriage was so obviously a love-match and it seemed to mock the emptiness of the relationship she shared with Gabe.

She turned to find his cool grey gaze on hers.

'Enjoying yourself?' he said.

She wondered what he would say if she told him the truth. That she felt blindsided with bewilderment about the future and fearful of being married to a man who gave nothing away.

But Leila was a princess who had been taught never to show her feelings in public. She could play her part as well as he was playing his. She could make her reply just as non-committal as the cool question he'd asked.

'It's been a very interesting day,' she conceded.

Unexpectedly, he gave a low laugh—as if her un-emotional response had pleased him. He bent his lips to her ear. 'I think we might leave soon, don't you?'

'I think that might be acceptable,' she said, swallowing in an effort to shift the sudden dryness in her throat.

'I think so too,' he agreed. 'So let's say goodbye to our guests and go.'

The unmistakeable intent which edged his words made Leila's heart race with excitement. But hot on that flare of anticipation came apprehension, because the sex they'd shared that afternoon in Qurhah now seemed like a distant dream.

What would it be like to make love with him again after everything that had happened? What if this time it was a disappointment—what then? Because she suspected that a man as experienced as Gabe would not tolerate a wife who didn't excite him. Wasn't that why men in the desert kept harems—to ensure that their sexual appetites were always gratified? Wasn't

it said in Qurhah that no one woman could ever satisfy a man?

Her heart was pounding erratically as he led her
outside to his waiting car. Leila slid inside and the
quicksilver gleam of his eyes was brighter than her
new platinum wedding ring as he joined her on the
back seat. Suddenly, she imagined what her life might
have been like if Gabe had refused to marry her, as he
could so easily have done. She imagined her brother's
fury and her country's sense of shame and she felt a
stab of gratitude towards the Englishman with the
hard body and the dark golden hair.

'Thank you,' she said quietly.

'For what?'

'Oh, you know.' She kept her voice light. 'For saving me from a life of certain ruin—that sort of thing.'

He gave a short laugh. 'I did it because I had to.
No other reason. Don't start thinking of me as some
benign saviour with nothing but noble intentions in
his heart. Because that man does not exist. I'm a cold-
hearted bastard, Leila—or so your sex have been telling me all my adult life. And since that is unlikely to
change, it's better that I put you straight right from
the start. The truth might hurt, but sometimes it's a
kinder pain than telling lies. Do you understand?'

'Sure,' said Leila, her voice studiedly cool as her
fingers dug into the wedding bouquet which she would
have liked to squash against his cold and impassive
face. Couldn't the truth have waited for another day?
Couldn't he have allowed her one day of fantasy before
the harshness of reality hit them? But men only did
that kind of mushy stuff in films. Never in real life.

'But understand something else,' he added softly.

'That my lack of emotion does not affect my desire for you. I have thought of nothing else but you and although I badly want to kiss you, you'll have to wait a little while longer. Because while I'm fairly confident the press haven't got hold of this story, I can't guarantee that the paparazzi aren't lying in wait outside my apartment. And we don't want them picturing you getting out of the car looking completely ravaged, do we, my beautiful blue-eyed princess?'

'We certainly don't,' said Leila, still reeling from his cold character assessment—followed by those contrasting heated words of desire.

But there were no paparazzi outside the apartment—just the porter who'd been sitting behind the desk the first time she'd been here and who now smiled as they walked into the foyer.

'Congratulations, Mr Steel,' the man said, with the tone of someone who realised that normal deference could be relaxed on such a day. 'Aren't you going to carry the lady over the threshold?'

Gabe gave a ghost of a smile as he stared down into Leila's eyes. 'My wife doesn't like heights,' he said. 'Do you, darling?'

'Oh, I absolutely loathe them,' she said without a flicker of reaction.

But irrationally, she felt a stab of disappointment as they rode upstairs in the elevator. Despite what he'd said in the car, it wouldn't have hurt him to play the part of adoring groom in front of the porter, would it? They said that men fantasised about sex—well, didn't he realise that women did the same thing about weddings, no matter how foolish that might be?

'Why are you frowning?' he questioned as the door of his apartment swung silently shut behind them.

'You wouldn't understand.'

Tilting her chin with his finger, he put her eyes on a collision course with his. 'Try me.'

She tried all right. She tried to ignore the sizzle of her skin as he touched her, but it was impossible. Even that featherlight brush of his finger on her chin was distracting. Everything about him was distracting. Yet his grey eyes were curious—as if he was genuinely interested in her reasons. And wasn't that as good a start as any to this bizarre marriage?

So start by telling him what it is you want. He has just advocated the use of truth, so tell him. Tell him the truth. She held his gaze. 'If you must know, I quite liked the idea of being carried over the threshold.'

Dark eyebrows arched. 'I thought you might find it hypocritical under the circumstances.'

'Maybe it is.' She shrugged. 'It's just that I've never been carried anywhere before—well, presumably I was, as a baby. But not as an adult and never by a man. And this might be the only stab at it I get.'

'Oh, I see,' he said. He took the bouquet from her hand and placed it on a nearby table. 'Would carrying you to bed compensate for my shocking omission as a bridegroom?'

She met the glitter of his eyes and excitement began to whisper over her skin. He was flirting with her, she realised. And maybe she ought to flirt right back. 'I don't know,' she said doubtfully. 'We could try it out and see.'

He gave a flicker of a smile as he bent and slid one arm under her knees, picking her up with an ease which didn't surprise her. Leila might have been tall for a woman but Gabe made her feel tiny. He made her feel all soft and yearning. He made her feel things she had no right to feel. Her arms fastened themselves around his neck as he carried her along a long, curving corridor into his bedroom.

She'd only been in here once before to unpack her clothes and find a home for her shoes. But then, as now—she had been slightly overwhelmed by the essential *masculinity* of the room. A vast bed was the centrepiece—and everything else seemed to be concealed. Wardrobes and drawers were tucked away out of sight, and she could see why. Any kind of clutter would have detracted from the floor-to-ceiling windows which commanded such a spectacular view over the river.

She tried to imagine bringing a baby into this stark environment and felt curiously exposed as he set her down on her gleaming wedding shoes.

'Won't we…be seen?' she questioned, her gaze darting over his shoulder as he began to unfasten her dress.

'The windows are made specially so that people can't see in from the outside,' he murmured. 'Like car windows. So there's no need to worry.'

But Leila had plenty to worry about. The first time they'd done this, there had been no time to think. This time around and she'd done nothing *but* think. How many women had stood where she had stood? Women who were far more experienced than she was. Who would have known where to touch him and how to please him.

His fingers had loosened some of the fastenings,

and the dress slid down to her waist, leaving her torso bare. She felt *exposed.* And vulnerable. He bent his head to kiss her shoulder, but she couldn't help stiffening as he traced the tip of his tongue along the arrowing bone.

He drew his head away from her and frowned. 'What's wrong?'

'I don't know. This feels so...' Awkwardly, her words trailed off. She could pretend that nothing was wrong but she remembered what he'd said in the car. That the truth could hurt, but lies could hurt even more. And if she kept piling on layer after layer of fake stuff, her life would be reduced to one big falsehood. In a marriage such as theirs—wasn't the truth the only way to safeguard her sanity? 'So cold-blooded,' she said.

'You're nervous?'

'I guess so.'

'You weren't nervous last time.'

'I know.' She licked her lips. 'But last time felt different.'

'How?'

'Because we weren't thinking or analysing. There was no big agenda. No frightening future yawning ahead of us. It just...happened. Almost like it was meant to happen.'

For a moment she wondered if she'd said too much. Whether that final sentence had sounded like the hopeless yearning of an impressionable young woman. The truth was all very well, but she didn't want to come over as *needy.*

He stroked his hand down over her cheek and moved it round to her neck. His grey eyes narrowed and then suddenly he dug his fingers into her hair and brought his mouth down on hers in a crushing kiss.

It was the kiss which changed everything. The kiss which ignited the fire. All the pent-up emotion she'd kept inside for weeks was now set free. And suddenly it didn't matter that Gabe had warned her about having ice for a heart because, for now at least, he was all heat and flame and maybe that was enough to melt him.

She clung to him as his mouth explored hers, and he began to pull the pins from her hair. Silken strands spilled down around her shoulders, one after another. She could feel them tickling her back as they fell. Cool air was washing over her skin as he unclipped her bra and her breasts sprang free.

He stopped kissing her and stood for a moment, just observing her. And then, very deliberately, he reached out and cupped a breast in the palm of his hand, his eyes not leaving her face as he rotated his thumb against the nipple.

'Gabe,' she said indistinctly.

'What?' The thumb was replaced by the brush of his lips as he bent his head to the super-sensitive nub, and Leila closed her eyes as pleasure washed over her. Her senses felt raw and alive—as if he'd just rehabilitated them from a long sleep. She reached towards his shirt buttons, but the effort of undoing even one seemed too arduous when his hand was skimming so possessively over her waist and touching the bare skin there.

With a low laugh which sounded close to a growl, he freed the last fastenings of her dress and let it slide to the ground.

Stepping out from the circle of concertinaed silk, she looked up at his dark face, and something about his expression made her heart miss a beat. All her doubts and fears were suddenly replaced by something infinitely more dangerous. Something which had happened the last time she'd been in this situation. Because wasn't there something about Gabe Steel which called out to her on a level she didn't really understand? Something which made her feel powerful and vulnerable all at the same time.

He was a cool English billionaire who could have just thrown her to the wolves. Who could have rejected his child and made her face the consequences on her own. But he had done no such thing. He had been prepared to shoulder the heavy burden of responsibility she had placed upon his shoulders. Gabe Steel was not a bad man, she decided. He might be a very elusive and secretive one—but he was capable of compassion. And wasn't she now better placed than any other female on the planet to discover more about a person who had captivated her from the start? Couldn't she do that?

Her torpor suddenly left her as she reached towards his shirt and began to slide the buttons from their confinement. Her confidence grew as she felt his body grow tense. She could hear nothing but the laboured sound of his breathing as she opened up his shirt and feasted her eyes on the perfection of the golden skin beneath.

Bending her head, she flickered her tongue at his tight, salty nipple and she felt a sharp thrill as she heard him groan. She had never undressed a man before—but how difficult could it be? She tugged the charcoal jacket from his shoulders and let it fall on top of her discarded wedding dress. The shirt followed— so that now he was completely bare-chested, like those men she'd seen fighting for coins in one of the provincial market squares outside Simdahab.

Undoing the top button of his trousers, she was momentarily daunted by the hardness beneath the fine cloth, which made unzipping him awkward. But his fingers covered hers, and he guided her hand down over the rocky ridge, and Leila's heartbeat soared, because that shared movement felt so gloriously intimate.

With growing confidence, she dealt with his socks and shoes—and he returned the favour by easing her out of her panties and stockings.

Before long, they were both completely naked, standing face to face next to the bed. His hands were splayed over her bottom and her breasts were brushing against his chest. She could feel his erection nudging her belly and the answering wetness of her sex as she wrapped her arms around his neck.

'Are you sure we can't be seen?' she whispered.

'Why, is that your secret fantasy?' he questioned, pushing her down onto the soft mattress. 'People watching and seeing what a *naughty* princess you can be?'

Leila said nothing as his mouth moved to her neck and he moved his hand between her legs. She closed her eyes and tried to concentrate on the stroking movement of his fingers. But even intense pleasure could not completely obliterate the sudden troubled skitter of her thoughts. Was this what playboy lovers enjoyed most, she wondered—to share fantasies? Didn't he realise that she was still too much of a novice to have any real fantasies?

His eyes were dark as he moved over her, but she could see the sudden tautness of his mouth. She wondered if he was wishing that this were just uncomplicated sex. That he was not tied to her for the foreseeable future, and that there was not a baby on the way.

'Is something *wrong*?' she whispered.

'Wrong?' he echoed unsteadily. 'Are you out of your mind? I'm just savouring every delicious moment. Because for the first time in my life I don't have to worry about contraception. I'll be able to feel my bare skin inside you—and it's a very liberating feeling.'

His description sounded more mechanical than affectionate but Leila told herself to be grateful for his honesty. At least he wasn't coating his words with false sentiment and filling her with false hopes. And why spoil this moment by wishing for the impossible, instead of enjoying every incredible second?

Tipping her head back, she revelled in the sensation of what he was doing to her.

The way his lips were moving over hers.

The way his fingers played so distractingly over her skin, setting up flickers of reaction wherever they alighted.

The way he…

'Oh, Gabe,' she breathed as she felt him brushing intimately against her.

Slowly, he eased himself inside her, the almost-entry of his moist tip followed by one long, silken thrust. For a moment he stilled and allowed her body to adjust to him.

'I'm not hurting you?' he questioned.

Hurting her? That was the last thing he was doing. She was aware that he fitted her as perfectly as the last piece of a jigsaw puzzle which had just been slotted into place. She had never felt as complete as she did in that moment, and wouldn't the cool Gabe Steel be horrified if he knew she was thinking that way?

'No,' she breathed, shaking her head. 'You're not hurting me.'

'And does it feel—different?'

She met the smoky question in his eyes. 'Different?'

'Because of the baby?'

Would it terrify him if she told him that yes, it did? That it felt unbelievably profound to have his flesh inside her, while their combined flesh grew deep in her belly. Much too profound for comfort. She pressed her lips against the dark rasp of his jaw.

'I don't really have enough experience for comparison,' she whispered.

He tilted her face upwards so that all she could see was the gleam of his silver gaze. 'That sounds like a blatant invitation to provide you with a little more.'

'D-does it?'

'Mmm. So I think I'd better do just that, don't you?'

She gasped as he began a slow, sweet rhythm inside her. Her fingertips slid greedily over the silken skin which cloaked his moving muscles. Eagerly, she began to explore the contours of his body—the power of his rock-hard legs and the taut globes of his buttocks.

She felt part of him.

All of him.

She felt in that moment as if anything was possible.

'Gabe,' she moaned, her body beginning to tense.

His mouth grazed hers. 'Tell me.'

'I c-can't.'

'Tell me,' he urged again.

'Oh. *Oh!*'

Gabe felt her buck beneath him in helpless rapture. His mouth came down hard on hers as her back arched, his fingers tightening over her narrow hips. He became aware of the softness of her belly as he pressed against her and then he let go—spilling his seed into her with each long and exquisite thrust.

For a while he was aware of nothing other than the fading spasms deep within his body and a sense of emptiness and of torpor. Automatically, he rolled away onto the other side of the bed where he lay on top of the rumpled sheet and sucked mouthfuls of air back into his lungs. His eyelids felt as if they'd been weighted with lead. He wanted to sleep. To sleep for a hundred years. To hold on to a sensation which felt peculiarly close to contentment.

But old habits died hard and he fought the feeling and the warm place which was beckoning to him, automatically replacing it with ice-cold logic. All he was experiencing was the stupefying effect of hormones as his body gathered up its resources to make love to her again. It was sex, that was all. Surprisingly good sex—but nothing more than that. How could it ever be more than that?

Meeting her bright blue gaze, he flickered her a non-commital smile.

'What a perfect way to begin a honeymoon,' he drawled.

CHAPTER EIGHT

It was a honeymoon of sorts.

Leila supposed that some people might even have considered it a successful honeymoon. With time and money at his disposal, Gabe set about showing her a London she'd only ever seen in films or books—and the famous city came to life before her eyes.

They visited Buckingham Palace and the famous Tower where two young princes had once been imprisoned. They took a ride on a double-decker bus, which thrilled Leila since she'd never been on public transport before. They went to galleries and museums and saw some of the long-running West End shows.

He showed her a 'secret' London too—a side to the city known only to the people who lived in it. Restaurants with flower-filled courtyards which were tucked away behind industrial grey streets and intimate concert halls where he took her to hear exquisite classical music.

And when they weren't sightseeing they were having sex. Lots of it. Inventive, imaginative and mind-blowing sex, which left her gasping and breathless with pleasure every time. She told herself she was lucky—and when she was kissing her gorgeous new husband, she *felt* lucky.

But while she couldn't fault the packed schedule Gabe had arranged for her, sometimes it felt as if she were spending time with a tour guide. Sometimes he was so...*distant*. So...*forbidding*. She would ask him questions designed to understand him better. And he would find a million ways not to answer them. He would change the subject and ask her about growing up in Qurhah. And although he seemed genuinely interested in her life as a princess, sometimes he made her feel as if she was a brand new project he was determined to get right.

He remained as enigmatic as he'd done right from the very beginning. She had married a man who kept his thoughts and feelings concealed and inevitably, that made anxiety start to bubble away beneath the glossy surface of her new life.

It was only during sex that she ever felt on the brink of a closeness which constantly eluded her. When he was making love he sometimes looked down at her, his face raw with passion and his eyes flaring with pewter fire. She wanted him to tell her what it was that kept him so firmly locked away from her. She wanted to look within his heart and see what secrets it revealed. But as soon as his orgasm racked his powerful body, she could sense him distancing himself again.

Oh, he would hold her tightly and bury his lips against her damp skin and tell her that she was amazing. Once he even told her that she was the best lover he'd ever had. But to Leila, his words seemed empty and she was scared to believe them. As if he was saying them because he knew he ought to say them, rather than because he meant them.

She would lie there hugging her still-trembling body while he went off to take a shower, forcing herself to remember that she was only here because of the life growing inside her. A life so new that sometimes it didn't seem as if it were real...

One morning they were lying amid a tumble of sex-scented sheets after a long and satisfying night of lovemaking, when she rolled onto her stomach and looked at him.

'You know, you've never even told me how you made your fortune.'

He stretched out his lean, tanned body and yawned. 'It's a dull story.'

'Every story has a point of interest.'

He looked at her. 'Why do you ask so many questions, Leila? You're always digging, aren't you?'

She met his cool gaze. 'Maybe I wouldn't keep asking if you actually tried answering some of them for a change.'

She could see the wariness in his eyes, but for once she refused to be silenced or seduced into changing the subject. Even if their marriage wasn't 'real' in the way that Sara and Suleiman's was—didn't her position as his wife give her some kind of right to know? To find out whether, beneath that cool facade, Gabe Steel had a few vulnerabilities of his own?

'So tell me,' she murmured and dropped a kiss on his bare shoulder. 'Go on.'

Gabe sighed as he felt her soft lips brushing against his skin. He had never planned to marry her. He hadn't wanted to marry her. Reluctantly, he had taken what he considered to be the best course of action in circumstances which could have ruined her. He had done the right thing by her. Yet instead of showing her gratitude by melting quietly into the background and making herself as unobtrusive as possible, she had proved a major form of distraction in ways he had never anticipated.

From the moment she opened her eyes in the morning to the moment those long black lashes fluttered to a close at night, she mesmerised him in all kinds of ways.

The way she rose naked from the rumpled sheets—a tall, striking Venus with caramel skin and endless legs. The reverse-heart swing of her naked bottom as she wiggled it out of the room. The way she slanted him that blue-eyed look, which instantly had his blood boiling with lust.

But he knew that women often mistook a man's lust for love; and that lust always faded. In the normal scheme of things, that wouldn't matter, but with Leila it did. He couldn't afford to let her fall in love with him and have the all too predictable angry outcome when she realised it wasn't ever going to be reciprocated. He didn't want to hurt her. He didn't want her to start thinking that he could feel things, like other men did. She was the mother of his child and she wasn't going anywhere. He might not have wanted to become a father, but he was going to make damned sure that this baby was an enduring part of his life. Which he guessed was why he found himself saying, 'What exactly do you want to know?'

'Tell me how you first got into advertising,' she said. 'Surely that's not too difficult.'

'Look it up on the internet,' he said.

'I already have.' She remembered how she'd checked him out before that fateful meeting in Simdahab. 'And although there's lots of stuff about you winning awards and riding motorbikes and being pictured with some of the world's most beautiful women—there's not much in the way of background. Almost as if somebody had been controlling how much information was getting out there.' She stroked her finger down his cheek. 'Is that down to you, Gabe?'

'Of course it is.' His response was economical. 'I'm sure your brother controls information about himself all the time.'

'Ah, but my brother is a sultan who rules an empire and has a lot of enemies. What's your excuse?'

She saw the flicker of irritation which crossed his face—a slightly more exaggerated irritation than the look she'd seen yesterday when he'd discovered a dirty coffee cup sitting on the side of his pristine bathtub and acted as if it were an unexploded bomb.

'My excuse is that I try to remain as private as possible,' he said. 'But I can see that you're not going to let up until you're satisfied. Where shall I begin?'

'Were you born rich?'

'Quite the opposite. Dirt poor, as they say—though I doubt whether someone like you has any comprehension of what that really means.'

His accusation rankled almost as much as his attitude, and Leila couldn't hide her hurt. 'You think because I was born in a palace that I'm stupid? That I have no idea what the vast majority of the world is like? I'm surprised at you, Gabe—leaping to stereotypical judgements like that.'

'Ah, but I'm an advertising man,' he said, a smile curving the edges of his mouth. 'And that's what we do.'

'I think I can work out what *dirt poor* means. I'm just interested to know how you went from that to…' the sweeping gesture of her hand encompassed the vast dimensions of the dining room, with its expensive view of the river '…well, *this*.'

'Fate. Luck. Timing.' He shrugged. 'A mixture of all three.'

'Which as usual tells me precisely nothing.'

He levered himself up against the pillows, his gaze briefly resting on the hard outline of her nipples. He felt the automatic hardening of his groin, wondering if that sudden flare of colour over her cheeks meant that she'd noticed it, too.

'I left school early,' he said. 'I was sixteen, with no qualifications to speak of, so I moved to London and got a job in a big hotel. I started in the kitchens—' He fixed her with a mocking look as he saw her eyes widen. 'Does it shock my princess to realise that her husband was once a kitchen hand?'

'What shocks this particular princess is your unbelievable arrogance,' she said quietly, 'but I'm enjoying the story so much that I'm prepared to overlook it. Do continue.'

She saw another brief flicker of sexual excitement in his eyes, but quickly she dragged the cotton sheet up to cover her breasts. She didn't want him seducing her into silence with his kisses.

'I didn't stay in the kitchens very long,' he said. 'I gravitated to the bar where the buzz was better and the tips were good. A big crowd of guys from a nearby advertising agency used to come in for drinks every Friday night—and they used to fascinate me.'

She stared at him. 'Because?'

For a moment, Gabe didn't answer because it was a long time since he'd thought about those days and those men. He remembered the ease with which they'd slipped credit cards from the pockets of their bespoke suits. He remembered their artful haircuts and the year-round tans which spoke of winter sun—at a time in his life when he'd never even had a foreign holiday.

'I wanted to be like them,' he said, in as candid an admission as he'd ever made to anyone. 'It seemed more like fun than work—and I felt I was owed a little fun. They would sit around and brainstorm and angst if they were short of creative ideas. They didn't really notice me hanging around and listening. They used to talk as if I wasn't there.' And hadn't it been that invisibility which had spurred him on—even more than his determination to break free from the poverty and heartbreak which had ended his childhood so abruptly? The sense that they had treated him like a nothing and he'd wanted to be someone.

'They had a deadline looming and a slogan for a shampoo ad which still hadn't been written,' he continued. 'I made a suggestion—and I remember that they looked at me as if I'd just fallen to earth. Some teenage boy with cheap shoes telling them what they should write. But it was a good suggestion. Actually, it was a brilliant suggestion—and they made me a cash offer to use it. The TV campaign went ahead using my splash line, the product flew off the shelves and they offered me a job.'

He remembered how surprised they'd been when he

had coolly negotiated the terms of his contract, instead of snatching at their offer, which was what they'd clearly expected. They'd told him that his youth and his inexperience gave him no room for negotiation, but still he hadn't given way. He had recognised that he had a talent and that much was non-negotiable. It had been his first and most important lesson in bargaining—to acknowledge his own self-worth. And they had signed, as he had known all along they would do.

'Then what happened?'

Gabe shrugged as her soft words floated into his head and tangled themselves up with his memories. He had often wondered about the particular mix of ingredients which had combined to make him such a spectacular success, yet the reasons were quite simple.

He was good with words and good with clients. A childhood spent honing the art of subterfuge had served him well in the business he had chosen. His rise to the top had been made with almost seamless ease. His prediction that digital technology was the way forward had proved unerringly correct. He had formed his own small company and before long a much bigger agency had wanted to buy his expertise. He had expanded and prospered. He'd discovered that wealth begot wealth. And that being rich changed nothing. That you were still the same person underneath, with the same dark and heavy heart.

'I just happened to be in the right place at the right time,' he said dismissively, because thoughts of the past inevitably brought with them pain. And he tried not to do pain. Didn't he sometimes feel that he'd bitten off his allotted quota of the stuff, all in one large and unpalatable chunk? He gave her a long, cool look.

'So if the interrogation is over, Leila, you might like to think about what you want to do today.'

Leila stiffened, her enjoyment of his story stifled by the sudden closure in his voice. Was this what all men did with women? she wondered as she swung her legs over the side of the bed and grabbed a tiny T-shirt and a pair of panties. Tell them just enough to keep them satisfied, but nothing more than that? Keep them at arm's length unless they were making love to them?

But she *knew* all this, didn't she? None of these facts should have surprised her. She'd seen the way her father had treated her mother. She'd seen how quickly women became expendable once their initial allure had worn off. So why the hell was she grasping at rainbows which didn't exist?

She tugged on the T-shirt and pulled on her panties before walking towards the window, suddenly unenthusiastic about the day ahead.

'Why don't you surprise me?' she said flatly. 'Since you're the man with all the ideas.'

She didn't hear the footfall of his bare feet straight away. She didn't even realise he was following her until his shadow fell over her and she turned round to meet the tight mask of his face. She could see the smoulder of sexual hunger in his eyes, but she could see the dark flicker of something else, too.

'What kind of surprise do you want, Leila?'

She could feel the beat of sexual tension as it thrummed in the air around them. He was angry with her for probing, she realised—and his anger was manifesting itself in hot waves of sexual desire. She told herself that she should walk away from him and that might make him realise that sometimes he treated her more like an object than a person. But she couldn't walk away. She didn't want to. And didn't they both want exactly the same thing? The only thing in which they were truly compatible...

She met the smoulder of his gaze and let the tip of her tongue slide along her bottom lip. 'If I tell you then it won't be a surprise, will it?'

'My, how quickly you've learnt to flirt,' he observed softly, his eyes following the movement hypnotically. 'My little Qurhahian virgin hasn't retained much of her innocence, has she?'

'I sincerely hope not,' she returned, 'because a wife who lacks sexual adventure will quickly lose her allure. The women of the harem learn that to their peril.'

Her assertion seemed to surprise him, for his eyes narrowed in response. His gaze drifted down to where the tiny T-shirt strained over her aching nipples.

'You are dressed for sex,' he said huskily.

She tilted her chin. 'I'm hardly dressed at all.'

'Precisely.'

He took a step towards her and backed her into the sitting room towards the L-shaped sofa which dominated one side of the room, and Leila felt excited by the dark look on his face, which made him appear almost *savage*.

She could feel the leather of the sofa sticking to her bare thighs as he pushed her down on it, and her heart began to hammer in anticipation.

'Gabe?' she said, because now he was kneeling on the ground in front of her and pulling her panties all the way down.

But he didn't answer. He was too busy parting her

knees and moving his head between them and, although this was not the first time he had done this, it had never felt quite so intense before.

'Gabe,' she said again, more breathlessly this time as his tongue began to slide its way up towards the molten ache between her legs.

'Shut up,' he said roughly.

But his harsh words were not matched by the exquisite lightness of his touch, and she couldn't help the gasp of pleasure which was torn from her lips. Her eyelids fluttered to a close as she felt the silkiness of his hair brushing against her thighs. Her lips dried as the tip of his tongue flickered against her heated flesh and she groaned.

She felt helpless beneath him—and for a moment the feeling was so intense that she felt a sudden jolt of fear. She tried to wriggle away but he wouldn't let her. He was imprisoning her hips with the grasp of his hands while he worked some kind of sweet torture with his tongue. And surely if she wanted him to stop, she shouldn't be urging him on by uttering his name. Nor clutching at his shoulders with greedy and frantic hands.

She could feel her orgasm building and then suddenly it happened violently, almost without warning. Her fingers dug into his hair as she began to buck beneath him and just when it should have been over, it wasn't over at all.

Because Gabe was climbing on top of her and straddling her—entering her with one hard, slick stroke which seemed to impale her. Gabe was moving inside her, and she was crying out his name again and tears were trickling down her cheeks—and what on earth was *that* all about? She wiped them away before he could see them.

Automatically, she clung to him as he shuddered inside her, his golden-dark head coming to rest on her shoulder and his ragged breath warm against her skin. She found herself thinking that one of life's paradoxes was that intense pleasure always made you aware of your own capacity for intense pain. And wasn't that what had scared her? The certainty that pain was lurking just around the corner and she wasn't sure why.

She closed her eyes and it seemed a long while before he spoke, and when he did his words were muffled against her neck.

'I suppose you're now going to demand some sort of apology.'

She turned her head to face him. She saw his thick lashes flutter open and caught a glimpse of the darkness which still lingered in his eyes. 'I'm not sure that making a woman moan with pleasure warrants an apology,' she said.

His face tightened as he withdrew from her and rolled onto his back, staring up at the ceiling and the dancing light which was reflected back from the river outside. He gave a heavy sigh. 'Maybe it does if that pleasure comes from anger. Or if sex becomes a demonstration of power, rather than desire.'

She didn't need to ask what had made him angry because she knew. Her questions had irritated a man who liked to keep his past hidden. A man who recoiled from real intimacy in the same way that people snatched their hands away from the lick of a flame and she still didn't know why.

Maybe she should just accept that she was wast-

ing her time. Leila's hand crept to her still-flat stomach. Shouldn't she be thinking about her baby's needs
and the practicalities of her current life, rather than
trying to get close to a man who was determined not
to let her?

But something made her reach out her hand and to
lay it softly over the thud of his heart. 'Well, whatever
your motivation was, we both enjoyed it—unless I'm
very much mistaken.'

At this he turned his head, and his grey eyes were
thoughtful as he studied her. 'Sometimes you surprise me, Leila.'

'Do I?'

'More frequently than I would ever have anticipated.' He stroked his hand over the curve of her hips.
'You know, we ought to think what you're going to
do next week.'

'Next week?' She drew her head back and looked
at him. 'Why—what's happening next week?'

'I'm going back to work. Remember?' He kissed
the curve of her jaw. 'Honeymoons don't last for ever
and I do have to work to pay the bills, you know.'

Suddenly she felt unsettled. Displaced. 'And in the
meantime, I'm going to be here on my own all day,'
she said slowly.

His grey eyes were suddenly watchful. 'Not necessarily. I can speak to some of my directors, if you
like. Introduce you to their wives so you can get to
know them. Some of them work outside the home,
but plenty of them are around during the day—some
with young children.'

Her heart suddenly heavy, Leila nodded. She didn't
want to seem ungrateful and, yes, it would be good

to meet women whose company she might soon welcome once her own baby arrived.

But Gabe's words made her feel like an irrelevance. As if she had no real identity of her own. Someone's daughter. Someone's sister and, now, someone's wife.

Well, she *did* exist as a relevant person in her own right and maybe she needed to show Gabe that—as well as to prove it to herself. Back in Qurhah, she had yearned for both personal and professional freedom and surely this was her golden opportunity to grab them.

'I don't want to just kill time while I wait for the baby to be born,' she said. 'I want a job.'

His eyes narrowed. 'A job?'

'Oh, come on, Gabe. Don't look so shocked. Wasn't that what I wanted the first time I ever met you?' She lifted her hand and touched the dark-gold of his hair. 'You thought my photos were good when I first showed them to you. You told me so—and I'd like to think you meant it. Wouldn't your company have work for someone with talent?'

'No,' he said.

Flat refusal was something Leila was used to, but it was no less infuriating when it was delivered so emphatically by her husband. She felt the hot rush of rebellion in her veins. 'I'm not asking you to pull any strings for me,' she said fiercely. 'Just show my work to someone in your company—anonymously, of course—and let them be the judge.'

'No,' he said again.

'You can't keep saying no!'

'I can say any damned thing I please. You're asking *me* for a job, Leila—remember? And I'm telling you that you can't have one. That's the way it works when you're an employer.'

She stared at him mulishly and thought that, at times, Gabe's attitude could be as severe as her brother's. 'Why not?' she demanded. 'I'd like to know exactly what it is you're objecting to. The accusations of nepotism, which won't stand up if I get the job on my own merits? Or is it something else—something you're not telling me?'

Gabe got off the sofa and began to walk towards the bedroom, shaking his head as if denying her question consideration. She thought that he was going to leave the room without answering when he suddenly turned back and it was only then that she realised that he was completely naked. And completely aroused. Again.

'It's your proximity I'm having a problem with,' he declared heatedly, wondering how she managed to get under his skin time and time again. 'I'll have to be with you the whole damned time, won't I? In the car. In the canteen—'

'Standing by the water cooler?' Her mouth twitched. 'Or does some minion bring you water on a silver tray in a crystal glass?'

'We're talking about my life—not yours, princess!' he iced back. 'And how can someone judge your work when you don't have it? You haven't even brought your portfolio with you, have you? You left it in Qurhah.'

'Yes, I did. But I have all the images on a USB stick,' she said sweetly. 'So that won't be a problem.'

Gabe made a stifled sound of fury as he walked away towards the bathroom, wishing for the first time ever that he had a door to slam. But he had chosen the apartment because there *were* no doors. Because one room flowed straight into the next, each characterised by a disproportionate amount of light and space. He had chosen it because it was the antithesis of the places he'd inhabited during his childhood—and now the very determined Princess Leila Scheherazade was making him want to lock himself away. She was invading his space even more than she had already done. And there didn't seem to be a damned thing he could do to stop it.

He would have someone show her portfolio to Alastair McDavid—at Zeitgeist's in-house photographic studio. And he would just have to hope that Alastair found her work *good*—if not quite good enough.

He turned on the shower and his mouth hardened as the punishing jets of icy water began to rain down on him. Because something told him that his hopes were futile and that Leila would soon have her exquisite foot in yet another door.

CHAPTER NINE

THE PANORAMIC VIEW outside his penthouse office gave him a moment's respite before Gabe refocused his gaze on the woman who was sitting at the other side of his desk.

Of course his hopes had been futile. And *of course* Leila got the job she'd secretly been lusting after. Leaning back in his swivel chair, he looked into the excited sparkle of his wife's blue eyes. Though maybe that was an understatement. She hadn't just 'got' the job, she had walked it—completely winning over Alastair McDavid, who had described her photos as 'breathtaking' and had suggested to Gabe that they employ her as soon as possible.

Gabe drummed his fingertips on the polished surface of his desk and attempted to speak to her in the same tone he would use to any other employee. But it wasn't easy. The trouble was that he'd never wanted to kiss another employee before. Or to lock the door and remove her clothes as quickly as possible. The X-rated fantasies which were running through his mind were very distracting, and his mouth felt as dry as city pavement in the summer. 'At work, I am your boss,' he said coolly. 'Not your husband or your lover. And I don't want you ever to forget that.'

'I won't.'

'While you are here, you will have nothing to do with the Qurhah campaign.'

'But—'

'No buts, Leila. I'm telling you no—and I mean it. It will only complicate matters. People working on the account might feel inhibited dealing with you—a woman who just happens to be a princess of the principality. Their creativity could be inhibited and that is something I won't tolerate.' He subjected her to a steady look, glad of the large and inhibiting space between them. 'Is that clear?'

'If you say so.'

'I do say so. And—barring some sort of emergency—you will not come to my office again unless you are invited to do so. While you are here at Zeitgeist, you will receive no deferential treatment—not from me, nor from anyone else. You are simply one of the four hundred people I employ. Got that?'

'I think I'm getting the general idea, Gabe.'

Gabe couldn't fail to notice the sardonic note in her voice, just as he couldn't fail to notice the small smile of triumph she was trying to bite back, having got her way as he had guessed all along she would. And maybe he should just try to be more accepting about the way things had turned out. Alastair McDavid was no fool—and he'd said that Leila had an extraordinarily good eye and that her photos were pretty near perfect. Her talent was in no doubt—and, since her work had been submitted anonymously, nobody could accuse him of nepotism.

But Gabe was feeling uncomfortable on all kinds of levels. For the first time ever his personal life had entered the workplace and he didn't like it. He didn't like it one bit. Despite years of occasional temptation and countless invitations, he'd never dated an employee or a client before. He had seen for himself the dangers inherent in that. There had never been some hapless female sobbing her eyes out in the women's washroom because of something *he'd* done. He'd never been subjected to awkward silences when he walked into boardroom meetings, or one of the Zeitgeist dining rooms.

The less people knew about him, the better, and he had worked hard to keep it that way. He was never anything less than professional with his workforce, even though he joined in with 'dress-down Friday' every week and drank champagne in the basement bar next door whenever a new deal was signed. People called him Gabe and, although he was friendly with everyone from the janitor to the company directors, he maintained that crucial personal distance.

But Leila was different.

She looked different.

She sounded different.

She was distracting—not just to him but to any other man with a pulse, it seemed. He had driven her to work this morning—her first morning—and witnessed the almost comical reaction of one of his directors. The man had been so busy staring at her that he had almost driven his car straight into a wall.

Her endless legs had been encased in denim as she'd climbed out of Gabe's low sports car, with one thick, ebony plait dangling down over one shoulder.

In her blue shirt and jeans, she was dressed no differently from any of his other employees, yet she had an indefinable head-turning quality which marked her out from everyone else. Was that because she'd been brought up as a princess? Because she had royal blood from an ancient dynasty pulsing through her veins, which gave her an innate and almost haughty bearing? When he looked at her, didn't he feel a thrill of something like pride to think that such a woman as this was carrying his child? Hadn't he lain there in bed last night just watching her while she slept, thinking how tender she could be, and didn't he sometimes find himself wanting to kiss her for absolutely no reason?

Yet he knew those kinds of thoughts were fraught with danger. They tempted him into blotting out the bitter truth. They ran the risk of allowing himself to believe that he was capable of the same emotions as other men. And he was not.

He frowned, still having difficulty getting his head round the fact that she was sitting in *his* office as if she had every right to be there. 'Anything you want to ask *me*?' he questioned, picking up a pencil and drawing an explosion of small stars on the 'ideas' notepad he always kept open on his desk.

'Do people know I'm pregnant?'

He looked up and narrowed his eyes. 'Why would they?'

'Of course. Why would they?' she repeated, and he thought he heard a trace of indignation in her voice. 'Heaven forbid that you might have told somebody.'

'You think that this is something I should boast about, Leila? That an obviously unplanned pregnancy has resulted in an old-fashioned shotgun marriage?

It hasn't exactly sent my reputation shooting up into the stratosphere.' He gave a dry laugh. 'Up until now, I'd always done a fairly good job of exhibiting fore-thought and control.'

Pushing back her chair, she stood up, her face suddenly paling beneath the glow of her olive skin. 'You b-bastard,' she whispered. 'You complete and utter bastard.

He'd never heard her use a profanity before. And he'd never seen a look of such unbridled rage on her face before. In an instant he was also on his feet. 'That didn't come out the way it was supposed to.'

'And how was it *supposed to* come out?' She bit her lip. 'You mean you didn't intend to make me sound like some desperate woman determined to get her hooks into you?'

'I was just pointing out that usually I don't mix my personal life with my business life,' he said, raking his fingers through his hair in frustration.

'I think you've made that abundantly clear,' said Leila. 'So if you've finished with your unique take on character assassination cunningly designed as a pep talk, perhaps I could go and start work?'

For once Gabe felt wrong-footed. He saw the hurt look on her face and the stupid thing was that he wanted to kiss her. He wanted to break every one of his own rules and pull her into his arms. He wanted to lose himself in her, the way he always lost himself whenever they made love. But he fought the feeling, telling himself that emotional dependence was a luxury he couldn't afford. He knew that. He knew there were some things in life you could never rely on and that was one of them.

But guilt nagged at him as he saw the stony expression on her face as she turned and walked towards the door. 'Leila?'

She turned around. 'What?'

'I shouldn't have said that.'

Her smile was wry. 'But you did say it, Gabe. That's the trouble. You did.'

Shutting his office door behind her, Leila was still simmering as she walked into the adjoining office to find Alice waiting for her and with an effort she forced herself to calm down. Because what she was *not* going to do was crumble. She could be strong—she knew that. And she needed to be strong—because she was starting to realise that she couldn't rely on Gabe to be there for her.

Oh, he might have put a ring on her finger and made her his wife, but she couldn't quite rid herself of the nagging doubt that this marriage would endure—baby or not.

Pushing her troubled thoughts away, she smiled at Alice. 'Gabe says you're to show me around the Zeitgeist building,' she said. 'Though judging by the size of it, I think I might need a compass to find my way around the place.'

Alice laughed. 'Oh, you'll soon get used to it. Come on, I'll show you the canteen first—that's probably the most important bit. And after that, I'll take you down to the photographic studios.'

Leila quickly learnt that paid employment had all kinds of advantages, the main one being that it didn't give you much opportunity to mope around yearning for what you didn't have.

Overnight, her first real job had begun and, although she was fulfilling a lifetime ambition just by *having* a job, she found it a bit of a shock. She'd grown up in a culture which encompassed both opulence and denial, but she had never set foot in the workplace before. She was unprepared for the sheer exhaustion of being on her feet all day and for being woken by the alarm clock every morning. Quickly, she discovered that dressing at leisure was very different from having to be ready to start work in the studio at eight-thirty. Her lazy honeymoon mornings of slow lovemaking were replaced by frantic clockwatching as she rushed for the shower and grappled with her long hair.

'You don't have to do this, you know,' said Gabe one morning as they sat at some red lights with Leila hastily applying a sweep of mascara to her long lashes.

'What? Wear make-up?'

'Very funny. I'm talking about putting yourself through this ridiculous—'

'Ridiculous what?' she interrupted calmly. 'Attempt to prove that I'm just like everyone else and that I need some sense of purpose in my life? Shock! Horror! Woman goes out to work and wears make-up!'

'What does the doctor say about it?' he growled.

'She's very pleased with my progress,' Leila answered, sliding her mascara back into her handbag. 'And it may surprise you to know that the majority of women work right up until thirty-six weeks.'

She sat back and stared out of the car window, watching the slow progress of the early-morning traffic. Gabe's car was attracting glances, the way it always did. She guessed that, when viewed from the outside, her life looked like the ultimate success story.

As if she 'had it all'. The great job. The gorgeous man. Even a little baby on the way.

From the inside, of course—it was nothing like that. Sometimes she felt as if her marriage was as illusory as the many successful advertising campaigns which Gabe's company had produced. Those ones which depicted the perfect family everyone lusted after with the artfully messy table with Mum and Dad and two children sitting around it, giggling.

Yet everyone at Zeitgeist knew that the model father in the advert was probably gay and that the model mum's supposedly natural beauty was enhanced by hair extensions and breast implants.

No, nothing was ever as it seemed.

Nothing.

Gabe was still Gabe. Compelling, charismatic but ultimately as distant as a lone island viewed from the shoreline. And she realised that was the way he liked it. The way he wanted to keep it. They weren't growing closer, she realised. If anything, they were drifting further apart.

One evening, they arrived back at the apartment after an early dinner out and Gabe went straight to their bedroom to change. Minutes later he reappeared in jeans and a T-shirt, with his face looking like thunder.

'What the hell has been going on?' he demanded. 'Have we been burgled?'

Leila walked over to where he stood, looking at the room behind him with a sinking heart. He had left early for a meeting this morning and somehow she'd slept through the alarm and had woken up really late. Which meant that she had left home in a rush, and it showed—particularly as today was the cleaner's day off.

Automatically, she moved forward and started to pick up some of the discarded clothes which lay like confetti all over the floor. A pair of knickers were lying on his laptop. 'I overslept,' she said, hastily grabbing them from the shiny surface. 'Sorry.'

Her words did nothing to wipe the dark expression from his face, for tonight he seemed to be on some kind of mission to get at her. 'But it isn't just when you oversleep, is it, Leila?' he demanded. 'It's every damned day. I keep finding used coffee cups around the place and apple cores which you forget to throw away. Did nobody ever teach you to tidy up after yourself, or were there always servants scurrying around to pick up after you?'

Leila flinched at the cold accusation ringing from his voice, but how could she possibly justify her general untidiness when his words were true?

'I did have servants, yes.'

'Well, you don't have servants now, and I value my privacy far too much to want any staff moving in—not even when the baby's born. So if we're to carry on living like this, then you're really going to have to learn to start being more tidy.'

The words leapt out at her like sparks from a spitting fire.

If we're to carry on living like this.

Biting her lip, she turned away, but Gabe caught hold of her arm and pulled her against him.

'I'm sorry.'

'It doesn't matter.'

'It does. That came out too harshly. Sometimes I

just…snap,' he said, his head lowering as he made to brush his lips over hers.

But Leila pushed him away. He thought that making love could cure everything—and usually it did. It was always easy to let him kiss her, because his kisses were so amazing that she always succumbed to them immediately. And when she was in his arms he didn't feel quite so remote. When he was deep inside her body, she could allow herself to pretend that everything was just perfect. Yet surely that was like just papering over a widening crack in the wall, instead of addressing the real problem beneath.

Sometimes she felt as if she was being a coward. A coward who was too scared to come out and ask him whether he wanted her out of his life. Too scared that he might say yes.

She went into the bathroom and showered, and when she emerged in a cotton dress which was beginning to feel snug against her expanding waist, it was to find him sipping at a cup of espresso.

He looked up as she entered the room, and suddenly his grey eyes were cool and assessing.

'I have a deal coming up which means that I need to go to the States,' he said. 'Will you be okay here on your own?'

'Of course,' she said brightly, but, coming in the wake of their recent spat, his words sounded ominous.

She walked over to the fridge and poured herself a glass of fizzy water, exaggeratedly wiping the few spilt drops from the work surface before going to perch on one of the bar stools.

'How long will you be gone?' she asked.

'Only a few days.'

Gabe saw the tremble of her lips, which she couldn't quite disguise, and suddenly the coffee in his mouth seemed to taste sour. Yet he knew exactly what he was doing. He was insightful enough to know that he was pushing her away, but astute enough to know that he could offer her no other option. Because the thought of getting close to her was making him *feel* stuff. And that was something he didn't do.

He put down his coffee cup with more force than he intended.

If only it could be different.

His mouth hardened as he stared into the bright blue of her eyes.

It could never be different.

That night they lay on opposite sides of the bed, the heavy silence indicating that neither was asleep, though neither of them spoke. His sleep was fractured, his disturbing dreams forgotten on waking— leaving him with a heavy headache which he couldn't seem to shift.

He was just sliding his cell phone into his jacket pocket when he walked into the sitting room to find Leila looking at his passport, which he'd left lying on the table.

'That's a very sombre photo,' she commented.

'You aren't supposed to smile in passport photos.'

Leila found herself thinking that he wouldn't have much of a problem with that. That unless the situation demanded it, his natural demeanour was unsmiling. Those chiselled cheekbones and cold eyes lent themselves perfectly to an implacable facade.

She glanced down at his birth date and her heart

gave a funny little twist as she glanced back up at him. 'Will you phone me?'

'Of course.' He took the passport from her and brushed his mouth over hers in a brief farewell kiss. 'And I'll be back on Sunday. Keep safe.'

But after he'd gone, all the energy seemed to drain from her. Leila sat down on the sofa and stared into space, her heart thumping like someone who had just run up an entire flight of stairs without stopping. The date on his passport was March fifteenth—the Ides of March. She knew that date. Of course she did. Wasn't it etched firmly in her mind as heralding the biggest change in her life?

She shook her head, telling herself not to be so stupid. It was a coincidence. Of course it was.

Over the next few days, she was grateful to be able to lose herself in the distraction of work—glad that its busy structure gave her little time to dwell on the uncomfortable thoughts which were building like storm clouds in her mind. Alastair McDavid announced that Zeitgeist had just landed a big contract to advertise a nationwide chain of luxury hotels and spas. And since spa clientele consisted mainly of women, it was in everyone's interest to use a female photographer.

'And we'd like to use you, Leila,' he told her with a smile.

Leila was determined not to let him down and the excitement of planning her first solo assignment was almost enough to quell the disquiet which was still niggling away inside her. Almost, but not quite.

Sunday arrived and Gabe texted to say that he was just about to catch his plane. She wished she was in a position to collect him from the airport, but she still hadn't learnt to drive. She had allowed her husband and his chauffeur to ferry her everywhere. It had been all too easy to lean on Gabe—and if she wasn't careful that could get to be a lasting habit.

Because for the first time she was beginning to acknowledge the very real fear that this marriage seemed destined to fail.

She remembered his cold rebuke about her general untidiness, yet she hadn't even factored in what the presence of a tiny baby was going to do to Gabe Steel's ordered existence. What if he hated having a screaming infant in his slick, urban apartment? Wouldn't he get irritated if she went off sex, as she'd been told that new mothers sometimes did?

Her distraction grew as she showered and washed her hair, then picked out a long tunic dress in palest blue silk, which she'd brought with her from Qurhah. She didn't question why she had chosen to wear that particular tunic on that particular day. All she knew was that it covered her body from neck to ankle and she wondered if she was seeking comfort in the familiar.

She pinned her hair into a simple up do and made tea while she tried not to feel as if she was waiting. But she *was* waiting. Waiting for some sort of answer to a question she wasn't sure she wanted to ask.

What was it that they said in Qurhah? That if you disturbed a nest of vipers, then you should expect to get bitten.

She heard the click of the front door opening and the sound of Gabe closing it again. He didn't call her name, but his footsteps echoed on the polished wooden floor as they approached, and her heart began to race as he walked into the room.

For a moment he stood very still and then he came over and kissed her, but she pulled away.

'How's Leila?' he questioned, his eyes narrowing as they stared into her face.

'I'm fine,' she said brightly. 'Shall I make some coffee?'

'I had some on the plane. Any more coffee and I'll be wired for a week.' He glanced down at the stack of unopened mail which was waiting for him before looking up again. 'So what's been happening while I've been away?'

'My…scan went well,' she said carefully, her fingers beginning to pleat at the filmy blue fabric of her tunic. 'And I have some good news. Alastair wants me to do the assignment for the new spa contract.'

'Good.'

She looked up from her fretful pleating and suddenly her throat felt so dry that she could barely get the words out. 'And March fifteenth is your birthday.'

He gave a short laugh. 'Interesting that you should tell me in an almost accusatory manner something I've known all my life.'

She told herself not to be intimidated by the coldness in his voice, nor to freeze beneath the challenge icing from his pewter eyes. 'That's the day we had… sex in Simdahab.'

'And?' His dark eyebrows elevated into two sardonic arcs. 'Aren't I allowed to have sex on my birthday?'

She shook her head. She was still a relative novice when it came to lovemaking, but she was intuitive enough to know that something about him that afternoon had been different. Something she hadn't seen since. There had been something *wild* about his behaviour that day. Something seeking and restless. She chose her words carefully. 'You gave me the distinct impression that having spontaneous sex with someone you'd only just met wasn't your usual style.'

'Maybe you were just too irresistible.'

'Is that true?'

Gabe met the steady stare of her bright blue eyes and, inwardly, he cursed. If she was a casual girlfriend, he would have told her it was none of her business, and then to get out and leave him alone. But Leila was his wife. He couldn't tell her to get out. *And the truth was that he didn't want to.*

He met her eyes. 'No, it's not true,' he said quietly. 'I seduced you that day because I was in Qurhah, a place where it's almost impossible to buy whisky, which is my usual choice of drink on my birthday.' There was a pause. 'And in the absence of the oblivion brought about by alcohol, I opted instead for sex.'

CHAPTER TEN

LEILA STARED INTO eyes as flat as an icy sea as Gabe's words hit her. Her fingernails were digging into the palms of her hands but she barely noticed the physical discomfort—not when this terrible pain was lancing through her heart and making it almost impossible for her to breathe. 'You used me?' she questioned at last. 'Because you couldn't get a drink?'

His laugh was bitter. 'There's no need to be quite so melodramatic about it. People have sex for all kinds of reasons, Leila. Sometimes it's because lust just gets the better of them and sometimes because it makes them forget.' He threw his passport down on the table and looked at her. 'I didn't use you any more than you used me that day. I wanted oblivion and you wanted to experiment. Am I right?'

Leila squirmed beneath the challenge of his gaze because his words were uncomfortably close to the bone. How could she deny his accusation when it was true? She *had* wanted to experiment, yes—but she'd had her reasons. What would he say if she told him that he had seemed to represent everything a man should be? Everything that she'd ever dreamed of.

That for the first time in her life, she'd actually *believed* all those romantic films she'd been hooked on.

Yet, in a way, maybe that had been seeking her own kind of oblivion. She had found pleasure with a devastatingly handsome and sexy man—and for a few brief moments she had forgotten the prison of her palace life. But she hadn't really known him as *Gabe*, had she?

She still didn't.

'What were you seeking to obliterate?' she asked carefully.

'It isn't relevant.'

'Oh, I think it is.' She sucked in a breath and held his gaze as she let it out again. 'Look, I get it,' she said. 'I get that you're a very private man who doesn't want to talk about emotions.'

'So don't ask me.'

She shook her head as she ignored the cold clamp of his words. 'But I *have* to ask you—don't you see? I know all the psychology books say that yesterday is gone. But I don't want to go on like this—not knowing stuff. I'm having your baby, Gabe. Don't you think that gives me the right to know something about your past, as well as the occasional speculation about what our future might hold?'

With an angry shake of his head, Gabe walked over to the window to stare out at one of the most expensive views in the world. It was ironic, he thought. You could buy yourself somewhere high in the sky, which was far away from the madding crowd. But no matter how much you spent or how much you tried to control your life—you could never keep the world completely at bay. You could only try. He could feel the hard beat of his heart as he turned round to face her.

'It isn't relevant,' he said again.

'It *is*,' she argued. 'We can't just keep burying our heads in the sand and pretending this isn't happening, because it is. We're going to have a baby, Gabe. A baby which needs to be cared for. Not just cared for. Loved,' she said, her voice faltering a little.

'Don't look to me for love, Leila,' he said tonelessly. 'I thought I'd made that clear from the beginning.'

'Oh, you did. You made it very clear, and I wouldn't dream of expecting you to love *me*,' she said. 'But surely our baby has the right to expect it. If you can't show our baby love—and believe me when I tell you I'm not judging you if that's the case—then don't I at least have the right to know why?'

For a moment there was silence while Gabe looked at the set of her shoulders and the steady blue gaze which didn't falter beneath his own deliberately forbidding stare. He knew what she wanted. What women always wanted. To find out why he didn't show emotion or even feel it. It was something he'd come up against time and time again—and women were the most tenacious of creatures. Countless numbers had tried—and failed—to work him out. Powerful women, rich women, successful women—they all wanted the one thing which eluded them. They saw his cold heart as a challenge; his emotional isolation as something they wished to triumph over.

Yet Leila's question had not been tinged with ambition—rather with the simple desire to understand. She was the mother of their baby and maybe what she said was true. Maybe she *did* have the right to know what had made him the person he was. But wasn't he scared to let her close? Scared of what might happen if he did?

He surveyed her from between half-shuttered eyes. 'What do you want me to tell you?'

Leila was so surprised at his sudden change of heart that it took a moment before she could speak, and all the time her head was telling her to go easy. Not to scare him off with a fierce interrogation.

'Oh, I don't know,' she said softly. 'All the usual things. Like, where you were born. I don't even know that.'

For a moment, there was silence. It reminded her of the moment before the start of a play, when the whole theatre was quiet and prepared for revelation. And then he began to speak.

'I was born in the south of France. But we moved back to England when I was a baby—to a place called Brighton.'

'Yes, Brighton. I've heard of it.' Leila nodded and began reciting, as if she were reading from a geographical textbook. 'It's a seaside town on the south coast. Is it very beautiful—this Brighton?'

In spite of everything, Gabe gave a glimmer of a smile. At times she seemed so foreign and so *naive* but of course, in many ways, she was. Maybe she thought he came from a background like hers and telling her that he had been born on the French Riviera would only feed into that fantasy.

The truth, he reminded himself. She needed to know the truth.

'Anywhere by the sea has the potential to be beautiful,' he said. 'But, like any town, there are rough parts—and those were the places we lived. Not that we stayed anywhere very long.'

'We?'

'My mother and me.'

'Your father wasn't around?'

Gabe could taste the sudden bitterness in his mouth. He wanted to stop this unwanted interrogation right now, but he realised that these questions were never going to go away unless he answered them.

And wasn't it time he told *someone*?

'No, my father wasn't around,' he said. 'He and my mother split up before I was born. Things ended badly and she brought me back to England, but she had no family of her own and no money. When she met my father, she'd been working as a waitress—and that was all she was qualified to do.'

'So, was your father French?' questioned Leila, thinking that he didn't look French.

He shook his head. 'No. He was Russian.'

Slowly, she nodded, because that made sense. Much more sense. The high, chiselled cheekbones, which made his face look so autocratic and proud. The icy grey eyes. The hair, which looked like dark, molten gold. 'So what kind of childhood did you have?' she asked quietly.

He shrugged, as if it didn't matter. 'It was largely characterised by subterfuge. My mother was always afraid that my father would try to find me and so we were always on the move. Always living just below the radar. Our life was spent running. And hiding.'

If he thought about it, he could still remember the constant sensation of fear. Of looking over his shoulder. Of being told never to give anything away to any stranger he might meet. He had quickly learnt how to appear impenetrable to those he met.

And hadn't the surveillance and masquerade skills he'd acquired stood him in good stead for his future career? He had discovered that the world of advertising was the world of illusion. That what you saw was never quite what you got. The masks he had perfected to keep his identity hidden had been invaluable in his role as a powerful executive. They were what had provided him with his chameleon-like reputation. As careers went, his background had been a perfect fit.

'My mother took what jobs she could,' he said. 'But it was difficult to juggle poorly paid work around childcare and I pretty much brought myself up. I soon learnt to look after myself. To rewire dodgy electrics and to shop for cheap food when the supermarkets were about to close.'

Leila blinked in surprise, because the image he painted was about as far away from the sophisticated billionaire she'd married as it was possible to imagine. But she still thought there was something he wasn't telling her. Some dark secret which was lurking just out of sight. *I need to know this for my baby*, she thought fiercely. *For our baby.*

'And?'

His mouth hardened. She saw the flash of something bleak in the depths of his eyes before it was gone again.

'I used to feel indignant that my father had never bothered to look us up. I wondered why he didn't seem to care how his son was doing—or why he'd never once offered to help out financially. It became something of an obsession with me. I used to ask my mother what he was like, but she never wanted to talk about him. And the more she refused to tell me, the more frustrating I found it.'

His words tailed off, and for a moment he said nothing. Leila held her breath but didn't speak, not wanting to break his concentration.

'As I grew older, I became more determined to find out something about him,' he continued. 'I didn't necessarily want to be with him—I just wanted to *know*.'

'Of course you did,' she said.

Their eyes met, and Gabe suddenly got a painful flash of insight. Maybe he'd wanted to know for exactly the same reasons that Leila wanted to know about *him*. Maybe everybody had a fundamental desire to learn about their roots. Or the roots of the child they carried…

'But my mother was scared,' he said. 'I can see that now. She was scared that I would run to a man she feared. That I would choose him over her.' He gave a bitter laugh. 'Of course, I only discovered this afterwards.'

'Afterwards?' she echoed as some grim ending glinted as darkly as thick blotting paper held over the beam of a flashlight.

He nodded, and the way he swallowed made Leila think of barbed wire; of something jagged and sharp lodging in his throat and making his words sound painful and distorted.

'It was the eve of my sixteenth birthday,' he said. 'We were living in this tiny hole of place. It was small and dark and I started wondering what kind of life my father had. Whether he was wealthy. Or whether he was reduced to eating food which was past its sell-by date and shivering like us, because it was the coldest spring in nearly thirty years. So I asked my mother the same question I'd been asking ever since I could remember. Did she have any idea where he was or what he did? And as always, she told me no.'

'And you believed her?' questioned Leila tentatively.

He shrugged. 'I didn't know what to believe, but I was on the brink of adulthood and I couldn't tolerate being fobbed off with evasive answers any more. I told her that the best birthday present she could give me would be to tell me the truth. That either she provided me with some simple facts about my parentage—or I would go and seek my father out myself. And that she should be under no illusion that I would find him. I was probably *harsher* than I should have been, but I had the arrogance of youth and the certainty that what I was doing was right.'

There was complete silence, and Leila's heart pounded painfully as she looked at him, for she had never seen an expression on a man's face like that before. Not even when her brother had returned from that terrible battle with insurgents in Port D'Leo and his two most senior commanders had been slain in front of him. There was a helplessness and a hopelessness glinting in Gabe's eyes which was almost unbearable to observe.

'She said she would tell me the next day, on my birthday. But…'

His words tailed off and Leila knew he didn't want to tell her any more, but she needed to know. *And he needed to say it.* 'But what?'

'I think she meant to tell me,' he said. 'But I also

think she was terrified of the repercussions. Afraid that she might lose me.' His mouth twisted. 'But when I got back from school the next day, she couldn't tell me anything at all because she was dead.'

Leila's heart lurched as she stared at him in alarm, not quite believing what he'd just said. *'Dead?'*

For a long moment, there was silence. 'At first I thought she was just sleeping. I remember thinking that I'd never seen her looking quite so peaceful. And then I saw...I saw the empty pill bottle on the floor.'

Leila's throat constricted as she struggled to say something, imagining the sight which must have greeted the young boy as he arrived home from school. She stared at him in utter disbelief. 'She... *killed herself*?'

'Yes,' he said flatly.

Leila felt a terrible sadness wrap itself around her heart. She had wanted to understand more about Gabe Steel and now she did—but she had never imagined this bleak bitterness at the very heart of his life. She could hardly begin to imagine what it must have been like for him. So that was why he had locked it all away, out of sight. That was why he kept himself apart—why he deliberately put distance between himself and other people.

She was stunned by what he had told her. Yet out of his terrible secret came a sudden growing sense of understanding. No longer did it surprise her that he didn't want to trust or depend on women—because hadn't the most important woman in his life left him?

And lied to him.

'Did you blame yourself?' she asked quietly.

'What do you think?' he bit out, his icy facade now completely shattered.

She saw emotion breaking through—real, raw emotion—and it was so rare that instinctively she went to him and he didn't push her away. He let her hold him. She wrapped her arms around him and hugged him tightly and she could feel his heart beating hard against her breast. Pressing her lips against his ear, she whispered, 'You mustn't blame yourself, Gabe.'

'No?' He pushed her away, like somebody who had learned never to trust words of comfort. 'If I hadn't been so persistent…if I hadn't been so damned stubborn—then my mother wouldn't have felt driven to commit such a desperate act. If I hadn't been so determined to find out about my *father*, she need never have died. She could have lived a contented old age and been cushioned by the wealth I was to acquire, but which she never got to see.'

For a moment Leila didn't answer, wondering if she dared even try. Because how could someone like her possibly empathise with Gabe's rootless childhood and its tragic termination? How could she begin to understand the depths of grief he must have experienced when he was barely out of boyhood? That experience had formed him and, emotionally, it had warped him.

Up until that moment, Leila had often thought herself hard done by. Her parents' marriage had been awful—everyone at court had known that. Her father had spent most of his time with his harem, while her mother had sat at home heartbroken—too distracted to focus on her only daughter. As if to compensate for that, Leila had been pampered and protected by her royal status but she had felt trapped by it too. She had been isolated and lost during a childhood almost as lonely as Gabe's.

But his circumstances had been different. He had been left completely on his own. He had lived with his guilt for so long that it had become part of him. 'Your mother must have been desperate to have taken such a drastic action,' she said quietly.

His voice was sardonic. 'I imagine she must have been.'

She stumbled on. 'And she wouldn't want you to carry on blaming yourself.'

'If you say so, Leila.'

She swallowed, because one final piece of the jig-saw was missing. 'And did you ever find your father? Did you track him down?'

There was a heartbeat of a pause before his mouth hardened. 'No.'

'Gabe—'

'No.' He shook his head. 'That's enough. No more questions, Leila. And no more platitudes either. Aren't you satisfied now?'

His eyes were blazing, and she wondered if she'd gone too far. If she'd pushed him to a point where he was likely to break. She wondered if he was going to walk out. To put distance between them, so that when they came face to face again he could pretend that this conversation had never happened.

But he didn't do any of that. Instead, he pulled her back into his arms. He stared down at her for a long moment before bending his head to kiss her— the fiercest kiss she could ever have imagined. She knew what he was doing. He was channelling his hurt and his anger and his pain into sex, because that was what he did. That was how he coped with the heavy burden he carried.

Leila clung to him, kissing him back with all the passion she was capable of, because she wanted him just as much. But she wanted so much more than just sex. She ached to give him succour and comfort. She wanted to show him that she was here for him and that she would always be here for him if only he would let her. She would warm his cold and damaged heart with the power of her love. Yes, love. She loved this cold, stubborn husband of hers, no matter how much he tried to withdraw from her.

'Gabe,' she whispered. 'My darling, darling Gabe.'

The breath he let out in response was ragged and that vulnerable sound only added to her determination to show him gentleness. Her hand flew up to the side of his face and, softly, she caressed his jaw. Did her touch soothe him? Was that why his eyelids fluttered to a close, as if he was unspeakably weary? She touched those too, her fingertips whispering tenderly over the lids, the way she had done all that time ago in Simdahab.

Beneath the tiptoeing of her fingers, his powerful body shuddered—shaking like a mighty tree which had been buffeted by a major storm. He opened his eyes and looked at her but there was no ice in his grey eyes now. Only heat and fire.

He picked her up and carried her over to the sofa, and she'd barely made contact with the soft leather before he was impatiently rucking up her filmy blue dress and sliding down her panties. His hand was shaking as he struggled with his own zip, tugging down his trousers with a frustrated little moan.

She was wet and ready for him and there were few preliminaries. But Leila didn't want them; she just wanted Gabe inside her. His fingers parted her slick, moist folds and she gasped as he entered her, closing her eyes as he filled her.

'Gabe,' she said indistinctly, but he didn't answer as he began to move.

It was fast and deep and elemental. It seemed to be about need as much as desire, and Leila found herself responding to him on every level. Whatever he demanded of her, she matched—but she had never kissed him quite as fervently as she did right then.

Afterwards, she collapsed against the heap of the battered cushions, her heart beating erratically as she made shallow little gasps for breath. She turned to look at him, but he had fallen into a deep sleep.

For a while she lay there, just watching the steady rise and fall of his chest. She thought about what he had told her and she flinched with pain as she took her mind back to his terrible story. He had known such darkness and bleakness, but that period of his life was over. He had taken all the secrets from his heart and revealed them to her—and she must not fail him now.

Because Gabe needed to be loved; properly loved. And she could do that. She could definitely do that. She would care for him deeply, but carefully—for fear that this bruised and damaged man might turn away from the full force of her emotions.

She must love him because he needed to be loved and not because she demanded something in return. She might wish for that, but it was not hers to demand.

She snuggled closer, feeling the jut of his hip against her belly. She ran her lips over the roughness of his jaw and then kissed the lobe of his ear as she wrapped her arms tightly around his waist.

'I will love you, Gabe Steel,' she whispered.

But Gabe only stirred restlessly in his sleep.

CHAPTER ELEVEN

THE DISTANT RUMBLE of thunder echoed Leila's troubled thoughts.

Had she thought it would be easy? That Gabe's icy heart would melt simply because he'd revealed all the bitter secrets he'd carried around with him for so long? That he'd instantly morph into the caring, sharing man she longed for him to be?

Maybe she had.

She glanced out of the window. Outside, the tame English skies were brewing what looked like the fiercest storm she had witnessed since she'd been here. Angry grey clouds billowed up behind St Paul's Cathedral and the river was the colour of dark slate.

She had tried to reassure herself with the knowledge that, on the surface, things in their marriage were good. Better than before. She kept telling herself that, as if to accentuate the positive. Gabe was teaching her card games and how to cook eggs, and she was learning to be tidier. He massaged her shoulders at the end of a working day and they'd started going for country walks on the weekend. Her pregnancy was progressing well and she had passed the crucial twelve weeks

SHARON KENDRICK   163

without incident. Her doctor had told her that she was blooming—and physically she had never felt better.

Her job, too, was more fulfilling than she could ever have anticipated. At first, Leila had suspected that most of the staff at Zeitgeist had been wary of the boss's wife being given a plum role as a photographer, but none of that wariness had lasted. According to Alastair, her outlook was fresh; her approach original—and she got along well with people.

Her photos for the spa campaign had confounded expectation—the expectation being that it was impossible to get an interesting shot of a woman wrapped in a towel.

But somehow Leila had pulled it off. Maybe it was the angle she had used, or the fact that her background had equipped her to understand that a woman didn't have to show lots of flesh in order to look alluring.

'And anyway,' she had said to Gabe as they were driving home from work one evening, 'these spas are trying to appeal to a female audience, not a male one. Which means that we don't always have to portray women with the not-so-subtle subtext that they're constantly thinking about sex.'

'Unlike you, you mean?' he had offered drily.

She had smiled.

Yes, on the surface things were very good.

So why did she feel as if something was missing—as if there was still a great gaping hole in her life which she couldn't fill? Was it because after that awful disclosure about his mother, Gabe had never really let down his guard again? Or because her expectations of a relationship were far more demanding than she'd realised? That she had been lying to herself about not wanting his love in return, when it was pretty obvious that deep down she craved it.

There were moments which gave her hope—when she felt as if they were poised on the brink of a new understanding. When she felt as close to him as it was possible to feel and her heart was filled with joy. Like the other day, when they had been lying in bed, she'd been wrapped in his arms and he'd been kissing the top of her head and the air had felt full of lazy contentment.

But then she'd realised that for the first time she could feel the distinct swell of her belly, even though she was horizontal at the time.

With an excited little squeal, she'd caught hold of his hand and moved it to her stomach. 'Gabe. Feel,' she'd whispered. 'Go on. Feel.'

She knew her husband well enough to realise that he would never give away his true feelings by doing something as obvious as snatching his hand away from her skin, as if he'd just been burned. But she felt his whole body tense as he made the most cursory of explorations, before disentangling himself from her embrace and telling her that he had to make an international call.

So what was going on beneath the surface of that cold and enigmatic face? Leila gave a sigh. She didn't know. You could show a man love, but love only went so far. Love couldn't penetrate brick walls if people were determined to erect them around their hearts. Love could only help heal a person if that person would allow themselves to be healed.

Gabe made her feel as if she'd wrested every secret from him and that he found any more attempts at soul-searching a bore. Maybe she just had to accept that this was as good as it got. That the real intimacy she longed for simply wasn't going to happen.

But that didn't mean she was going to stop loving him.

She turned away from the thundery skyline to where he was lying sprawled out on the leather sofa, and her heart gave a little twist.

She could never stop loving him.

'Gabe?'

'Mmm?'

'I was wondering if we could give a party?'

He looked up and frowned. 'What kind of party?'

'Oh, you know—something revolutionary. Invite some people along, give them food and drink, maybe play a little music. That sort of thing.'

'Very funny.' Stretching his arms above his head, he gave a lazy yawn. 'What exactly did you have in mind?'

She drew in a deep breath. 'Well, we've never really had a wedding party, have we? I mean, we had that lunch with Sara and Suleiman, but that was all. And I've become quite friendly with Alice and a few of the others from work, so I'd quite like to invite them. And then there's my brother. I'd quite like to see him.' She wriggled her shoulders. 'I'd just like a bit of a celebration before the baby comes. Some kind of acknowledgement that the wedding actually happened.'

He didn't answer straight away.

'As long as it's not here,' he said eventually. 'But if you want to hire a hotel or a restaurant, then that's fine by me.'

'Oh, Gabe,' she said, and walked back across the

room to hug him and when she stopped hugging him she could see that he was actually *smiling*.

Leila threw herself into a frenzy of organisation. She booked the award-winning wedding room at the Granchester Hotel and hired a party planner who came highly recommended by Alice.

The party's colour scheme of gold and indigo was chosen to reflect the colours of the Qurhahian flag and the cuisine was intended to offer delicacies from both cultures. A group of barber-shop singers had been booked for a cabaret spot at ten and dozens of fragrant crimson roses were on order.

Responses soon came flooding in. Everyone at Zeitgeist who'd been invited said yes. Sara and Suleiman were going to be there and also Sara's brother. Even Murat accepted his invitation, much to Leila's pleasure and surprise. It seemed that everybody wanted to attend the wedding celebration of a desert princess and a man known for never giving parties. Leila bought a new dress for the occasion—a gorgeous shimmery thing with threads of silver running through a grey silky material, which reminded her of the mercurial hue of Gabe's eyes.

She took off the day before the party but Gabe was tied up with wall-to-wall meetings all morning.

He was frowning as he kissed her goodbye. 'I'll meet you for lunch,' he said. 'And for goodness' sake—calm down, Leila. You're wearing yourself out with this damned party.'

Something in his tone had made her tilt her head back to look at him. 'You do *want* this party, don't you?'

For a moment there was silence and his smile was

faintly rueful as he shook his head. 'I never said I wanted it, did I? I agreed to it because it makes you happy.'

She stared at the door as it closed behind him.

Wanting to make her happy was a step forward, she guessed—even if it made her feel a bit like a child who needed to be placated with a new toy. Like a spoilt little princess who'd stamped her foot and demanded a party. The same spoilt princess who had finally remembered to throw away her apple cores and to remember that there wasn't a squad of servants poised to tidy up after her.

In an effort to subdue her sudden feeling of restlessness, she decided to try a little displacement therapy. Walking over to the concealed wardrobe, she pulled out her new skyscraper grey heels, which were jostling for room with the rest of her shoes. She really was going to have to ask Gabe to give her more cupboard space, since she had far more clothes than he did. Or maybe she should just do the sensible thing and acquire some for herself.

She practised walking around the bedroom in her new shoes and decided that they didn't hurt a bit. Then she jigged around a little and decided they would be fine to dance in. And in spite of all her reservations, she felt a soaring sense of excitement to think that she might get to dance with her husband for the first time ever.

Pulling open one of the wardrobe doors which Gabe rarely used, she was relieved to find it almost empty. She could shift some of her clothes in here. She took off her shoes and bent down to place them neatly on the rack at the bottom, when she noticed the

corner of a drawer protruding, spoiling the otherwise
perfect symmetry of the wardrobe's sleek interior.

She wondered what drew her eyes to the manila colour of an envelope inside, but it was enough to make
her hesitate. Was that why she didn't immediately
push the drawer shut, but slowly open it as curiosity
got the better of her?

She didn't know why her heart was beating so fast,
only that it was. And she didn't know why her husband should have wedged an envelope in some random drawer when he kept all his paperwork in the
bureau in his study next door. Fingers trembling, she
flipped open the top of the envelope because she could
see that inside there were photos. Photos of a man. A
stranger, yet…

Her heart missed a beat as she pulled out another
photo. This time there were two men and one she recognised instantly because it was Gabe. But of course
she recognised the other man too, because his features
were unmistakeable.

High, slashed cheekbones. Piercing pewter eyes
and dark golden hair. She swallowed. Two men standing outside what looked like a Parisian café. One of
them her husband and the other very obviously his
father.

But Gabe had never met his father! He'd told her
that. She remembered the way his mouth had tightened and the bitter look which had darkened his eyes
as he'd said it.

The envelope slipping from her fingers, Leila slid
to her knees. He *had* met his father. There was photographic evidence of it right in front of her eyes. He
had told her that this marriage would be based on

truth, but it seemed that it was based on nothing but a tissue of lies.

Lies.

She felt the acrid taste of bile rising up in her throat and in that moment she felt utter defeat, wondering how she could have been so blind. So *stupid*. They didn't have love, no matter how much she wanted it—and now it seemed that they didn't even have trust either.

But she had ignored all the signs. She had blithely done what women were so good at doing. She had refused to listen to all the things he'd told her, because it hadn't suited her to listen. He'd told her that he didn't do love but she had thought—arrogantly, it seemed now—that she might just be able to change his mind.

And in that showy-off way, she had decided to throw a party which he clearly had no appetite for—*he'd even told her that, too*. She was planning to dress up in her new, shimmery party frock and her slightly too-high grey shoes and to explode into the flower-decked wedding room of the Granchester and make as if it were all okay. As if she were just like every other bride—happy and contented and expecting a baby. But she wasn't, was she?

Maybe she could have been that bride. Maybe she could have settled for sex and affection and companionship, without the magic ingredient of love. She knew that plenty of people were happy enough with that kind of arrangement. But not lies. Because lies were addictive, weren't they? You told one and you might as well tell a million.

The walls felt as if they were closing in on her, even

though they were made of glass. But claustrophobia was all in the mind, wasn't it? Just like trust.

She scrabbled around and found a sweater and pulled it on, because suddenly she was shivering. Shivering as if she'd caught a violent bout of flu. She grabbed her handbag and took the elevator downstairs and the porter she'd seen on her wedding day was there.

She rarely saw him these days, because usually she was rushing past with Gabe, or because they took the elevator straight down to the underground car park. It was as much as she could do to flash him a smile, but something on her face must have alarmed him for he rose to his feet, a look of concern on his face.

'Everything all right, Mrs Steel?'

The unfamiliar use of her married name startled her but, with an effort, Leila pinned a smile to her face. 'I'm fine. I just want some fresh air.'

'Are you sure? Looks like rain,' he said doubtfully.

Yes. And it felt like rain, too. Inside her heart, it felt as if the storm had already broken.

She started walking; she didn't know where. Somewhere. Anywhere. She didn't really pay attention to the route she was taking. She wasn't used to the streets of London, but she didn't care. A reckless gloom came over her. Maybe it was best that she got used to these streets now, so that when she was living on her own she would have a better idea of the geography of the city.

The rain began to fall. Slowly at first and then harder and more relentlessly, but Leila barely felt it, even though after a few minutes she was soaked right through. During the gaps between the loud thunderclaps above her, she could hear her phone vibrating in her handbag, but she ignored it.

She walked and walked until the riverbank became unfamiliar and the houses and shops less glitzy and much closer together. She saw people with angry dogs straining at their leashes. She saw youths huddled in shop doorways sheltering from the rain, dragging cigarette smoke deep into their lungs.

She didn't know how long she'd been walking when she found a café. Her wet hair hung in stringy rat's tails as she sat dripping in a steamy corner and ordered a mug of strong tea. Her phone began to ring and, uninterestedly, she pulled it out. She saw that it was Alice and that she had four missed calls—three of them from Gabe.

She pressed the answer button. 'Hello.'

'Leila, is that you?' Alice sounded frantic.

'Yep. It's me.'

'Are you okay? Gabe's been going out of his mind with worry. He says he hasn't been able to get hold of you.'

Leila stared at the steam which rose from her mug like smoke from a bonfire. 'I'm fine,' she said tiredly. 'I just needed some fresh air.'

'Leila.' Alice's voice now dipped to soft and cautious. 'Where *are* you?'

'It doesn't matter.'

'It does. You sound…strange. Let me send a car for you.'

'No.'

'Then at least tell me where you are,' pleaded Alice. 'Just to put my mind at rest.'

Wearily, Leila looked down at the laminated menu

and gave the name of the café. She would leave before Alice had a chance to send anyone, which was clearly what she had in mind. But her feet were aching and she was cold. Like, really cold. As if somebody had taken her bones and turned them into ice. So she just sat there as the minutes ticked away and the chatter of the other customers seemed to be taking place in a parallel universe.

She felt hungry, too. Hungry in a way which was unfamiliar to her and she knew that this was the baby speaking to her. Finding herself unable to ignore the unfamiliar cravings of her body, she ordered a white bread sandwich stuffed with thick slices of cheese and smothered in a sharp and pungent brown chutney.

She fell on it with an instinctive greed which seemed beyond her control and that was how Gabe found her. He walked into the humble café, his face sombre and his dark golden hair so wet that it looked almost black. Raindrops were running down over the high slash of his cheekbones and for one crazy moment it looked almost as if he were crying.

But Gabe didn't do tears, she reminded herself. Gabe didn't do emotions because he didn't *feel*. Gabe's hurt and pain had made him immune from the stuff which afflicted normal human hearts, like hers.

He walked straight over to her and leant over the table. Holding on to the back of a chair, he seemed to be having difficulty controlling his breathing and it was a moment before he could ice out his incredulous question.

'What the hell do you think you're doing, Leila?'

'What does it look like I'm doing? I'm eating a cheese and pickle sandwich.' She finished chewing a mouthful which now tasted like sawdust and stared at him. 'Anyway, I thought you were in meetings.'

'I cancelled them when I didn't hear from you. I've been going out of my mind with worry.'

'So Alice said.'

'So Alice said,' he repeated, and then his eyes narrowed. 'Don't you *care*?'

At this, she put the rest of the sandwich down on the plate but her hands were still trembling as she met the accusation in his eyes.

'Don't I *care*?' She gave a short laugh. 'I did. I cared very much. But I realise now how incredibly stupid I've been. I mean, how could I possibly think that ours was a marriage worth saving? You told me that our relationship was to be based on truth and you lied. A loveless marriage I could just about live with, but not lies, Gabe. Not lies.'

And with that, she pushed back her chair and ran out of the café.

CHAPTER TWELVE

THE COOL RAIN hit Leila's face as she met the fresh air, but Gabe was hot on her heels. She ran straight past the chauffeur-driven car which was obviously his, but he caught up with her before she'd reached the end of the street.

His hands on her elbows, he hauled her round to face him and held on to her tightly, even though she tried to struggle out of his grip.

'You can't run away,' he said grimly.

'I can do anything I like. And I want to be as far away from you as possible. So go away and leave me alone.'

'I'm not going anywhere without you and I'm not having this discussion in the middle of the street in the pouring rain.'

'Terrified it will ruin your ice-cool image?' she mocked.

'Terrified that you'll catch a cold—especially in your present condition,' he said. 'You're pregnant, Leila. Remember?'

'Oh!' She gave a howl of frustrated rage as she struggled again. 'As if I could ever forget!'

But he was levering her gently towards the waiting

car, and the chauffeur had leapt out to open the door.
Gabe was easing her onto the back seat and Leila was
appalled at how relieved she felt as warmth and luxury wrapped themselves round her body like a soft
and comforting mantle.

That's just the external stuff, she reminded herself
bitterly. *Money just makes things more comfortable.
It doesn't change anything. It doesn't make the hurt
and betrayal go away.*

She turned to face him as he slid onto the seat beside her. 'I'm not going back to your apartment!'

'We don't have to do that,' he said evenly. 'Where
would you like to go instead?'

And wasn't that the saddest thing of all—that
she couldn't think of anywhere? The place she most
wanted to be was in his heart, and there was no place
for her there.

'I don't care,' she said.

'Then let's just drive around for a while, shall we?
And you can tell me what's wrong.'

'What's wrong? *What's wrong?*' She hated the way
he was talking to her as if she were aged a hundred
and had forgotten where she lived. It was as much as
she could do not to bang her fists frustratedly against
his chest. And sudden all her hurt and pain and disappointment came bubbling out. 'I'll tell you what's
wrong! You told me that our marriage was to be based
on truth. You told me you couldn't promise me love,
but you could promise me that. And I believed you.'
Tears sprang from her eyes and began to trickle down
her cheeks. 'I believed you even though I wanted the
impossible from you. I wanted your love, but I was
prepared to settle for the truth.'

'Leila—'

'And then this morning.' Angrily, she shook away the hand which he'd placed on her arm. 'This morning I found some photos stuffed away in a drawer in the wardrobe.'

He went very still. 'So you've been spying on me, have you?'

'Don't you dare try to turn this on me! I was actually looking for a bigger home for my shoe collection—but that's not the point! The point is that I found photos of you with a man who was clearly your father. A man you told me you'd never met. You lied to me, Gabe. You *lied to me.*'

There was silence in the car, punctuated only by the muffled sound of her sobs and, reluctantly, she took the handkerchief he withdrew from his pocket and buried her nose in it.

'Yes, I lied to you,' he said heavily. 'I lied to you because…'

His voice faded away and it was so unlike Gabe to hesitate that Leila lifted her nose from the handkerchief to look at him. Her vision was blurred through her tears but she saw enough to startle her, for his eyes looked like two empty holes in a face so ravaged with emotion that for a moment he didn't look like Gabe at all.

'Because, what?'

He shook his head and turned to her as the words began to spill from his lips, as if he'd been bottling them up for a long time. 'What if you were a man and you met a woman who just blew you away, in a way you didn't recognise at the time—because it had never happened to you before? Maybe you were determined not to recognise it because it was something you didn't believe in. Something which, deep down, you feared.'

Leila sniffed. 'None of that makes sense.'

'Hear me out.' He sucked in a deep breath. 'So you walk away from this woman, telling yourself that you've made the best and the only decision you could possibly make. But you're not sure. In fact, you're starting to realise that you've just done the dumbest thing imaginable, when she turns up at your home in London. And you look at her and realise what an idiot you've been. You realise that here you have a chance for happiness right in front of your eyes, but you're scared. And then...'

His voice tailed off and she saw his features harden.

'Then?'

'Then she tells you she's pregnant and you're even more scared. Because this is a double-edged sword. On the one hand, it means you can be together legitimately without having to delve too deeply into your own emotions. Yet on the other...'

'Gabe!' Her anger forgotten now, she leaned forward—wondering what on earth could have put such a haunted expression on his face. 'Will you please stop talking in riddles? The fact is that you lied about seeing your father and nothing can change that.'

'No. Nothing can change that. But what if I told you there was a reason why my mother kept his identity from me?' He raked his fingers back through his plastered hair and his fingertips came away wet. For a moment he just stared at them, as if he might find some kind of answer gleaming back at him from that damp, cold skin.

'After she died, I felt angry and bitter—and guilty

too. But I went to London and I started working and, as I told you, success came pretty quickly.'

'Yes,' she said quietly. 'You told me.'

'I embraced my new role as a successful business-man but sometimes—not often—I would think about my father. I couldn't eradicate the curiosity which still niggled away at me. I didn't know if he was dead or alive. I wanted to confront him. I wanted to know why he'd abdicated all his responsibilities towards me. I wanted to tell him that a woman had died sooner than reveal his identity.' He clenched his fist, as if he wanted to hit something. Or someone. 'I guess I was looking for someone to blame for her death. Some-one who wasn't me.'

'Go on,' she said.

'I was rich by this point. Rich enough to find any-one I wanted and it didn't take long to track my fa-ther down in Marseilles, which is where he'd moved to when he'd left Provence. And suddenly I under-stood my mother's behaviour. I understood why she'd wanted to protect me from him. Why she'd feared his influence on me…'

His words tailed off as if he couldn't bear to say them but Leila leaned forward, her wet hair falling over her shoulders as she peered into his face. 'What, Gabe? *What?*'

'Which particular title shall I give him? Gangster or hoodlum?' he questioned bitterly. 'Because he an-swered to both. He was an underworld figure, Leila. A powerful and ruthless individual. I discovered that he had killed. Yes, killed. I discovered this when we met in Paris and not long afterwards he was gunned down in some gangland shootout himself. That photo was taken by one of his associates and it's the only one of us together. Time after time I went to burn it, but something always stopped me and I still don't know what that something is.'

'Oh, Gabe,' she whispered, her voice distorted with shock and pain. 'Why the hell didn't you tell me?'

'Because I *couldn't*. Don't you see, Leila?' His eyes were blazing as his voice cracked with emotion. 'His blood is my blood. And it's our baby's blood too. How could I knowingly pass on a legacy like that to you? How could I possibly tell the sister of the Sultan about her baby's forebears? Not just a grandmother who had committed suicide, but a grandfather who was a murderer. How could I subject you to a life of fear that those tainted genes will have been passed down to the next generation?' There was silence for a moment as his eyes burned into hers. 'I'm damaged, darling. Badly damaged. Now do you understand?'

Leila nodded. Yes, she understood. She understood this powerful man's pride and fear, but also about his deep desire to protect. And Gabe had been trying to protect her. From hurt and pain and worry. He had been trying to protect their baby too—from the heartache and fear that evil might be inherited, like blue eyes or the ability to draw.

He wanted to reach out to her, but he didn't know how.

She looked into his haunted face and her heart went out to him, but she knew that this was her golden opportunity and that she must not shrink from it. She had wanted to be his equal, hadn't she? And she wanted to be strong.

So show him that you're still there for him. Love him the way you really want to love him. Why let him shoulder this burden on his own, when you're more than willing to share it with him?

Her voice was low and trembling as her words came tumbling out. 'Do you have any idea of the history of Qurhah?' she demanded.

He looked at her as if this was the last thing in the world he had expected her to say. 'I can't see how that is relevant.'

'Can't you? Actually, it's *very* relevant. I'll have you know that my family is descended from mighty warriors and ruthless tyrants. There have been Al-Maisan sultans conquering neighbouring lands ever since our people first settled in the desert, and there has been much bloodshed along the way. Nobody's history is whiter than white, Gabe. Not yours and especially not mine.'

He shook his head. 'That's not the same,' he said stubbornly.

She laid her hand on his arm. 'It *is* the same—just different. Our baby isn't a clone of your father, you know. Nor of you—or me. Our baby is unique and I know for sure that the best and only legacy we can give him—or her—is love. We must love this baby with all our hearts, Gabe. Even if you don't feel that way about me—do you think you can find it in your heart to love our baby?'

He shook his head and for a minute his face was contorted with pain. 'What a brute of a man you must think I am,' he declared bitterly, 'that I would be in-

capable of feeling something for an innocent scrap
of humanity.'

'Not a brute,' she said gently. 'A man who has been
wounded—badly wounded. But I am your wife and
I am going to help you heal, but I can only do that
if you let me. If you can bear to open up your heart,
Gabe—and let me in.'

She saw a muscle flickering at his temple as he
caught hold of her wet shoulders and looked into her
face.

'Only if you can you forgive me,' he said. 'Can
you ever forgive me for what I have done, my darling Leila?'

'There's nothing to forgive,' she said softly, her
hand reaching up to touch the hard contours of his
face. She ran her fingertip along the high slash of his
very Slavic cheekbones and the firm curve of his lips.
She looked into the pewter eyes and her heart turned
over with love. One day soon she would tell him to
learn to understand his father, and then to let the bitterness go. That there was a little bit of bad in the best
of people, and a little bit of good in the worst.

But not now.

Now she must be focused on the most important
things.

'We're both very cold and very wet,' she said as
she snuggled up against him. 'Do you think we should
go home?'

Gabe stroked a straggly strand of damp hair away
from her face and smiled, but the lump in his throat
meant that it took a moment or two before he could
speak. 'Right here is home,' he said unevenly. 'Wher-

ever you are. I love you, my compassionate and passionate princess. I love you very much.'

He tapped on the glass and the car moved away, and that was when he started to kiss her.

EPILOGUE

'HE LOOKS VERY Qurhahian,' said Gabe as he gazed into the crib where the sleeping infant lay.

Leila smiled, giving one last unnecessary twitch of the snowy cashmere blanket which now covered the crescent curve of Hafez's perfect little foot. 'Do you know, that's exactly what Murat said to me today.'

'Did he?'

She nodded as she looked down at their tiny son. His skin was faintly tinged with olive and already he had a hint of the slightly too-strong nose which had been the bane of her life, but which Gabe always told her was the most beautiful nose in the world. Deep down she suspected that her husband was relieved to discover that their firstborn looked more like her than him. But Leila was confident that, with time, his few remaining reservations about his heritage would melt beneath the power of her love.

Today had been Hafez's naming ceremony, here in the palace in Simdahab where she'd grown up—and it had been the most glorious of visits. All the servants had clucked excitedly around the princess's new baby. That was when they hadn't been buzzing round the Western guests who had flown out for the occasion and who mingled with the dignitaries and kings from the neighbouring desert countries.

It had been a day of immense happiness and joy, but Leila thought that Murat seemed rather pensive and she wondered if it was because the woman he had been destined to marry had found happiness with another man.

She put her arms around Gabe and pressed her lips to his cheek. 'My brother said something very strange to me today.'

'Tell me.' He started to kiss her neck.

Leila closed her eyes as shivers of sensation began to whisper over her skin. 'He said that at least there was another generation of the Al-Maisan family, in case he never produced an heir of his own. He seemed to imply that he would never marry—and that he'd be contented with a long line of mistresses instead.'

Gabe smiled as he brushed his mouth over her scented skin. Hadn't he once thought that way himself? When his heart had been so dark and cold that it had felt as if a lump of ice had been wedged in his chest. 'All it takes is the right woman,' he said. 'And once she comes along, it seems that a man will happily change his entire life to please her. Just as I have done for you.'

'Oh, darling,' she said, closing her eyes with dreamy pleasure as she thought back to everything that had happened to them since Hafez had been born.

They had sold his apartment and moved to a large house overlooking Hampstead Heath, because Gabe realised that Leila had been right. That his minimalistic high-rise apartment was no place to bring up a baby—it had suited a phase of his life which was now over. Hafez needed grass and flowers, she had told him firmly. He needed a nearby nursery and hopefully a school he could walk to.

So a studio had been built for her in the basement of their new house, from which she would work as a freelance photographer. That way she got all the pleasures of working, but none of the regular commitment which would keep her away from their son.

Gabe lifted his hand and stroked back the glorious fall of hair from her face so that it streamed down over her shoulders in a cascade of ebony. The roseate curves of her lips were an irresistible invitation, and he kissed her with a steadily increasing hunger before drawing away from her.

'I love you,' he said.

'I know. The feeling is shared and returned.'

'And there's a spare hour to fill before the palace banquet,' he said a little unsteadily. 'Shall we go to bed?'

She opened her eyes. 'You're insatiable.'

'I thought you liked me that way.'

'I like you any way I can get you,' she whispered back. 'But preferably without any clothes on and nobody else around.'

'You are a shameless woman, Leila Steel.'

'Lucky that's the way you like *me*,' she teased.

'I know,' he said. 'I never stop reminding myself how lucky I am.'

And this was the greatest of the many truths he'd discovered in a life now lived without pretence, or fear or regret.

Next week was his birthday but he wouldn't be seeking to blot out the past with a bottle of Scotch and oblivion. He would be embracing the golden and glorious present with his wife and their beloved baby son.

And he would be telling Leila how much he loved her, just as he did every single day of his life. His beautiful Qurhahian princess who had brought his heart to life with the power of her love. Just as the rains fed the dormant flower seeds, to bring the desert miracle to the Mekathasinian Sands.

* * * * *

'Samantha.' Rafaele smiled. **'Aren't you going to ask me in? It's cold out here.'**

Sam's hand clenched tightly around the door. Panic rushed into her blood. Finally rousing her.

'Now isn't a good time. I thought I made it clear that I'm not interested.'

A dull flush accentuated Rafaele's cheekbones, but Sam was barely aware of it when she heard the high-pitched, *'Mummy!'* which was accompanied by small feet running at full speed behind her.

She felt Milo land at her legs and could almost visualise his little round face peeping out to see who was at the door. As if she were trying in vain to halt an oncoming train, Sam said in a thready voice, 'Now *really* isn't a good time.'

Rafaele stared at Milo for what seemed like an age. He frowned and then looked as if someone had just hit him in the belly. Dazed, he glanced up at Sam and she knew exactly what he was seeing. Her eyes were wide and stricken, set in a face leached of all colour.

Panicked. Guilty.

Just like that something in his eyes turned to ice and she knew that he knew.

BLOOD BROTHERS

Power and passion run in their veins

Rafaele and Alexio have learned that to feel emotion is to be weak. Calculated ruthlessness brings them immense success in the boardroom and in the bedroom. But a storm is coming with the sudden appearance of a long-lost half-brother and three women who will change their lives for ever…

*Read **Rafaele Falcone's** story in:*
WHEN FALCONE'S WORLD STOPS TURNING
February 2014

Only one woman has come close to touching this brooding Italian's cold heart, and he intends to have her once more. But Samantha Rourke has a secret that will rock his world in a very different way…

*Read **Alexio Christakos's** story in:*
WHEN CHRISTAKOS MEETS HIS MATCH
April 2014

His legendary Greek charm can get him any woman he wants—and he wants Sidonie Fitzgerald for one, hot night. But when that night isn't enough will he regret breaking his own rules?

And coming soon…
***Cesar Da Silva's** story*
June 2014

The prodigal son is tormented by his dark past. Can one woman save this Spanish billionaire's tortured soul, or is he beyond redemption?

WHEN FALCONE'S WORLD STOPS TURNING

BY
ABBY GREEN

Published in Great Britain 2014
by Mills & Boon, an imprint of Harlequin (UK) Limited,
Eton House, 18-24 Paradise Road, Richmond, Surrey, TW9 1SR

© 2014 Abby Green

ISBN: 978 0 263 90825 1

Harlequin (UK) Limited's policy is to use papers that are natural,
renewable and recyclable products and made from wood grown in
sustainable forests. The logging and manufacturing processes conform
to the legal environmental regulations of the country of origin.

Printed and bound in Spain
by Blackprint CPI, Barcelona

Abby Green spent her teens reading Mills and Boon® romances. After repeatedly deferring a degree to study Social Anthropology (long story!) she ended up working for many years in the film and TV industry as an assistant director.

One day, while standing outside an actor's trailer waiting for him to emerge, in the rain, holding an umbrella in gale force winds, she thought to herself, *Surely there's more than this and it involves being inside and dry?*

Thinking of her love for Mills and Boon, and encouraged by a friend, Abby decided to submit a partial manuscript. After numerous rewrites, chucking out the original idea and starting again with a new story, her first book was accepted and an author was born.

She is happy to report that days of standing in the rain outside an actor's trailer are a rare occurrence now. She loves creating stories that will put the reader through an emotional wringer (in a good way, hopefully!), and yet leave her feeling satisfied and uplifted.

She lives in Dublin, Ireland, and you can find out more about her and her books here: www.abby-green.com

Recent titles by the same author:

FORGIVEN BUT NOT FORGOTTEN?
EXQUISITE REVENGE
ONE NIGHT WITH THE ENEMY
THE LEGEND OF DE MARCO

Did you know these are also available as eBooks?
Visit www.millsandboon.co.uk

This is for Gervaise Landy, without whose influence I would most likely still be speaking into a walkie-talkie outside an actor's trailer in a car park somewhere, in the rain, trying to explain what the delay is. Thank you for all the great conversations about Mills & Boon, and that first memorable one in particular all those years ago. As soon as we recognised a fellow fanatic in each other we were kindred spirits. You were the one who put the idea in my head in the first place about writing for Mills & Boon, and you were the one with the tape on how to write one—which I still have, and which I will return to you as soon as you promise me you're going to sit down and finish that manuscript. With much love and thanks for sowing the seed of a dream in my head!

In thanking Gervaise I also have to dedicate this book to Caitríona Ní Mhurchú, at whose party I first met Gervaise. From the age of sixteen I have idolised this glamorous, confident, sexy, intelligent woman, so if you see any of those traits in my heroines it comes from a deep well of inspiration.

PROLOGUE

RAFAELE FALCONE LOOKED at the coffin deep inside the open grave. The earth they'd thrown in was scattered on top, along with some lone flowers left by departing friends and acquaintances. Some of them had been men, inordinately upset. Evidently there was some truth to the rumours that the stunning Esperanza Christakos had taken lovers during her third marriage.

Rafaele felt many conflicting emotions, apart from the obvious grief for his dead mother. He couldn't say that they'd ever had a close relationship; she'd been eternally elusive and had carried an air of melancholy about her. She'd also been beautiful. Beautiful enough to send his own father mad with grief when she left him.

The kind of woman who'd had the ability to make grown men completely lose all sense of dignity and of themselves. Not something that would ever happen to *him*. His single-minded focus was on his career and rebuilding the Falcone motor empire. Beautiful women were a pleasant diversion—nothing more. None of his lovers were ever under any illusions and expected nothing more than the transitory pleasure of his company.

His conscience pricked at this confident assertion—there had only been one lover who had taken him close to the edge but that was an experience he didn't dwell on... not any more.

His half-brother, Alexio Christakos, turned to him now and smiled tightly. Rafaele felt a familiar ache in his chest. He loved his half-brother, and had done from the moment he'd been born, but their relationship wasn't easy. It had been hard for Rafaele to witness his brother growing up, sure in the knowledge of his father's success and support—so different from his own experience with his father. He'd felt resentful for a long time, which hadn't been helped by his stepfather's obvious antipathy towards the son that wasn't his.

They both turned and walked away from the grave, engrossed in their own thoughts. Their mother had bequeathed to both her sons her distinctive green eyes, although Alexio's were a shade more golden than Rafaele's striking light green. Rafaele's hair was thicker and a darker brown next to his brother's short-cut ebony-black hair.

Differing only slightly in height, they were both a few inches over six foot. Rafaele's build was broad and powerful. His brother's just as powerful, but leaner. Dark stubble shadowed Rafaele's firm jawline today, and when they came to a stop near the cars Alexio observed it, remarking dryly, 'You couldn't even clean up for the funeral?'

The tightness in Rafaele's chest when he'd stood at the grave was easing slightly now. He curbed the urge to be defensive, to hide the vulnerability he felt, and faced his brother, drawling with a definite glint in his eye, 'I got out of bed too late.'

He couldn't explain to his brother how he'd instinctively sought the momentary escape he would find in the response of an eager woman, preferring not to dwell on how his mother's death had made him feel. Preferring not to dwell on how it had brought up vivid memories of when she'd walked out on his father so many years ago, leaving him a broken man. He was still bitter, adamantly refusing to pay his respects to his ex-wife today despite Rafaele's efforts to persuade him to come.

Alexio, oblivious to Rafaele's inner tumult, shook his head and smiled wryly. 'Unbelievable. You've only been in Athens for two days—no wonder you wanted to stay in a hotel and not at my apartment...'

Rafaele pushed aside the dark memories and quirked a mocking brow at his brother, about to dish out some of the same, when he saw a latecomer arrive. The words died on his lips and Alexio's smile faded as he turned to follow Rafaele's gaze.

A very tall, stern-faced stranger was staring at them both. And yet...he looked incredibly familiar. It was almost like looking into a mirror. Or at Alexio...if he had dark blond hair. It was his eyes, though, that sent a shiver through Rafaele. Green, much like his and Alexio's, except with a slight difference—a darker green, almost hazel. Another take on their mother's eyes...? But how could that be?

Rafaele bristled at this stranger's almost belligerent stance. 'May we help you?' he asked coolly.

The man's eyes flickered over them both, and then to the open grave in the distance. He asked, with a derisive curl to his lip, 'Are there any more of us?'

Rafaele looked at Alexio, who was frowning, and said, '*Us*? What are you talking about?'

The man looked at Rafaele. 'You don't remember, do you?'

The faintest of memories was coming back: he was standing on a doorstep with his mother. A huge imposing door was opening and there was a boy, a few years older than him, with blond hair and huge eyes.

The man's voice sounded rough in the still air. 'She brought you to my house. You must have been nearly three. I was almost seven. She wanted to take me with her then, but I wouldn't leave. Not after she'd abandoned me.'

Rafaele felt cold all over. In a slightly hoarse voice he asked, 'Who *are* you?'

The man smiled, but it didn't meet his eyes. 'I'm your older brother—*half-brother*. My name is Cesar Da Silva. I came today to pay my respects to the woman who gave me life...not that she deserved it. I was curious to see if any more would crawl out of the woodwork, but it looks like it's just us.'

Alexio erupted beside Rafaele. 'What the *hell*—?'

Rafaele was too stunned to move. He knew the Da Silva name. Cesar was behind the renowned and extremely successful Da Silva Global Corporation. His mind boggled to think that he might have met him and not known that they were brothers. With a sickening sense of inevitability, he didn't doubt a word this man had just said. Their fraternal similarities were too obvious. They could be non-identical triplets.

That half-memory, half-dream had always been all too real—he'd just never known for sure, because whenever he'd mentioned it to his mother she'd always changed the subject. Much in the way she had never discussed her life in her native Spain before she'd met his father in Paris, where she'd been a model.

Rafaele gestured to his brother, 'This is Alexio Christakos...our younger brother.'

Cesar Da Silva looked at him with nothing but ice in his eyes. 'Three brothers by three fathers...and yet she didn't abandon either of *you* to the wolves.'

He stepped forward then, and Alexio stepped forward too. The two men stood almost nose to nose, with Cesar topping his youngest brother in height only by an inch.

Cesar, his jaw as rigid as Alexio's, gritted out, 'I didn't come here to fight you, brother. I have no issue with either of you.'

Alexio's mouth thinned. 'Only with our dead mother, *if* what you say is true.'

Cesar smiled, but it was thin and bitter. 'Oh, it's true, all right — more's the pity.'

He stepped around Alexio then, and walked to the open grave. He took something out of his pocket and dropped it down into the dark space, where it fell onto the coffin with a distant hollow thud. He stood there for a long moment and then came back, his face expressionless.

After a charged silent moment between the three men he turned to stride away and got into the back of a waiting dark silver limousine, which moved off smoothly.

Rafaele turned to Alexio, who looked back at him, gob-smacked.

'What the…?' he trailed off.

Rafaele just shook his head. 'I don't know…'

He looked back to the space where the car had been and reeled with this cataclysmic knowledge.

CHAPTER ONE

Three months later...

'SAM, SORRY TO bother you, but there's a call for you on line one...someone with a very deep voice and a sexy foreign accent.'

Sam went very still. *Deep voice...sexy foreign accent.* The words sent a shiver of foreboding down her spine and a lick of something much hotter through her pelvis. She told herself she was being ridiculous and looked up from the results she'd been reading to see the secretary of the research department at the London university.

Kind eyes twinkled mischievously in a matronly face. 'Did you get up to something at the weekend? Or should I say some*one*?'

Again that shiver went down Sam's spine, but she just smiled at Gertie. 'Chance would be a fine thing. I spent all weekend working on Milo's playschool nature project with him.'

The secretary smiled and said indulgently, 'You know I live in hope, Sam. You and Milo need a gorgeous man to come and take care of you.'

Sam gritted her teeth and kept smiling, restraining herself from pointing out how well she and Milo were doing without a man. Now she couldn't wait to take the call. 'Did you say line one?'

Gertie winked and disappeared, and Sam took a deep breath before picking up the phone and pressing the flashing button. 'Dr Samantha Rourke here.'

There was silence for a few seconds, and then came the voice. Low, deep, sexy—and infinitely memorable. '*Ciao*, Samantha, it's Rafaele…'

The prickle of foreboding became a slap in the face. He was the only one apart from her father who had ever called her Samantha—unless it had been *Sam* in the throes of passion. All the blood in her body seemed to drain south, to the floor. Anger, guilt, emotional pain, lust and an awful treacherous tenderness flooded her in a confusing tumult.

She only realised she hadn't responded when the voice came again, cooler. 'Rafaele Falcone…perhaps you don't remember?'

As if that was humanly possible!

Her hand gripped the phone and she managed to get out, 'No… I mean, yes. I remember.'

Sam wanted to laugh hysterically. How could she forget the man when she looked into a miniature replica of his face and green eyes every day?

'*Bene*,' came the smooth answer. 'How are you, Sam? You're a doctor now?'

'Yes…' Sam's heart was doing funny things, beating so hard she felt breathless. 'I got my doctorate after…' She faltered and the words reverberated in her head unspoken. *After you came into my life and blew it to smithereens.* She fought valiantly for control and said in a stronger voice, 'I got my doctorate since I saw you last. How can I help you?'

Again a bubble of hysteria rose up in her: *how about helping him by telling him he has a son?*

'I am here in London because we've set up a UK base for Falcone Motors.'

'That's…nice,' Sam said, a little redundantly.

The magnitude of who she was talking to seemed to

hit her all of a sudden and she went icy all over. Rafaele Falcone. Here in London. He'd tracked her down. Why? *Milo*. Her son, her world. *His son.*

Sam's first irrational thought was that he must know, and then she forced herself to calm down. No way would Rafaele Falcone be calling her up sounding so blasé if he knew. She needed to get rid of him, though—fast. And then think.

'Look…it's nice to hear from you, but I'm quite busy at the moment…'

Rafaele's voice took on a cool edge again. 'You're not curious as to why I've contacted you?'

That sliver of fear snaked down Sam's spine again as an image of her adorable dark-haired son came into her mind's eye.

'I…well…I guess I am.' She couldn't have sounded less enthusiastic.

Rafaele's voice was almost arctic now. 'I was going to offer you a position with Falcone Motors. The research you're currently conducting is exactly in the area we want to develop.'

Sheer blind panic gripped Sam's innards at his words. She'd worked for this man once before and nothing had been the same since. Her tone frigid, she said, 'I'm afraid that's impossible. I'm committed to working on behalf of the university.'

Silence for a few taut seconds and then Rafaele responded with a terse, 'I see.'

Sam could tell that Rafaele had expected her to drop at his feet in a swoon of gratitude, even just at the offer of a job, if nothing more personal. It was the effect he had on most women. He hadn't changed. In spite of what had happened between them.

The words he'd left lingering in the air when he'd walked away from her resonated as if it had happened yesterday: *'It's for the best,* cara. *After all, it wasn't as if this was ever anything serious, was it?'*

He'd so obviously wanted her to agree with him that Sam had done so, in a flat and emotionless voice. Her body had seemed drained of all feeling. Relief had been a tangible force around him. It was something that she hadn't forgotten and which had helped her to believe she'd made the right decision to take full responsibility for Milo on her own. Even so, her conscience pricked her now: *you should have told him.*

Panic galvanised Sam, so that Rafaele Falcone's offer of a job barely impinged on her consciousness. 'Look, I really am quite busy. If you don't mind…?'

'You're not even interested in discussing this?'

Sam recalled the bile that had risen within her when Rafaele had made his uninterest in her all too clear and bit out curtly, 'No, I'm not interested. Goodbye, Signor Falcone.'

Goodbye, Signor Falcone, and this from a woman he knew intimately.

Rafaele looked at the phone in his hand for a long moment. Not comprehending the fact that she had just hung up on him. Women did not hang up on him.

Rafaele put the phone down and his mouth firmed. But Samantha Rourke had never been like other women. She'd been different from the start. He felt restless and got up from his seat to pace over to the huge window that overlooked operations at his new UK base on the outskirts of London. But for once his attention wasn't on operations.

She'd come to his factory in Italy as an intern after completing her Masters in Mechanical Automotive Engineering. The youngest and only woman in a group of men. Scarily bright and intelligent. He would have had no compunction hiring her on the spot and paying her whatever she asked just to keep her working for him…but he'd become distracted.

Distracted by her sexily studious air and her tall, slim body. Distracted by the mannish clothes she'd insisted on wearing which had made him want to peel them off to see the curves hinted at but hidden underneath. Distracted by her flawless pale Celtic skin and those huge almond-shaped eyes set in delicate features. Grey eyes…like a stormy sea.

Distracted by the way she would look at him and blush when he caught her eye, the way she would catch her lower lip between small white teeth. Distracted by that fall of inky black hair which she'd kept tucking behind her ear. And, as time had worn on, distracted by the slow-burning licking flames of desire that had grown hotter and stronger every time he saw her.

Rafaele had fought it. He hadn't liked it—and especially not in the workplace. There were plenty of females working in his factory and yet none of them had ever turned his head. His life was run on strict lines and he'd always kept his personal life well away from his work. But she had been so far removed from the kind of woman he normally went for: polished, sophisticated. Worldly wise. Women who were sexy and knew it and knew what to do with it. Cynical, like him.

Sam had been none of those things. Except sexy. And he'd known she didn't know that. She'd seemed to have absolutely no awareness of the fact that men's gazes lingered on her as she passed by. It had enraged Rafaele. The hot spurt of possessiveness had been an alien concept to him. Before they'd even kissed!

In the end sexual frustration had been such a tight ball of need inside him that one day he'd called her to his office and, without being able to say a word, had taken her face in his hands and kissed her, drowning in an intoxicating sweetness he'd never tasted before.

Even now that memory alone had an effect on Rafaele's libido and body. He cursed. He'd thought of her months ago, at his mother's funeral. He thought of her more often than he liked to admit. Sam was the one who had taken him too close to the edge. They had shared more than just a brief sexual history. They had almost shared...*a child*.

Even now a shiver of fear snaked down Rafaele's spine. How close he'd come to dealing with something he never wanted to deal with. That was what he needed to remember.

He swung around and stared blankly into his huge office. Clearly she wanted nothing to do with him, and he should want to have nothing to do with her.

He should not have given in to the compulsion to track her down. He should steer well clear of Samantha Rourke and put her out of his mind. For good.

Samantha woke up on Saturday morning when a small warm body burrowed into the bed beside her. She smiled sleepily and wrapped her arms around her sturdy son, breathing in his sweet scent.

'Morning, handsome.'

'Morning, Mummy, I love you.'

Sam's heart clenched so hard for a second that she caught her breath. She kissed the top of his head. 'I love you too, sweetheart.'

Milo pulled his head back and Sam cracked open an eye and grimaced at the morning light.

He giggled. 'You're funny.'

Sam started to tickle Milo and he screeched with glee. Soon they were both wide awake and he was scrambling back out of the bed to clatter down the stairs.

She shouted after him. 'Don't turn on the TV yet!'

She heard him stop and could imagine his thwarted expression, and then he called back, 'Okay. I'll look at my book.'

Sam's heart clenched again. He would too. She knew when she went downstairs he'd be looking at his book studiously, even though he couldn't really read yet. He was such a good boy. Such a bright boy. Sometimes it scared her, how intelligent he was, because she felt as if she didn't have the means to handle it.

Bridie, her father's housekeeper, who had stayed on after he'd died two years previously, would often look at her with those far too shrewd Irish eyes and say, 'Well, where do you think he got it from? His grandfather was a professor of physics and you had your head in books from the age of two.'

Then she would sniff in that way she had and say, 'Now, obviously, as I don't know anything about his father, I can't speculate on that side of things...' which was Sam's cue to give her a baleful look and change the subject.

If it hadn't been for Bridie O'Sullivan, though, Sam reminded herself as she got out of bed, she would never have been able to get the PhD which had got her onto the lucrative research programme at the university, and which now helped pay for food, clothes *and* Bridie's wonderful care for Milo five days a week.

Bridie lived in the granny flat that had been built onto the side of the house some years before.

As Sam tied the belt on her robe, and prepared to go downstairs to get breakfast ready for herself and Milo, she tried to suppress the resurgence of guilt. The guilt that had been eating at her insides all week since she'd had *that* phone call. The guilt that had been a constant presence for four years, if she was completely honest with herself.

It unsettled her so much that she slept badly every night, tortured with memories while awake and by dreams while asleep, full of lurid images. *Hot* images. She woke tangled in the sheets, her skin damp with sweat, her heart racing, her head aching.

Rafaele Falcone. The man who had shown her just how colourless her world had been before demonstrating how easily he could deposit her back into perpetual greyness. As if she'd had no right to experience such a lavish, sensual dream.

Even now she wondered what on earth it had been about her that had caught his eye. But whatever it had been, to her everlasting shame, she would never forgive herself for believing that it had been more. For falling for him like some lovestruck teenager.

She reassured herself for the umpteenth time that week that he didn't deserve to know about Milo because he'd never wanted him in the first place. She would never forget how his face had leached of all colour when she'd told him she was pregnant.

Sam sagged back onto the side of the bed, the onslaught of memories coming too thick and fast to escape. He'd been away on a trip for three weeks and during that time Sam had found out she was pregnant. He'd asked to see her as soon as he'd returned, and after three weeks of no contact Sam hadn't been able to stop her heart from pumping with anticipation. Maybe he hadn't meant what he'd said before he'd gone on the trip…

'It might be no harm, cara, *for us to spend some time apart. My work is beginning to suffer…you're far too distracting…'*

But when she'd walked into his office he'd looked stern. Serious. Before she could lose her nerve Sam had blurted out, 'I have to tell you something.'

He'd looked at her warily. 'Go on, then.'

Sam had blushed and nervously twisted her hands, suddenly wondering if she was completely crazy to have a feeling of optimism that he might welcome her news. They'd only spent a month together. One heady, glorious month. Four weeks. Was that really enough time—?

'Sam?'

She'd looked at him, taken a deep breath and dived in. 'Rafaele…I'm pregnant.'

The words had hung ominously between them and a thick silence had grown. Rafaele's face had leached of all colour and Sam had known in that instant with cold clarity that she'd been a complete fool. About everything.

He'd literally gone white, his eyes standing out starkly green against the pallor. She'd thought he might faint and had moved towards him, but he'd put out a hand and asked hoarsely, 'How?'

She'd stopped in her tracks, but hadn't been able to halt the spread of ice in her veins. 'I think…when we were careless.'

An understatement for the amount of times they had been careless…in the shower, in the living room of Rafaele's *palazzo* when they'd been too impatient to make it to the bedroom, in the kitchen of her flat one evening, when he'd pushed her up against the counter and pulled down her trousers…

Sam had felt hot and mortified all at once. It felt so… *lurid* now. So desperate. It had been *sex*, not romance. Had she ever really known him? The vulnerability she'd felt in that moment was a searing everlasting memory.

He'd looked at her accusingly. 'You said you were on the pill.'

Sam got defensive. 'I was—I *am*. But I told you it was a low-dosage pill not specifically for contraception. And I had that twenty-four-hour bug a few weeks ago…'

Rafaele had sat down heavily into his chair. He looked as if he'd aged ten years in ten seconds. 'This can't be happening,' he'd muttered, as if Sam weren't even there.

She had tried to control her emotions, stop them from overwhelming her. 'It's as much of a shock to me as it obviously is to you.'

He'd looked up at her then and his face had tightened. 'Are you sure it's a shock? How do I know this wasn't planned in some attempt to trap me?'

Sam had almost staggered backwards, her mouth open, but nothing had come out. Eventually she'd managed, 'You think…you truly think I did this on purpose?'

Rafaele had stood up and started to pace, some colour coming back into his cheeks, highlighting that stunning bone structure. He'd laughed in a way that had chilled Sam right to her core, because she'd never heard him laugh like that before. Harsh.

He'd faced her. 'It's not unheard of, you know, for a woman who wants to ensure herself a lifetime of security from a rich man.'

The depth of this heretofore unrevealed cynicism had sent her reeling. Sam had stalked up to Rafaele's desk, her hands clenched to fists. 'You absolute *bastard*. I would never do such a thing.'

And then she'd had a flash of his expression and his demeanour when she'd come into the room, before she'd given him a chance to speak. A very bitter and dark truth had sunk in.

'You were going to tell me it was over, weren't you? That's why you asked to see me.'

Rafaele had had the grace to avoid her eye for a moment, but then he'd looked at her, his face devoid of expression.

'Yes.'

That was all. One word. Confirmation that Sam had been living in cloud cuckoo land, believing that what she'd shared with one of the world's perennial playboys had been *different*.

She'd been so overcome with conflicting emotions and turmoil at his attitude to her news and his stark lack of emotion that she'd been afraid if she tried to speak she'd start crying. So she'd run out of his office. Not even caring that she'd humiliated herself beyond all saving.

She'd hidden in her tiny apartment, avoiding Rafaele, avoiding his repeated attempts to get her to open the door.

And then it had started. The bleeding and the awful cramping pain. Terrified, Sam had finally opened the door to him, her physical pain momentarily eclipsing the emotional pain.

She'd looked at Rafaele and said starkly, 'I'm bleeding.'

He'd taken her to a clinic, grim and pale, but Sam hadn't really noticed. Her hands had been clutching her belly as she'd found herself willing the tiny clump of cells to live, no matter what. For someone who hadn't ever seriously contemplated having children, because she'd lost her own mother young and had grown up with an emotionally absent father, in that moment Sam had felt a primitive need to become a mother so strong that it had shaken her to her core.

At the clinic the kindly doctor had informed her that she wasn't, in fact, miscarrying. She was just experiencing heavier spotting than might be normal. He'd said the cramps were probably stress-induced and reassured her that with rest and avoiding vexatious situations she should go on to have a perfectly normal and healthy pregnancy.

The relief had been overwhelming. Until Sam had remembered that Rafaele was outside the door, pacing up and down, looking grim. He was a 'vexatious situation' personified. She could remember feeling the cramps come back even then, at the very prospect of having to deal with him, and again that visceral feeling had arisen: the need to protect her child.

She'd dreaded telling him that she hadn't miscarried after all.

And then a nurse had left the room, leaving the door ajar, and Rafaele's voice had floated distinctly into the room from just outside.

Everything within her stilling, Sam had heard him say tightly, *'I'm just caught up with something at the moment... No, it's not important... I will resolve this as soon as I can and get back to you.'*

And just like that the small, traitorous flame of hope she'd not even been aware she was pathetically harbouring had been extinguished. Obviously because of doctor/patient confidentiality Rafaele was none the wiser as to whether or not she'd actually miscarried. He believed that she had.

He'd terminated his conversation and come into the room. Sam had looked out of the window, feeling as if she was breaking apart inside. She'd forced herself to be calm and not stressed. The baby was paramount now.

Rafaele had stopped by the bed. 'Sam...'

Sam hadn't looked at him. She'd just answered, 'What?'

She'd heard him sigh. 'Look, I'm sorry...really sorry that this has happened. We should never have become involved.'

Sam had felt empty. 'No,' she'd agreed, 'we shouldn't have.'

Even then a small voice had urged her to put him straight, but she'd felt so angry in that moment and had already felt her stress levels rising, her body starting to cramp. Dangerous for the baby.

Feeling panicked, she'd finally turned her head to acknowledge Rafaele and said, 'Look, what's done is done. It's over. I have to stay in for a night for observation but I'm leaving tomorrow. I'm going home.'

Rafaele had been pale but Sam had felt like reaching

up to slap him. He felt no more for her than he did for the fact that as far as he was aware he'd just lost a baby. He just wanted to be rid of her. *'I will resolve this as soon as I can...'*

'Just go, Rafaele, leave me be.' *Please,* she'd begged silently, feeling those stress levels rising. Her hands had tightened on the bedcover, knuckles white.

Rafaele had just looked at her, those green eyes unfathomable. 'It's for the best, *cara.* Believe me... You are young...you have your career ahead of you. After all, it wasn't as if this was ever anything serious, was it?'

Sam's mouth had twisted and she'd resolved in that moment to do her utmost to focus on her career...and her baby. No matter what it took. 'Of course not. Now, please, just *go.*'

Sam's control had felt so brittle she'd been afraid it would snap at any moment and he'd see the true depth of her agony.

Rafaele had stepped back a pace. 'I will arrange for your travel home. You won't have to worry about anything.'

Sam had stifled a semi-hysterical giggle at the thought of the monumental task and life-change ahead of her. She'd nodded abruptly. 'Fine.'

Rafaele had been almost at the door by then, relief a tangible aura around him. 'Goodbye, Sam.'

Feeling a sob rise, and choking it down with all of her will and strength, Sam had managed a cool-sounding, 'Goodbye, Rafaele.' And then she'd turned her head, because her eyes had been stinging. She'd heard the door close softly and a huge sob had ripped out of her chest, and tears, hot and salty, had flowed down her cheeks.

By the time Sam had been at home for a week she'd begun veering wildly between the urge to tell Rafaele the truth and the urge to protect herself from further pain. Then she'd seen on some vacuous celebrity TV channel that Rafaele was already out and about with some gorgeous Italian TV personality, smiling that devilishly sexy smile. As she'd looked at Rafaele, smiling for the TV cameras, his arm around the waist of the sinuous dark-haired Latin beauty, she'd known that she could never tell him because he simply wasn't interested.

'Mummy, I want Cheerios!'

Sam blinked and came back to reality. Milo. Breakfast. She pushed aside the memories, tried to ignore the guilt and got up to attend to her son.

That evening when the doorbell rang Sam looked up from washing the dinner things in the sink. Milo was playing happily on the floor in the sitting room with his cars, oblivious. As she went to answer it she assured herself it was probably just Bridie, who had forgotten her keys to the flat again.

But when she opened the door on the dusky late winter evening it wasn't Bridie, who stood at five foot two inches in heels. It was someone over a foot taller and infinitely more masculine.

Rafaele Falcone.

For a long, breathless moment, the information simply wouldn't compute. Suspended in time, Sam seemed to be able to take in details almost dispassionately. Faded jeans. Battered leather jacket. Thin wool jumper. Thick dark brown hair which still had a tendency to curl a little too much over his collar. The high forehead. The deep-set startling green eyes. The patrician bump of his nose, giving him that indelible air of arrogance. The stunning bone structure and that golden olive skin that placed him somewhere more exotic than cold, wet England.

And his mouth. That gorgeous, sculpted-for-wicked-things mouth. It always looked on the verge of tipping into a sexy half-smile, full of the promise of sensual nirvana.

Unless it was pulled into a grim line, as it had been when she had seen him last.

Reality slammed into Sam like a fist to her gut. She actually sucked in a breath, only realising then that she'd been starving her lungs for long seconds while she gawped at him like a groupie.

'Samantha.'

His voice lodged her even more firmly in reality. And the burning intensity of his green eyes as they swept down her body. Sam became acutely aware of her weekend uniform of skinny jeans, thick socks and a very worn plaid shirt. Her hair was scraped up into a bun and she wore no make-up.

Rafaele smiled. 'Still a tomboy, I see. Despite my best efforts.'

A memory exploded into Sam's consciousness. Rafaele, in his *palazzo*, presenting her with a huge white box. Under what had seemed like acres and acres of silver tissue paper a swathe of material had appeared.

Sam had lifted it out to reveal a breathtaking evening gown. Rafaele had stripped her himself and dressed her again. One-shouldered and figure-hugging, in black and flesh-coloured stripes, the dress had accentuated her hips, her breasts, and a long slit had revealed her legs. Then he'd taken her out to one of Milan's most exclusive restaurants. They'd been the last to leave, somewhere around four o'clock in the morning, drunk on sparkling wine and lust, and he'd taken her home to his *palazzo*…

'*Still a tomboy, I see…*'

The memory vanished and the backdrop of Sam's very suburban street behind Rafaele came back into view.

Sexy smile. 'Aren't you going to ask me in? It's cold out here.'

Sam's hand clenched tight around the door. *Milo.* Panic rushed into her blood. Finally. Rousing her.

'Now isn't a good time. I don't know why you've come here. I thought I made it clear the other day that I'm not interested.'

Sam forced herself to look at him. Four years had passed and in that time she'd changed utterly. She felt older, more jaded. Whereas Rafaele only looked even more gorgeous. The unfairness of it galvanised her. He'd known nothing of her life the last few years. *Because you didn't tell him*, a voice pointed out.

'Why did you come here, Rafaele? I'm sure you have more important things to do on a Saturday evening.'

The bitterness in Sam's voice surprised her.

Rafaele's jaw tightened, but he answered smoothly. 'I thought if I came to see you in person you might be persuaded to listen to my offer.'

A dull flush accentuated Rafaele's cheekbones, but Sam was barely aware of it as she heard a high-pitched 'Mummy!' which was accompanied by small feet running at full speed behind her.

She felt Milo land at her legs, clasping his arms around them, and could almost visualise his little round face peeping out to see who was at the door. Like trying in vain to halt an oncoming train, Sam said in a thready voice, 'Like I said, now really isn't a good time.'

She could see awareness dawn on Rafaele's face as he obviously took in the fact of a child. He started to speak stiltedly. 'I'm sorry. I should have thought… Of course it's been years…you must be married by now. Children…'

Then his eyes slid down and she saw them widen. She didn't have to look to know that Milo was now standing beside her, one chubby hand clinging onto her leg. Wide green eyes would be staring innocently up into eyes the exact same shade of green. Unusual. Lots of people commented on how unusual they were.

Rafaele stared at Milo for what seemed like an age. He

frowned and then looked as if someone had just hit him in the belly...dazed. He looked up at Sam and she knew exactly what he was seeing as clearly as if she was standing apart, observing the interplay. Her eyes were wide and stricken, set in a face leached of all colour. Pale as parchment. Panicked. *Guilty.*

And just like that, something in his eyes turned to ice and she knew that he knew.

CHAPTER TWO

'MUMMY, CAN WE watch the cars on TV now?'

Sam put her hand to Milo's head and said faintly, 'Why don't you go on and I'll be there in a minute, okay?'

Milo ran off again and the silence grew taut between Sam and Rafaele. He knew. She felt it in her bones. He'd known as soon as he'd looked into his son's eyes. So identical. She hated that something about his immediate recognition of his own son made something soften inside her.

He was looking at her so hard she felt it like a physical brand on her skin. Hot.

'Let me in, Samantha. Now.'

Feeling shaky and clammy all at once, Sam stepped back and opened the door. Rafaele came in, his tall, powerful form dwarfing the hallway. He smelt of light spices and something musky, and through the shock Sam's blood jumped in recognition.

She shut the door and walked quickly to the kitchen at the end of the hall, passing where Milo sat cross-legged in front of the TV watching a popular car programme. His favourite.

She was about to pull the door shut when a curt voice behind her instructed, 'Leave it.'

She dropped her hand and tensed. Rafaele was looking at Milo as he sat enraptured by the cars on the screen. He was holding about three of his favourite toy cars in his hands. If his eyes and pale olive skin hadn't been a fatal giveaway then this might have been the worst kind of ironic joke.

Sam stepped back and walked into the kitchen. She couldn't feel her legs. She felt sick, light-headed. She turned around to see Rafaele follow her in and close the door behind him, not shutting it completely.

Rafaele was white beneath his dark colouring. And he looked murderous.

He bit out, 'This is where you tell me that by some extraordinary feat of genetic coincidence that little boy in there *isn't* three years and approximately three months old. That he *didn't* inherit exactly the same colour eyes that I inherited from my own mother. That he *isn't* my son.'

Sam opened her mouth. 'He is…' Even now, at this last second, her brain searched desperately for something to cling onto. Some way this could be justified. *He was his father.* She couldn't do it. She didn't have the right any more. She'd never had the right. 'He is your son.'

Silence, stretching taut and stark, and then he repeated, 'He is my son?'

Sam just nodded. Nausea was churning in her belly now. The full implications of this were starting to hit home.

Rafaele emitted a long stream of Italian invective and Sam winced because she recognised some of the cruder words—they were pretty universal. Her belly was so tight she put a hand to it unconsciously. She watched as Rafaele struggled to take this in. The enormity of it.

'No wonder you were so keen to get rid of me the other day.'

He paced back and forth in the tiny space. She could feel his anger and tension as it lashed out like a live electrical wire, snapping at her feet.

Suddenly he stopped and looked at her. 'Are you married?'

Sam shook her head painfully. 'No.'

'And what if I hadn't decided to pay you a visit? Would you have let me remain in blissful ignorance for ever?'

Stricken, Sam whispered, 'I don't…I don't know.' Even as she admitted that, though, the knowledge seeped in. She wouldn't have been able to live with the guilt. She would have told him.

He pinned her to the spot with that light green gaze which had once devoured her alive and was now colder than the arctic.

'You bitch.'

Sam flinched. He might as well have slapped her across the face. It had the same effect. The words were so coldly and implacably delivered.

'You didn't want a baby,' she whispered, unable to inject more force into her voice.

'So you just lied to me?'

Sam could feel her cheeks burning now, with shame. 'I thought it was a miscarriage, as did you. But at the clinic, after the doctor had done his examination, he told me that I wasn't miscarrying.'

Rafaele crossed his arms and she could see his hands clenched to fists. She shivered at the threat of violence even though she knew he would never hit her. But she sensed he wanted to hit something.

'You knew then and yet you barefaced lied to me and let me walk away.'

Clutching at the smallest of straws, Sam said shakily, 'I didn't lie…you assumed…I just didn't tell you.'

'And the reason you didn't inform me was because…?'

'You didn't…didn't want to know.' The words felt flimsy and ineffectual now. Petty.

'Based on…?'

It was as if he couldn't quite get out full sentences, Sam felt his rage strangling his words.

Her brain felt heavy. 'Because of how you reacted when I told you in the first place…'

Sam recalled the indescribable pain of realising that Rafaele had been about to break it off with her. His abject shock at the prospect of her pregnancy. It gave her some much needed strength. 'And because of what you said afterwards…at the clinic. I heard you on the phone.'

Rafaele frowned and it was a glower. 'What did I say?'

Sam's sliver of strength started to drain away again like a traitor. 'You were talking to someone. You said you were caught up in something *unimportant*.' Even now those words scored at Sam's insides like a knife.

Rafaele's expression turned nuclear. His arms dropped, his hands were fists. '*Dio*, Samantha. I can't even recall that conversation. No doubt I just said something—anything—to placate one of my assistants. I thought you'd just miscarried. Do you really think I was about to announce *that* in an innocuous phone call?'

Sam gulped and had to admit reluctantly, 'Maybe… maybe not. But how did I know that? All I could hear was your relief that you didn't have to worry about a baby holding your life up and your eagerness to leave.'

He all but exploded. 'Need I remind you that I was also in shock, and at that point I thought there was no baby!'

Sam was breathing hard and Rafaele looked as if he was about to kick aside the kitchen table between them to come and throttle her.

Just then a small, unsure voice emerged from the doorway. 'Mummy?'

Immediately Sam's world refracted down to Milo, who stood in the doorway. He'd opened it unnoticed by them and was looking from one to the other, his lower lip quivering ominously at the explosive tension.

Sam flew over and picked him up and he clung to her.

Her conscience struck her. He was always a little intimidated by men because he wasn't around them much.

'Why is the man still here?' he asked now, slanting sidelong looks to Rafaele and curling into Sam's body as much as he could.

Sam stroked his back reassuringly and tried to sound normal. 'This is just an old friend of Mummy's. He's stopped by to say hello, that's all. He's leaving now.'

'Okay,' Milo replied, happier now. 'Can we look at cars?'

Sam looked at him and forced a smile, 'Just as soon as I say goodbye to Mr Falcone, okay?'

'Okey-dokey.' Milo used his new favourite phrase that he'd picked up in playschool, squirmed back out of Sam's arms and ran out of the kitchen again.

Sam watched Rafaele struggle to take it all in. Myriad explosive emotions crossing his face.

'You'll have to go,' she entreated. 'It'll only confuse and upset him if you stay.'

Rafaele closed the distance between them and Sam instinctively moved back, but the oven was behind her. Rafaele's scent enveloped her, musky and male. Her heart pounded.

'This is not over, Samantha. I'll leave now, because I don't want to upset the boy, but you'll be hearing from me.'

After a long searing moment, during which she wasn't sure how she didn't combust from the anger being directed at her, Rafaele turned on his heel and left, stopping briefly at the sitting room door to look in at Milo again.

He cast one blistering look back at Sam and then he was out through the front door and gone. Sam heard the powerful throttle of an engine as it roared to life and then mercifully faded again.

It was then that she started to shake all over. Grasping

for a chair to hold onto, she sank down into it, her teeth starting to chatter.

'Mummeeee!' came a plaintive wail from the sitting room.

Sam called out, 'I'll be there in one second, I promise.'

The last thing she needed was for Milo to see her in this state. Her brain was numb. She couldn't even quite take in what had just happened—the fact that she'd seen Rafaele again for the first time since those cataclysmic days.

When she was finally feeling a little more in control she went in to Milo and sat down on the floor beside him. Without even taking his eyes off the TV he crawled into her lap and Sam's heart constricted. She kissed his head.

Rafaele's words came back to her: *'This is not over, Samantha. I'll leave now, because I don't want to upset the boy, but you'll be hearing from me.'*

She shivered. She didn't even want to think of what she'd be facing when she heard from Rafaele again.

On Monday morning Sam filed into the conference room at the university and took a seat at the long table for the weekly budget meeting. Her eyes were gritty with tiredness. Unsurprisingly she hadn't slept all weekend, on tenterhooks waiting for Rafaele to appear again like a spectre. In her more fanciful moments she'd imagined that she'd dreamt it all up: the phone call; his appearance at the house. *Coming face to face with his son.* A small, snide voice pointed out that it was no less than she deserved but she pushed it down.

Robustly she told herself that if she'd had to go back in time she would have done the same again, because if she hadn't surely the stress of Rafaele being reluctantly bound to her and a baby would have resulted in a miscarriage for real?

Gertie, the secretary, arrived then and sat down breathlessly next to Sam. She said urgently, 'You'll never guess what's happened over the weekend…'

Sam looked at her, used to Gertie's penchant for gossip. She didn't want to hear some salacious story involving students and professors behaving badly, but the older woman's face suddenly composed itself and Sam looked to see that the head of their department had walked into the room.

And then her heart stopped. Because right on his heels was another man. *Rafaele*.

For a second Sam thought she might faint. She was instantly light-headed. She had to put her hands on the edge of the table and grip it as she watched in mounting horror and shock as Rafaele coolly and calmly strode into the room, looking as out of place in this unadorned academic environment as an exotic peacock on a grubby high street.

He didn't even glance her way. He took a seat at the head of the table alongside their boss, looking stupendously handsome and sexy. He sat back, casually undoing a button on his pristine suit jacket with a big hand, long fingers…

Sam was mesmerised.

This had to be a dream, she thought to herself frantically. She'd wake up any moment. But Gertie was elbowing her none too discreetly and saying *sotto voce*, 'This is what I was about to tell you.'

The stern glare of their boss quelled any chat and then, with devastating inevitability, Sam's stricken gaze met Rafaele's and she knew it wasn't a dream. There was a distinct gleam of triumph in those green depths, and a more than smug smile was playing around that firmly sculpted mouth.

Her boss was standing up and clearing his throat. Sam couldn't look away from Rafaele, and he didn't remove his gaze from hers, as if forcing her to take in every word now being spoken, but she only heard snippets.

'Falcone Industries…most successful…honoured that

Mr Falcone has decided to fund this research out of his own pocket...delighted at this announcement...funding guaranteed for as long as it takes.'

Then Rafaele got up to address the room. There were about thirteen people and, predictably, you could have heard a pin drop as his charismatic effect held everyone in thrall. He'd finally moved his gaze from Sam and she felt as if she could breathe again, albeit painfully. Her heart was racing and she took in nothing of what he said, trying to wrap her sluggish brain around the ramifications of this shocking development.

'Samantha...'

Sam looked up, dazed, to see her boss was now addressing her, and that Rafaele had sat down. She hadn't noticed, nor heard a word.

'I'm sorry, Bill, what did you say?' She was amazed she'd managed to speak.

'I *said*,' he repeated with exaggerated patience, clearly disgruntled that she appeared to be on another planet while in such illustrious company, 'that as of next week you will be working from the Falcone factory. You're to oversee setting up a research facility there which will work in tandem with the one here in the university.'

He directed himself to the others again while this bomb detonated within Sam's solar plexus.

'I don't think I need to point out the significance of being allowed to conduct this research within a functioning factory, and especially one as prestigious as Falcone Motors. It'll put us streets ahead of other research in this area and, being assured of Falcone funding for at least five years, we're practically guaranteed success.'

Sam couldn't take any more. She rose up in a blind panic, managed to mumble something vague about needing air and fled the room.

* * *

Rafaele watched Sam leave dispassionately. Since the other evening he'd been in shock. Functioning, but in shock. His anger and rage was too volcanic to release, fearsome in its intensity. And fearsome for Rafaele if he contemplated for a second why his emotions were so deep and hot.

Sam's boss beside him emitted a grunt of displeasure at her hasty departure, but Rafaele felt nothing but satisfaction to be causing her a modicum of the turbulence in his own gut. Through his shock Rafaele had felt a visceral need to push Sam off her axis as much as she'd pushed him off his.

He recalled bitterly how reluctant she'd been to talk to him in the first place about the job he was offering, all the while knowing her secret. Harbouring his son. With one phone call to his team Rafaele had put in motion this audacious plan to take over the research programme at her university and had relished this meeting.

While Sam's boss continued his speech Rafaele retreated inwardly, but anyone looking at him would have seen only fierce concentration.

He breathed in and realised that he hadn't taken a proper breath since he'd seen Sam looking at him with that stricken expression on her face in the doorway of her house the other evening. The initial punch to his gut he'd received when he'd first thought that Sam was married, with someone else's child, was galling to remember—and more exposing than he liked to admit.

Nothing excused her from withholding his son from him for more than three years. Rafaele had been about Milo's age when his world had imploded. When he'd witnessed his father, on his knees, sobbing, prostrating himself at Rafaele's mother's feet, begging her not to leave him.

'I love you. What am I if you leave? I am nothing. I have nothing...'

'Get up, Umberto,' she'd said. *'You shame yourself in front of our son. What kind of a man will he be with a crying, snivelling wretch for a father?'*

What kind of a man would he be?

Rafaele felt tight inside. The kind of man who knew that the most important things in life were building a solid foundation. Security. Success. He'd vowed never to allow anything to reduce him to nothing, as his father had been reduced, with not even his pride to keep him standing. Emotions were dangerous. They had the power to derail you completely. He knew how fickle women were, how easily they could walk away. Or keep you from your child.

Rafaele had driven back to Sam's house on Sunday, fired up, ready to confront her again, but just as he'd pulled up he'd seen them leaving the house. Milo had been pushing a scooter. He'd followed them to a small local park and watched like a fugitive as they played. Dark emotions had twisted inside him as he'd watched Sam's effortless long-legged grace and ease. He'd known that if he hadn't reappeared in their lives this would have just been another banal Sunday morning routine trip to the park.

Seeing his son's small sturdy body, watching him running around, laughing gleefully, something alien inside him had swelled. It was…pride. And something else that he couldn't name. But it had reminded him of that day again—the darkest in his memory—when his mother had gripped his hand painfully tight and pulled him in her wake out of their family *palazzo* outside Milan, leaving his father sobbing uncontrollably on the ground. A pathetic, broken man.

That was one of the reasons Rafaele had never wanted to have children. Knowing how vulnerable they were had always felt like too huge a responsibility to bear. No one knew better than he how events even at that young age could shape your life. And so he'd never expected that, when faced with his son, there would be such a torrent of feelings within him, each one binding him invisibly and indelibly to this person he didn't even know properly yet. Or that when he'd watched him running around the other day there would be a surge of something so primal and protective that he just knew without question, instantly, that he would do anything to prevent his son from coming into harm's way.

From far too early an age Rafaele had been made aware that the absence of a father corroded at your insides like an acid.

Resolve firmed like a ball of concrete inside him. There was no way on this earth that he was going to walk away from his son now and give him a taste of what he'd suffered.

Cutting off Sam's boss curtly, Rafaele stood up and muttered an excuse, and left the room. There was only one person he wanted to hear talk right now.

Sam's stomach felt raw after she'd lost her breakfast, minute as it had been, into a toilet in the ladies' room. She felt shaky, weak, and looked as pale as death in the reflection of the cracked mirror. She splashed water on her face and rinsed her mouth out, knowing that she had to go back out there and face—

The door suddenly swung open and Sam stood up straight, hands gripping the side of the sink. For once she prayed it might be Gertie, even though she knew it wasn't when every tiny hair seemed to prickle on her skin.

She turned around and saw Rafaele, looking very tall and very dark as he leant back against the door, hands thrust deep into his pockets. Even now her body sang, recognising the man who had introduced her to her own sensuality, and she clamped down on the rogue response, bitterly aware that not even the harsh fluorescent lighting could strip away his sheer good looks.

Welcome anger rose up and Sam seized on it, crossing her arms over her chest. Her voice felt rough, raw. 'What the hell do you think you're playing at, Rafaele? How dare you come in here and use your might to get back at me? These are people you're playing with—people who have invested long years of study into their area—and suddenly you sweep in and promise them a glimpse of future success when we both know—'

'Enough.'

Rafaele's voice sounded harsh in the echoing silence of the cavernous tiled ladies' bathroom.

'I am fully committed to following through on my promise of funding and support to this university.' His mouth tightened. 'Unless you've already forgotten, I *had* contacted you initially to ask you to work for me. I had every intention of using your expertise to further this very research for my own ends.'

He shrugged minutely. 'There's nothing new in that— any motor company worth its salt is on the lookout for new research and ways of beating the competition with new technology. You have single-handedly elevated this research to a far more advanced level than any other facility, in a university or otherwise.'

His words sent Sam no sense of professional satisfaction. She was still in shock. 'That may be the case,' she bit out tightly, 'but now that you know about Milo you're seeking to get back at me personally.'

She couldn't keep the bitterness from her voice.

'It just so happens that you have the means to be able to come in and take over the entire department to do your bidding.'

Fresh panic gripped her when she recalled her boss saying something about Sam herself going to work from his

factory. Her arms grew tighter over her chest when she recalled the hothouse environment of working in Rafaele's
Milan factory four years ago and how easily he'd seduced
her. The thought of going back into a similar environment,
even if Rafaele would prefer to throttle her than sleep with
her, made her clammy.

'I will not be going to work for you. I will remain here
at the university.'

Rafaele took a few paces forward and Sam saw the
light of something like steel in his eyes and his expression. Her belly sank even as her skin tightened with betraying awareness.

'You *will* be coming to work for me—or I will pull out
of this agreement and all of your colleagues are back to
square one. Your boss has informed me that if I hadn't
come along with the promise of funding he was going to
have to let some people go. He can't keep everyone on the
payroll due to reduced projected funding this year. You
would have been informed of that at this very meeting.'

Vaguely Sam was aware of the veracity of what he
said. It had been rumoured for weeks. Once again she
was struck by how little she'd appreciated how ruthless
Rafaele was. 'You bastard,' she breathed.

Rafaele looked supremely unperturbed. 'Hardly, when
I'm saving jobs. It's very simple if you do the right thing
and accede to my wishes. And this is just the start of it,
Samantha.'

Ice invaded her bloodstream. 'Start of what?'

To her shock she realised belatedly how close Rafaele
had come when he reached out a hand and cupped her jaw.
She felt the strength of that hand, the faint calluses which
reminded her of how he loved tinkering with engines despite his status. It was one of the things that had endeared
him to her from the start.

In an instant an awful physical yearning rose up within

her. Every cell in her body was reacting joyously to a touch she'd never thought she'd experience again. She was melting, getting hot. Damp.

Softly, he sliced open the wound in her heart. 'The start of payback, Samantha. You owe me for depriving me of my son for more than three years and I will never let you forget it.'

For a moment Rafaele almost forgot where he was, who he was talking to. The feel of Sam's skin under his hand was like silk, her jaw as delicate as the finest spun Murano glass. He had an almost overwhelming urge to keep sliding his hand around to the back of her neck, to tug her towards him so that he could feel her pressed against him and crush that pink rosebud mouth under his— Suddenly Rafaele realised what he was doing.

With a guttural curse he took his hand away and stepped back. Sam was looking at him with huge grey eyes, her face as pale as parchment with two pink spots in each cheek.

She blinked, almost as if she'd been caught in a similar spell, and then something in her eyes cleared. The anger was gone.

She changed tack, entreated him. She held out a hand and her voice was husky. 'Please, Rafaele, we need to talk about this—'

'No.' The word was harsh, abrupt, and it cut her off effectively. Everything within Rafaele had seized at her attempt to try and take advantage of a moment when she might have perceived weakness on his part. To play on his conscience. With the shadows under her eyes making her look fragile and vulnerable.

He'd witnessed his mother for years, using her wiles to fool men into thinking she was vulnerable, fragile. Only to see how her expression would harden again once they were no longer looking and she'd got what she wanted. She'd been so cold the day she'd left his father, showing not an ounce of remorse.

Once, he mightn't have believed Sam was like that, but that was before she'd kept his son from him, demonstrating equal, if not worse, callousness.

Rafaele took another step back and hated that he felt the need to do so. That volcanic anger was well and truly erupting now. He gritted out, 'If you were a man...'

Sam tensed and her chin lifted. Gone was the soft look of before, the husky entreaty.

'If I were a man...what? You'd thrash me? Well, what's stopping you?'

Rafaele could see where her hands had clenched to fists by her side. He looked at her disgustedly. 'Because I don't raise my hands to women—or anyone, for that matter. But I felt like it for the first time when I realised that boy was my son.'

He couldn't stop the words spilling out. That initial shock was infusing him all over again.

'My *son*, Sam, my flesh and blood. He's a Falcone. *Dio*. How could you have played God like that? What gave you the right to believe you had the answer? That you alone could decide to just cut me out of his life?'

Sam seemed to tense even more, her chin going higher. Those spots of red deepened, highlighting her delicate bone structure. 'Do I need to remind you *again* that you practically tripped over your feet in your hurry to get out of the clinic that day? You could barely disguise your relief when you thought there was nothing to worry about. You just assumed the worst. It didn't even occur to you to question whether or not I'd actually had a miscarriage, because you didn't want a baby.'

Rafaele coloured, his conscience pricked by the reminder of how eager he'd been to get away from those huge bruised eyes, the raw emotion. The shock. The awareness that Sam had strayed too far under his skin.

Tightly he admitted, 'I never had any intention of having children. But you gave me no reason to doubt the inevitable conclusion of what we'd both believed to be a miscarriage.'

Sam choked out, 'You were quite happy to wash your hands of me, so don't blame me now if I felt the best course was to leave you out of my decision-making process.'

Rafaele looked at Sam across the few feet that separated them and all he could see was her eyes. Huge, and as grey as the rolling English clouds. She was sucking him in again but he wouldn't let her. She'd wilfully misdirected him into believing she'd miscarried when all the while she'd held the knowledge of their baby, *living*, in her belly.

He shook his head. 'That's just not good enough.'

Sam's voice took on a defensive edge. 'I was hardly encouraged to get in touch and tell you the truth when I saw you with another woman only a week after that day.'

She was breathing heavily under her shirt and he could see her breasts rise and fall. A flash of heat went straight to his groin and Rafaele crushed it ruthlessly. He focused on her face and tried to forget that he actually hadn't slept with another woman for about a year after Sam had left, despite appearances and despite his best efforts. Every time he'd come close something inside him had shut down. And since then…? His experiences with women had been anything but satisfactory. To be reminded of this now was galling.

He narrowed his eyes. 'Don't you dare try to put this on me now, just to deflect your own guilt.'

But the guilt that had struck Rafaele wouldn't be banished, much as he wanted it to be. Damn her! He wouldn't let her do this to him now. She'd borne his child. His son. And said nothing.

Sam's voice was bitter. 'God forbid that I would forget what our relationship was about. *Sex.* That was pretty much it, wasn't it? Forget conversation, or anything more intimate than being naked in bed. It wasn't as if you didn't make that abundantly clear, Rafaele, telling me over and over again not to fall for you because you weren't *about* that.'

'But you did anyway, didn't you?' Rafaele couldn't keep the accusing note out of his voice and he saw Sam blanch.

'I thought I loved you.' Her mouth twisted. 'After all, you were my first lover, and isn't it normal for a virgin to develop an attachment to her first? Isn't that one of the helpful warnings you gave me?'

Rafaele saw nothing right then but a memory of Sam's naked and flushed body as she'd lain on his bed before him, her breasts high and round, her narrow waist, long legs. Skin so pure and white it had reminded him of alabaster—except she'd been living, breathing, so passionate. And she'd been innocent. He'd never forget how it had felt to sink into that slick, tight heat for the first time. It was his most erotic memory. Her gasp of shock turning to pleasure.

She continued, 'But don't worry. I soon got over it and realised how shallow those feelings were. Once I was faced with the reality of pregnancy and a baby.'

'A reality,' Rafaele gritted out, angry at that memory and at how easily it had slipped past his guard, 'that you decided to face *alone.*'

Reacting against her ability to scramble his thought-processes, Rafaele changed tack.

'Was it a punishment, Sam? Hmm?' He answered himself. 'Punishment for my being finished with you? For not wanting more? For letting you go? For not wanting to have a baby because that's not what our relationship was about?'

Rafaele couldn't stop the demon inside him.

'I think the problem is that you fell for me and you were angry because I didn't fall for you, so you decided to punish me. It's so obvious…'

CHAPTER THREE

SAM CLOSED the distance between them, her hand lifted and she hit Rafaele across the face before she even registered the impulse to do so. She realised in the sickeningly taut silence afterwards that she'd reacted because he'd spoken her worst fears out loud. Here in this awful, stark, echoey room.

With a guttural curse, and his cheek flaring red where Sam had hit him, Rafaele hauled her into his arms and his mouth was on hers. He was kissing her angrily, roughly.

It took a second for Sam to get over the shock, but what happened next wasn't the reaction she would have chosen if she'd had half a brain cell still working. Her reaction came from her treacherous body and overrode her brain completely.

She started kissing him back, matching his anger with her own. For exposing her. For saying those words out loud. For making her feel even more ashamed and confused. For being *here*. For making her want him. For making her remember. For kissing her just to dominate her and prove how much she still wanted him.

Her hands were clutching Rafaele's jacket. She tasted blood and yet it wasn't pain that registered. It was passion, and it sent her senses spiralling out of all control. Rafaele's hands were bruisingly hard on her arms and tears pricked behind Sam's eyelids at the tumult of desire mixed with frustration.

She opened her eyes to see swirling green oceans. Rafaele pulled away jerkily and Sam could hear nothing but the thunder of her own heartbeat and her ragged breathing. She was still clutching his jacket and she let go, her hands shaking.

'You're bleeding…'

The fact that Rafaele's voice was rough was no comfort. He was just angry, not overcome with passion.

Sam reached up and touched her lip and winced when it stung slightly. Her mouth felt swollen. She knew she had to get out of there before he saw something. Before he saw that very close behind her anger in that exchange had been an awful yearning for something else.

'I have to go. They'll be wondering where we are.' Her insides were heaving, roiling. She was terrified she might be sick again, and this time all over Rafaele's immaculate shoes. She couldn't look at him.

'Sam—'

'No.' She cut him off and looked at him. 'Not here.'

His jaw tightened. 'Fine. I'll send a car for you this evening. We'll talk at my place.'

Sam was too much in shock to argue. Too much had happened—too much physicality. Too much of a reminder that he aroused more passion in her just by looking at him than she'd ever felt in her life with anyone else. She simply didn't have it in her right then to say anything other than a very reluctant, 'Fine.' She needed to get away from this man before he exposed her completely.

That evening, Sam waited for Rafaele in an exclusive townhouse in the middle of Mayfair, demesne of the rich and famous. Anger and an awful sense of futility had simmered in her belly all day as she'd had to put up with her colleagues excitedly discussing the great opportunity Rafaele Falcone had presented them with while knowing that it was only to ensure he gained as much control of her life as he could.

She was afraid of the volatility of her emotions after what had happened in that bathroom earlier and, worse, at the thought of working for him again. She forced herself to take deep breaths and focused on her surroundings. Luxurious sofas and chairs, dressed in shades of grey and white and cream. Low coffee tables and sleek furnishings. Seriously intimidating.

She felt very scruffy as she was still in her work uniform of narrow black trousers, white shirt and black jacket. Flat shoes. Hair pulled back. No make-up. These surroundings were made for a much more sensual woman. A woman who would drape herself seductively on a couch in a beautiful silk dress and wait for her lover.

It reminded Sam painfully of Rafaele's *palazzo* on the outskirts of Milan, where sometimes she had fooled herself into believing nothing existed beyond those four walls. And that she was one of those beautiful seductive women.

'Sorry to keep you waiting.'

Sam whirled around so abruptly when she heard his voice that she felt dizzy. She realised she was clutching her leather bag to her chest like a shield and lowered it.

She really wasn't prepared to see Rafaele again so soon, and that swirling cauldron of emotions within her was spiked with a mix of anger and ever-present shame. And the memory of that angry kiss. Her lips were still sensitive. He looked like the Devil himself, emerging from the shadows of the doorway. Tall, broad, hard, muscled. And mean. His face was harsh, his mouth unsmiling. Making a mockery of his apology for keeping her waiting.

Nothing had changed from earlier. But despite her anger Sam's conscience stung. Tightly, she said, 'I'm sorry…for hitting you earlier. I don't know what came over me…but what you said…it was wrong.'

Liar. She burned inside. She might as well have held her tongue. She was lying to herself as much as to him.

Rafaele came further in. Grim. 'I deserved it. I provoked you.'

Sam blanched and looked at him. She hadn't expected that, and somewhere treacherous a part of her melted.

He walked past her and over to a drinks board, helping himself to something amber that swirled in the bottom of a bulbous glass. He looked at her over his shoulder, making heat flood her cheeks. She hadn't even realised that she'd been making a thorough inspection of his broad back, tapering down to lean hips and firm buttocks.

'Drink?'

She shook her head hurriedly and got out a choked, 'No. Thank you.'

'Suit yourself.' He gestured to a nearby couch. 'Sit down, Sam—and you can put down your bag. You look as if your fingers might break.'

She looked down stupidly to see white knuckles through the skin of her fingers where they gripped the leather. Forcing herself to take a breath, she moved jerkily over to the couch and perched on the edge, resisting the design of it, which wanted to seduce her into a more relaxed pose.

Rafaele came and sat down opposite her, clearly far more relaxed than her as he sank back into the couch, resting one arm across the top. Sam fought the desire to look and see how his shirt must be stretched across his chest.

'What kind of a name is Milo anyway? Irish?'

Sam blinked. It took a minute for his words to sink in because they were so unexpected. 'It's…it was my grandfather's name.'

Sam was vaguely surprised he remembered that detail of her heritage. She was one generation removed from Ireland, actually, having been born and brought up in England because her parents had moved there after her brilliant father had been offered a job at a London university.

Sam sensed his anger building again. 'I did intend to tell you…some day. I would never have withheld that information from Milo for ever.'

Rafaele snorted a harsh laugh. 'That's big of you. You would have waited until he'd built up a childhood full of resentment about his absent father and I wouldn't have even known.'

Rafaele sat forward and put down his glass with a clatter. He ran his hand impatiently through his hair, making it flop messily onto his forehead. Sam's insides clenched when she remembered how she'd once felt comfortable running her hands through his hair, using it to hold him in place when he'd had his face buried between—

Shame flared inside her at the way her thoughts were going. She should be thinking of Milo and extricating them both from the threat that Rafaele posed, not remembering lurid X-rated memories.

In a smaller voice she admitted, 'I've been living day to day…it didn't seem to be urgent right now. He…he doesn't ask about his father.'

Rafaele stood up, towering over her. 'I'd say it became urgent about the time you gave birth, Sam. Don't you think he must be wondering why other kids have fathers and he doesn't?'

Words were locked in Sam's throat. Milo mightn't have mentioned anything yet, but she had noticed him looking at his friends in playschool when their fathers picked them up. It wouldn't be long before he'd start asking questions.

She stood up too, not liking feeling so intimidated.

Rafaele bit back the anger that threatened to spill over and keep spilling. Looking as vulnerable, if not more so than she had earlier, Sam said tightly, 'Look, I can't stay too long. My minder is doing me a favour. Can we just… get to what we need to discuss?'

He'd been unable to get Sam's pale face out of his mind all day. Or the way he'd hauled her into his arms like a Neanderthal, all but backing her up against that sink to ravish her in a tacky bathroom. The feel of her against him, under his mouth, had dragged him back to a place he'd locked away deep inside, unleashing a cavalcade of desire more hot and urgent than anything he'd ever encountered.

He struggled to curb some of the intense emotion he was feeling.

'What's going to happen is this: I am going to be a father to my son and you will do everything in your power to facilitate that—because if you don't, Samantha, I won't hesitate to use full legal force against you.'

Rafaele delivered his ultimatum and Sam just looked at him, trying not to let him see how his words shook her to her core. *I won't hesitate to use full legal force against you.*

'What exactly do you mean, Rafaele? You can't threaten me like this.'

Rafaele came close to Sam—close enough for his scent to wind around her, prompting a vivid memory of how it had felt to have her mouth crushed under his earlier that day. He looked at her for such a long, taut moment that she stopped breathing. And then he moved back to the couch to sit down again and regarded her like a lounging pasha.

'It's not a threat. It's very much a promise. I want to be in Milo's life. I am his father. We deserve to get to know one another. He needs to *know* that I am his father.'

Panic boosted Sam's adrenalin. She couldn't have sat down if she'd wanted to. Every muscle was locked. 'You can't just barge in and announce that you're his father. He won't understand. It'll upset him.'

Rafaele arched a brow. 'And whose fault is that? Who

kept this knowledge from him and from me? One person, Sam. *You*. And now you have to deal with the consequences.'

'Yes,' Sam admitted bitterly, 'I recognise that, and you've already made your sphere of influence obvious—but not at the cost of my son's happiness and sense of security.'

Rafaele leant forward. 'You have cost our son his happiness and security already. You've wilfully cost him three years of knowing he had a father. You've already irreparably damaged his development.'

Our son. Sam's insides contracted painfully. She was feeling shocked again at the very evident emotion on Rafaele's face. Quickly masked, though, as if he was surprised by his own vehemence.

'So what are you proposing, Rafaele?'

A part of Sam, deep down inside, marvelled at that moment that there had ever been intimacy between them. That she had ever lain beside him in bed and gazed deep into his eyes. On their last night together…before he'd gone on his business trip…she'd reached out and touched his face as if learning every feature. He'd taken her hand and pressed a kiss to her palm, and there had been something she'd never seen before darkening his eyes, making her breath grow short and her heart pound…

'What I'm proposing is that, as I'm due to be here in England for the foreseeable future, I want to be a part of Milo's daily life so that he can get to know me.'

Sam struggled to take it in. '"The foreseeable future"? What does that mean? You can't get to know him and then just walk away, Rafaele, when your business is done.'

Rafaele stood up and put his hands deep in his pockets, as if he was having second thoughts about physical violence. Silkily he replied, 'Oh, don't worry, Sam, I have no intention of walking away—ever—no matter where my business takes me. Milo is my son just as much as he is yours. You've had unfettered access to him for over three years of his life and you will never deny me access again. I want him here—with me.'

Sam's mouth opened and closed again before she could manage to articulate, 'Here with you? But that's preposterous. He's *three!*'

Rafaele clarified with clear reluctance, 'Naturally you would also have to come.'

Sam emitted a scared laugh, because even though what Rafaele was saying was insane he sounded eminently reasonable. 'Oh, thanks! Should I be grateful that you would allow me to stay with my son?'

Rafaele's face darkened. 'I think any judge in any courtroom would look unfavourably upon a mother who kept her son from his father for no apparent good reason.'

Sam blanched and tried to appeal to him. 'Rafaele, we can't just…uproot and move in with you. It's not practical.' And the very thought of spending any more time alone with this man than she had to scared the living daylights out of her.

His voice sounded unbearably harsh. 'I am going to be under the same roof as my son, as his father, and I will not negotiate on that. You can either be part of it or not. Obviously it will be easier if you are. And, as we're going to be working together again, it can only be more practical.'

Anger surged again at Rafaele's reminder of that small detail and his intractability. 'You're being completely unreasonable. Of course I need to be with my son…*that's* non-negotiable.'

Rafaele took a step closer, and even though his hands were in his pockets Sam felt the threat reach out to touch her.

'Well, then, you have a measure of how I'm feeling, Samantha. I will expect you back here with your bags and

Milo by this time tomorrow evening or else we take it to the courts and they will decide how he will divide his time between us.' He added, 'You've proved that you believe one parent is dispensable—what's to stop me testing out the theory with you?'

Sam gritted out, 'I do recognise that you've missed out on time with Milo…and I should have told you before now. But I had my reasons and I believed they were valid.'

'Very noble of you, Samantha,' Rafaele mocked, with an edge.

Trying to concentrate and not be distracted by him, she said, 'It's just not practical for us to come here. This might be your home, and it's beautiful—'

'It's not mine,' Rafaele bit out. 'It belongs to a friend. I'm renting it.'

Sam lifted her hands in an unconscious plea for him to listen. 'All the more reason why this isn't a good idea—it's not even your permanent home. Milo is settled into a good routine where we are. We have a granny flat attached to the house and that's where Bridie lives.'

Rafaele arched a brow. 'His minder?'

Sam nodded. 'She was my father's housekeeper since I was two, after my mother died. She cared for me while I grew up and she stayed on after my father passed away two years ago.'

'I'm sorry,' Rafaele offered stiffly, 'I didn't know.'

'Thank you…' Sam acknowledged. 'The thing is,' she continued while she had Rafaele's attention, 'Bridie has known Milo since he was born. She…helped me.'

Sam coloured as she imagined the acerbic retorts going through Rafaele's mind and she rushed on. 'We have a good arrangement. Regular affordable childcare like I have is gold dust in London.'

Rafaele asserted, 'I don't think I need to point out that

affording childcare would be the least of your worries if you let me organise it.'

Sam was tense enough to crack, and all of a sudden she felt incredibly light-headed. She must have shown it, because immediately Rafaele was beside her, holding her arm and frowning.

'What is it? *Dio*, Sam, you look like death warmed up.'

His use of *Sam* caught her somewhere vulnerable. She cursed herself inwardly. She was no wilting ninny and she hated that Rafaele was seeing her like this. She pulled away from his strong grip jerkily. 'I'm fine…'

Rafaele all but forcibly manoeuvred her to the couch and made her sit down again. Then he went to the drinks cabinet and poured some brandy into a glass. Coming back, he handed it to her.

Hating herself for needing the fortification, Sam took it.

She took a sip, and as the pungent and strong alcohol filtered down her throat and into her belly, felt a bit steadier. She put the glass down and looked directly at Rafaele, where he too had taken his seat again, opposite her.

'Look, you've said yourself that you're just renting this place. It would be insane to uproot Milo from the only home he's known since he was a baby.' She pressed on, 'My father's house is perfectly comfortable. Bridie lives right next door. His playschool is at the end of the road. We have a nearby park. He goes swimming at the weekends to the local pool. He plays with the children from the surrounding houses. It's a safe area. Everyone looks out for everyone and they all love Milo.'

Rafaele's face was unreadable. Sam took a breath. She'd just spoken as if in a lecture, in a series of bullet points. Never more than right now did she appreciate just how much Rafaele could upset their lives if he wanted to. And it was entirely her fault.

He drawled, 'The picture you paint is positively idyllic.'

She flushed at the sarcasm in his voice. 'We're lucky to be in a good area.'

'How have you managed financially?'

Rafaele's question blindsided Sam for a minute. 'It... well, it wasn't easy at first. I had to defer my PhD for a year. My father was ill... But I had some savings to tide us over. And he had his pension. When he died the mortgage was protected, so that was paid off. Bridie looked after Milo while I did my doctorate and I was lucky enough to be taken onto the research programme soon afterwards. We get by. We have enough.'

Unmistakable pride straightened Sam's spine. Rafaele could see it in the set of her shoulders and he had to hand it to her—grudgingly. She hadn't come running to him looking for a hand-out as soon as she'd known her pregnancy was viable. He didn't know any woman who wouldn't have taken advantage of that fact. And yet Sam had been determined to go it alone.

'Would you have come to me if you'd needed money?'

Rafaele could see her go pale at the prospect and something dark rushed to his gut. She would have preferred to struggle than to see him again. Since last Saturday's cataclysmic revelation Rafaele had been avoiding looking at the fact that he'd felt so compelled to see Sam again he'd ignored his earlier warning to himself to stay away and had gone to her house with more than a sense of anticipation in his belly. It had been something bordering much closer to a *need*. He'd tried to ignore it, but he'd been incensed that she'd been so dismissive. Uninterested.

Rafaele stood up. 'I fail to see what all this has to do with me getting what I want—which is my son.'

Sam stood up too, her cheeks flushing, making her eyes stand out like glittering pools of grey. Desire, dark and urgent, speared Rafaele.

'That's just it. You don't get it, do you? It's not about you or me. It's about Milo and what's best for *him*. He's not a pawn, Rafaele, you can't just move him around at will to get back at me. His needs must come first.'

Rafaele felt stung at her tirade. She had the right to maternal indignation because she'd experienced the bonding process. He hadn't. But he knew that she was right. He couldn't just waltz in and pluck his son out of his routine, much as he wanted to. But he hated her for this.

Tightly he asked, 'So what is your suggestion, then?'

The relief that moved across her expressive fine features made him even angrier. Did she really think it would be this easy?

'We leave Milo where he is, at home with me. And you can come and see him…we'll work something out while you're here in England…and then, once we see how it goes, we can work out a longer term arrangement. After all, you won't be here for ever…'

He could see her spying her bag nearby and she moved to get it. His eyes were drawn against his will to her tall, slim form as she bent and then straightened, her breasts pushing against her shirt, reminding him of how badly he'd ached to touch them for the first time, and what it had felt like to cup their firm weight, made perfectly to fit his palms. The fact that the memory was so vivid was not welcome.

Sam was the only woman who'd ever had this ability to make him feel slightly out of his comfort zone. Coasting on the edge of extreme danger. And not the kind he liked, where he ultimately had control, say in a car.

Danger zone or no danger zone, something primal gripped Rafaele deep inside at seeing Sam preparing to leave, looking so relieved—as if she could just lay it all on the line like this and he'd agree.

She was backing away, tucking some loose hair behind her ear, and it was that one simple familiar gesture that pushed Rafaele over an edge. 'Do you really think it's that easy? That I'll simply agree to your terms?'

She stopped. 'You can't do this, Rafaele—insist on having it your way. It's not fair on Milo. If he's going to get to know you then it should be in his own safe environment. He's going to be confused as it is.'

Rafaele moved closer to Sam, almost against his will. 'And whose fault is that?' he reminded her, as an audacious plan formed in his brain. 'What do you hope for, Sam? That after a couple of visits I'll grow bored and you'll be left in peace?'

She swallowed visibly and looked faintly guilty. 'Of course not.'

But *she did*. He could tell. She hoped that this was just a passing display of anger and might. She was probably congratulating herself on the fact that he now knew and that she and her son—*his son*—would be left in peace to get on with their lives once he'd lost interest.

Suddenly Rafaele wanted to insert himself deep into Sam's life. *Deep into her*. He remembered what that had felt like too—that moment of exquisite suspension when neither of them could draw in a breath because he was embedded so deep inside her—

'This will work *my way* or no way,' he gritted out, ruthlessly crushing those incendiary images, exerting a control over his body he rarely had to call on.

'Rafaele—'

'No, Samantha. I will concede that you are right that Milo must come first, so I agree that he should stay where he is most secure.'

'You do?'

Rafaele didn't even bother to agree again, he just continued, 'So, with that concern in mind, I will compromise.'

She swallowed again. Now she looked nervous. *Good. She should*. Rafaele smiled and got a fleeting moment of satisfaction from the way her eyes dropped to his mouth and flared with something hot.

'I'll move in with you.'

Sam's eyes met his and grew wider. He saw her struggling to compute the information. She even shook her head slightly.

'I'm sorry… I don't think I heard you properly… You said you'll what?'

Rafaele smiled even more widely now, enjoying himself for the first time in days. 'You heard me fine, Samantha, I said I'll move in with you. Then you will have no reason to deny me access to my son as I'll be doing everything in my power to accommodate you—isn't that right?'

Sam felt as if she was suspended in time, disbelieving of what she'd just heard. But then the smug look on Rafaele's face told her she hadn't misheard. *Twice.*

'But…you can't. I mean…' Her brain seemed to have turned to slush. 'There's no room.'

Rafaele quirked a brow. 'It looks like a decent-sized house to me. I would imagine there's at least three bedrooms? All I need is one.'

Sam cursed his accuracy and diverted her thoughts away from remembering Rafaele's palatial bedroom in his *palazzo*, with the bed big enough for a football team. They'd covered every inch of it.

Stiffly she said, 'It's not a good idea. You wouldn't be comfortable. It's not exactly up to this standard.' She gestured with her arm to take in the surrounding opulence.

Rafaele grimaced. 'This place is too big for just me.' And then his eyes glinted with sheer wickedness. 'I find my preferences running to much more modest requirements all of a sudden.'

Sam felt old bitterness rise. No doubt he meant much in the same way his preferences had become more 'modest' when he'd found himself briefly in thrall to her. Seduced, presumably, by her complete naivety and innocence because he'd become momentarily jaded by the far more sophisticated women he usually went for. This had been evidenced by the fact that he'd never even taken her out in too public a social setting, preferring to keep their dates secluded and *secret*.

Sam shook her head, the mere thought of Rafaele in her house for an extended period making her seize inwardly. Not to mention the fact that he expected her to work for him.

'No. This is not going to happen. Maybe if you moved closer—'

Suddenly Rafaele was far too close and Sam's words faltered. Any hint of wickedness was gone.

'No, Samantha. I am moving in with you and there is nothing you can do or say to put me off this course. I've missed important milestones already in my son's life and I'm not about to miss another moment.'

Shakily Sam said, 'Please, there must be another way to do this.'

Rafaele stepped even closer. Sam could smell him now and see the lighter flecks of green in his eyes. See the dark shadowing of stubble on his jaw. He'd always needed to shave twice a day. Her insides cramped.

'The reason you don't want me to stay, Sam… It wouldn't be because there's still something there…would it?'

Had his voice grown huskier or was it her imagination? Sam just looked at him and blinked. His eyes were molten green, hot. And she was on fire. It was only when she saw something very cynical and dark in their depths that she managed to shake herself free of his spell. She was terrified he'd touch her again, like earlier, and stepped back, feeling cold all over.

The thought that she'd given herself away, that he might

analyse her reaction and suspect that there had been something deeper there than anger made her sick with mortification and shame.

In as cool a voice as she could muster, Sam said, 'Don't be ridiculous, Rafaele. I'm no more attracted to you any more than you are to me. That died long ago.'

His eyes flashed. 'So there should be no problem with my sharing your house to facilitate me getting to know my son, who you have kept from me for the last three years?'

It wasn't really a question. Much as in the way he had ridden roughshod over her department at work, ensuring she would be under his control. With a sinking sense of inevitability Sam knew that if she fought Rafaele further he'd only dig his heels in deeper and deeper. And perhaps he'd even feel like toying with her again, proving a point, and perhaps this time she'd really give herself away.

The thought made her go clammy. She must never forget his cruel rejection or let him know how badly he'd hurt her.

She reassured herself that he was a workaholic, after all, so she'd probably barely see him. And for all his lofty talk she didn't seriously see him lasting for longer than a week in the leafy but very boring London suburbs.

A man like Rafaele—son of an Italian count and a renowned Spanish beauty—was accustomed to beautiful things and especially beautiful women. Accustomed to getting what he wanted.

Seizing on that, and also anticipating his realisation that her house would not be a haven for his mistresses and would soon bore him to tears, Sam lifted her chin and said, 'When do you propose to move in?'

CHAPTER FOUR

FOUR DAYS LATER it was Friday evening, and Sam was tense enough to crack in two, waiting for Rafaele's appearance. He was moving in tonight, and all week his staff had been arriving at the house to prepare it for his arrival.

When she'd come home from his house the previous Monday evening she'd had to come clean and tell Bridie what had happened. The older woman had reacted with admirable nonchalance.

'He's his father, you say?'

'Yes,' Sam had replied, *sotto voce*, giving Bridie a look to tell her to be mindful of small ears nearby as Milo had been in the sitting room, watching a cartoon before bed.

Unfortunately Bridie had been enjoying this revelation far too much. She'd taken a sip of tea and then repeated, 'His father… Well, I never, Sam. You're a dark one, aren't you? I always thought it might have been a waiter or a mechanic at the factory or something…but it's actually himself—the Falcone boss…'

Sam had gritted out, 'He's only moving in temporarily. He'll be bored within a week, believe me.'

Bridie had sniffed disapprovingly. 'Well, let's hope not for Milo's sake.'

Sam's hands stilled under the water now, as she washed the dinner dishes. She could hear Milo's chatter to Bridie nearby. She was doing this for him. She had to stop thinking about herself and think of him. It was the only way she'd get through this, because if she focused for a second on what it meant for her to be thrown into such close proximity with Rafaele again she felt the urgent compulsion to run fast and far away.

Bridie bustled into the kitchen then, and Sam noticed her badly disguised expression of anticipation. She might have smiled if she'd been able.

'You really don't have to wait till he gets here.'

The housekeeper smiled at her sunnily and started drying dishes. 'Oh, I wouldn't miss this for the world, Sam. It's better than the Pope's visit to Dublin back in the seventies.'

Suddenly the low, powerful throb of an engine became obvious outside. To Sam's chagrin she found that she was automatically trying to analyse the nuances of the sound, figuring out the components of the engine.

Milo's ears must have pricked up, because he came into the kitchen excitedly and announced, 'Car!'

They didn't have a car themselves, much to his constant disappointment, and Sam couldn't stop him running towards the door now. When the bell rang her palms grew sweaty. Before she could move, though, Bridie was beating her to it, and Sam only noticed then that Bridie, who never wore an apron, had put one on. She wanted to roll her eyes.

But then the door opened and Sam's world condensed down to the tall dark figure filling the frame against the dusky evening. She hadn't seen him since Monday and she hated the way her heart leapt in her chest.

Milo said with some surprise from beside Bridie, 'It's the man.' And then, completely oblivious to the atmosphere, 'Do you have a car?'

Rafaele's gaze had zeroed in immediately on Sam, and she was glad now that she had the buffer of Bridie at the door. Bridie was doing her thing now, extending her hand, introducing herself, practically twinkling with Irish charm.

Lots of *'sure'* and *'Won't you come in out of that cold?'*. Ridiculously, Sam felt betrayed.

Rafaele stepped in and Sam's chest constricted. He looked so alien, foreign. Too gorgeous for this environment. Finally she found her legs and moved forward to pick Milo up. His eyes were huge as he took Rafaele in, again.

Milo repeated his question. 'Do you have a car, mister?'

Rafaele looked at Milo and Sam could see how his cheeks flared with colour. His eyes took on a glow that she'd never seen before…or maybe she thought she had… once. Her arms tightened fractionally around Milo. Bridie had bustled off somewhere, saying something about tea and coffee. Now it was just the three of them.

His voice was so deep it resonated within Sam.

'Yes, I do have a car… I'm Rafaele…and what's your name?'

The fact that Rafaele's voice had gone husky made Sam's guilt rush to the fore again. Milo buried his head in Sam's neck, his little arms tight around her neck.

She said to Milo's obscured face, 'Don't you remember me telling you that Mr Falcone would be moving in to live with us for a while?' Milo nodded against her neck, still hiding. She looked back at Rafaele. 'He's just a bit shy with strangers at first.'

Rafaele's eyes flashed dangerously at that reminder of his status and Sam said quickly, 'You can leave your jacket and things in the hall.'

He started to divest himself of his expensive black coat, revealing a dark suit underneath. Bridie reappeared then, unusually pink in the cheeks, and took Milo from Sam's arms, saying, 'I think it's bedtime for someone…there's refreshments in the drawing room.'

Sam wanted to roll her eyes again. Since when had Bridie referred to the main reception room as *the drawing room*? Or said *refreshments*? Or got pink in the cheeks from preparing tea?

She called after them. 'I'll be up to read a story in a little while.'

All she could hear, though, was Milo's plaintive, 'I want to see the car,' and Bridie reassuring him briskly that he could see it in the morning if he was a good boy and brushed his teeth before bed.

Hating Rafaele right then, for imposing himself on them like this and upsetting their equilibrium, Sam forced herself to look at him and bit out, 'I'll give you a tour, shall I?'

Rafaele smiled, but it didn't reach his eyes. 'That would be lovely.'

As perfunctorily as she could, while uncomfortably aware of Rafaele breathing down her neck, Sam showed him around the ground floor of the house.

He stopped in the study and took in the impressive array of equipment set up for his benefit, surprising her by saying, 'This was your father's study?'

'Yes,' Sam answered, more huskily than she would have liked, caught by a sudden upsurge of emotion at remembering her scatty, absent-minded father spending hours on end in here, oblivious to everything. Her chest tightened. *Oblivious to his daughter.*

'They should not have set up in here...it's not appropriate.'

Sam looked at Rafaele, surprised by this assertion. By this evidence of sensitivity.

'No...it's fine. It's been lying empty. It should be used.' Her mouth twisted wryly. 'Believe me, you could have set all this up here while he was still alive and he wouldn't have even noticed.'

Feeling exposed under Rafaele's incisive green gaze, Sam backed out of the room.

'Upstairs. I'll show you your room.'

She hurried up the stairs, very aware of Rafaele behind her, conscious of her drab work uniform. Again.

She opened and closed doors with almost indecent speed, and they passed where Milo was chattering nineteen to the dozen with Bridie as she helped him brush his teeth in the bathroom, standing on a little box so he could reach the sink.

Rafaele stopped outside for a long moment, and when he finally turned to keep following Sam she shivered at the look of censure in his eyes. That brief moment of sensitivity had evidently passed.

When she didn't open the door to her bedroom, but just gestured at it with clear reluctance, Rafaele pushed past her and opened the door. He looked in for a long moment, before slanting her an unmistakably mocking look. She burned inside with humiliation and hated to imagine what he must think of the room. It hadn't been redecorated since she'd left home for college and still sported dusky pink rose wallpaper.

The faded décor now seemed to scream out her innermost teenage fantasies of *not* being the school nerd, of her deeply secret wish to be just like all the other girls. No wonder Rafaele had seduced her so easily. He'd unwittingly tapped into the closet feminine romantic that Sam had repressed her whole life in a bid to be accepted by her father, turning herself into a studious tomboy.

Aghast to be thinking of this now, she swallowed her mortification, reached past Rafaele and pulled the door firmly closed in his face. Then she led him to his room.

Thankfully it was at the other end of the house from her room and Milo's, which was opposite hers. And, even better, it had an *en suite* bathroom. After that cataclysmic moment in the university the other day she had no intention of running into a half-naked Rafaele on his way to the bathroom.

Rafaele barely gave the room a cursory once-over. As she led him back downstairs Sam sent up another silent prayer that he was already chafing to get back to his own rarefied world, where his every whim was indulged before he'd even articulated it out loud.

Bridie had indeed set out tea and coffee in the front room. Sam poured coffee and handed it to him, watching warily as he sat down on the comfy but decidedly thread-bare sofa.

He looked around, taking in the homely furnishings. 'You have a nice house.'

Sam took a seat as far away from Rafaele as possible. She all but snorted. 'Hardly what you're used to.'

He levelled her a look that would have sent his minions running. 'I'm not a snob, Samantha. I may have had a priv-ileged upbringing, but when I set out to resurrect Falcone Industries I had nothing but the shirt on my back. I lived in an apartment the size of your porch and worked three jobs to put myself through college.'

Sam frowned, a little blindsided by this revelation. 'But your stepfather—he was a Greek billionaire…'

Rafaele's mouth twisted. 'Who hated my guts because I wasn't his son. The only reason he put me through school at all was because of my mother. He washed his hands of me as soon as he could and I paid him back every cent he'd doled out for my education.'

He'd never told her this before—had always shied away from talking about personal things. She'd always assumed that he'd been given a hand-out to restart Falcone Indus-tries. It was one of the most well-documented resurrections of a company in recent times. Spectacular in its success. She recalled his mother ringing from time to time, and their clipped conversations largely conducted in Spanish, which was her first language.

At a loss to know what to say, Sam went for the easiest thing. 'How *is* your mother?'

Rafaele's face tightened almost imperceptibly but Sam noticed.

'She died three months ago. A heart attack.'

'I'm sorry, Rafaele,' Sam responded. 'I had no idea…' She gestured helplessly. 'I must have missed it in the papers.'

His Spanish mother had been a world-renowned beauty and feted model. Her marriages and lovers had been well documented. The rumour was that she had cruelly left Rafaele's father when it had become apparent that he'd lost everything except his title. But this was only hearsay that Sam had picked up when she'd gone to Milan to work for Falcone Industries as an intern.

Rafaele shook his head, his mouth thin. 'It was overshadowed by the economic crisis in Greece so it barely made the papers—something we welcomed.'

Sam could remember how much Rafaele had hated press intrusion and the constant glare of the paparazzi lens. He put down his cup and stood abruptly. Sam looked up, her breath sticking in her throat for a minute as he loomed so large and intimidating. *Gorgeous*. Lord, how was she going to get through even twenty-four hours of him living under the same roof, just down the hall? Did he still sleep naked—?

'…will you tell him?'

Sam flushed hotly when she registered Rafaele looking at her expectantly. He'd just asked her a question and she'd been so busy speculating on whether or not he still slept naked that she hadn't heard him.

She stood up so quickly her knees banged against the coffee table and she winced. 'Tell who what?'

Rafaele looked irritated. 'When are you going to tell Milo that I am his father?'

Sam crossed her arms over breasts that felt heavy and tingly. 'I think…I think when he's got used to you being here. When he's got to know you a bit…then we can tell him.' She cursed herself for once again proving that her mind was all too easily swayed by this man.

He nodded. 'I think that's fair enough.'

Sam breathed out, struck somewhere vulnerable at seeing Rafaele intent on putting Milo's needs first, over his wish to punish her.

Just then Bridie put her head around the door. 'I'm off, love, and Milo is waiting for his story. If you need me over the weekend just call me. Nice to meet you, Mr Falcone.'

Sam moved towards the door, more in a bid to get away from Rafaele than a desire to see Bridie out, but the older woman waved her back with a definite glint in her eyes.

'Stay where you are.'

Rafaele murmured goodnight and then Bridie was gone. Sam heard the sound of the front door opening and closing. And now she really was alone in the house with the man she'd hoped never to see again and her son. *Milo.* The incongruity of Rafaele Falcone, international billionaire and playboy, here in her suburban house, was overwhelming to say the least.

She backed towards the door. 'I should go to Milo. He'll come looking for me if I don't.' Why did she suddenly sound as if she'd just been running?

Rafaele inclined his head. 'I have some work to attend to, if you don't mind me using the study?'

Sam was relieved at the prospect of some space. 'Of course not.'

And then she fled, taking the stairs two at a time as she had when she'd been a teenager.

Rafaele heard Sam take the stairs at a gallop and shook his head. He looked around the room again. Definitely not the milieu he was accustomed to, in spite of his defence to

Sam. Those gruelling years when he'd done nothing but work, study, sleep and repeat were a blur now.

He felt slightly shell-shocked at how easily he'd told Sam something he never discussed. It was no secret that he'd turned his back on his stepfather to resurrect his family legacy, but people invariably drew their own conclusions.

His mouth tightened. He'd resisted the urge to spill his guts before—had been content to distract them both from talking by concentrating on the physical. Avoiding a deeper intimacy at all costs.

Rafaele cursed and ran his hands through his hair, feeling constricted in his suit. He'd come straight here from a meeting in town. As soon as he'd walked in through the front door he'd felt the house closing in around him claustrophobically and he'd had a bizarre urge to turn on his heel, get back into his car and drive very fast in the opposite direction.

For a wild few seconds when he'd looked at Sam waiting in the hall the only thing he'd been able to remember was how he'd all but devoured her only days before. He'd assured himself that he could just send in his lawyers and have her dictated to, punished for not telling him about Milo.

But then he'd seen Milo, held in her arms, and the claustrophobia had disappeared. *That* was why he was here. Because he didn't want more months to go by before he got a chance to let his son know who he was. More months added on top of the three years he'd already missed. Rafaele had never really forgiven his own father for falling apart and checking out of his life so spectacularly. For investing so much in a woman who had never loved him. For allowing himself to turn into something maudlin and useless.

For years Rafaele had been jealous of his younger

brother, Alexio, who had grown up bathed in his father's love and support. So much so, however, that Rafaele knew how stifling Alexio had found it, prompting him to turn his back on his own inheritance. He smiled grimly to himself. Maybe that just proved one could never be happy?

He made his way to the study and sat down behind the desk, firing up various machines. He stopped abruptly when he heard movement above his head. His heart twisted at the realisation that he must be underneath Milo's room. Obeying an urge he couldn't ignore, Rafaele stood up and walked out of the room and up the stairs, as silent as a panther.

He saw the half-open door of Milo's room and stopped when he could see inside. The scene made him suck in a breath. Sam was leaning back against a headboard painted in bright colours with Milo in her embrace. She held a book open in front of them and was reading aloud, putting on funny voices, making Milo giggle.

Rafaele had forgotten that she wore glasses to read and write. They made her look seriously studious, but also seriously sexy. Her mouth was plump and pink. Even in the plain white shirt and trousers her slim curves were evident. This sight of her was hugely disconcerting. He'd never expected to see her in this situation. And yet something about it called to him—an echo of an emotion he'd crushed ruthlessly when she'd first told him she was pregnant. Before the shock had hit, and the cynical suspicion that she'd planned it, had come something far more disturbing. Something fragile and alien.

He hated her right then for still having an effect on him. For still making him want her. For invading his imagination when he'd least expected it over the last four years. He would find it hard to recall his last lover's name right now, but Sam…her name had always been indelible. And this was utterly galling when she'd proved to be as treacherous as his own mother in her own way. When she'd kept the most precious thing from him. His son.

For a moment Rafaele questioned his sanity in deciding to take over funding the research programme at the university in a bid to get to Sam. But then he remembered looking down into Milo's green eyes and recognising his own DNA like a beacon winking back at him.

As much as there was a valid reason behind his rationale, it had also come from that deeper place not linked solely to rationale and he hated to admit that.

His eyes went to his son and Rafaele put a hand to his chest, where an ache was forming. He would make it his life's mission to keep Sam from sidelining him from his own son's life. Whatever it took. Even if it meant spending twenty-four hours a day with her. He could resist her. How could he desire a woman who had denied him his most basic right of all? His own flesh and blood.

Later, when Sam was in bed, the familiar creakings of the old house which normally comforted her sounded sinister. Rafaele Falcone was separated from her only by some bricks and mortar. And reality was slowly sinking in. Her new reality. Living and working with Rafaele Falcone. She suspected that he'd flexed his muscles to get her to work for him as much to irritate her as for any *bona fide* professional reason, even if that was why he'd first contacted her.

The thought of going back into that factory environment made her feel clammy. Although she'd loved it the first time around—it had been so exciting, getting an internship with one of the most innovative and successful motor companies in the world.

Rafaele had made his initial fortune by devising a computer software program which aided in the design of cars, and that was how he'd first come onto the scene, stunning the world with its success. That was how he'd been able to fund getting Falcone Motors off the ground again—injecting it with new life, turning around the perception of the Falcone car as outdated and prehistoric. Now Falcone cars were the most coveted on the race track *and* on the roads.

And Sam had been in the thick of it, working on new cutting edge designs, figuring out the most fuel-efficient engine systems. From her very first day, though, she'd been aware of Rafaele. She'd gone bright red whenever she saw him, never expecting him to be as gorgeous in the flesh as he was in press photos.

He'd surprised her by being very hands-on, not afraid to get dirty himself, and invariably he knew more than all of them put together, displaying an awesome intelligence and intellect. And, in a notoriously male-dominated industry, she'd met more females working in his factory than she'd encountered in all her years as a student. Clearly when he said equal opportunities he meant it.

Sam had found that each day she was seeking him out… only to look away like a naive schoolgirl if he met her gaze, which he'd appeared to do more and more often. She'd been innocent—literally. A childhood spent with an emotionally distant father and with her head buried in books hadn't made for a well-rounded adolescence. While her peers had been experimenting with boys Sam had been trying in vain to connect with her scatty but brilliant father. Bridie had been in despair, and had all but given up encouraging Sam to get out and enjoy herself, not to worry so much about studying or her father.

The irony of it all was that while the more predominantly masculine areas *did* appeal to her—hence her subsequent career—she'd always longed to feel more feminine. And it was this very secret desire that Rafaele had unwittingly tapped into so effectively. Just by looking at her, he had made Sam feel like a woman for the first time in her life.

One of their first conversations had been over an intricate engine. The other interns and engineers had walked away momentarily and Sam had been about to follow them when Rafaele had caught her wrist. He'd let her go again almost immediately but her skin had burned for hours afterwards, along with the fire in her belly.

'So,' he'd drawled in that sexy voice, 'where did your interest and love for engines come from, Miss Rourke?'

The *Miss Rourke* had sounded gently mocking, as if some sort of secret code had passed between them. Sam had been mesmerised and it had taken a second for her to answer. She'd shrugged, looking away from the penetrating gaze that had seemed to see her in a way that was both exhilarating and terrifying.

'My father is a professor of physics, so I've grown up surrounded by science. And my grandmother…his mother…she was Irish, but she ended up in England during the Second World War, working in the factories on cars. Apparently she loved it and had a natural affinity for working with engines—so much so that she kept her job after the war for a few years, before returning home to marry.' She'd shrugged again. 'I guess it ran in the family.'

Sam looked back at her young naive self now and cringed. She'd been so transparent, so easy to seduce. It had taken one earth-shattering kiss in Rafaele's office and she'd opened herself up for him, had forgotten everything her upbringing had taught her about protecting herself from emotionally unavailable people.

He'd whispered to her that she was sensual, sexy, beautiful, and she'd melted. A girl who had grown up denying her very sexuality had had no defence mechanism in place to deal with someone as practised and polished and seductive as Rafaele.

She'd fallen for him quicker than Alice in Wonderland had fallen down the rabbit hole. And her world had changed as utterly as Alice's: beautiful dresses, intoxicating dates—one night he'd even flown them to Venice in his helicopter for dinner.

And then there had been the sex. He'd taken her innocence with a tenderness she never would have expected of a consummate seducer. It had been mind-blowing, addictive. Almost overwhelming for Sam, who had never imagined her boring, almost boyish body could arouse someone— never mind a man like Rafaele Falcone, who had his pick of the world's most beautiful women.

During their short-lived affair, even though he'd told her, 'Samantha…don't fall for me. Don't hope for something more because I have nothing to give someone like you…' she hadn't listened. She'd told herself that he had to feel *something*, because when they made love it felt as if they transcended everything that bound them to this earth and touched something profound.

At the time, though, she'd laughed and said airily, belying her own naivety, 'Relax, Rafaele! It is possible, you know, for not every woman you meet to fall in love with you. I know what this is. It's just sex.'

She'd made herself say it out loud, even though it had been like turning a knife towards her own belly and thrusting it deep. Because she'd been so far out of her depth by then she might as well have been in the middle of the Atlantic Ocean. She'd been lying, of course. She'd proved to be as humiliatingly susceptible to Rafaele's lethal charm as the next hapless woman.

If anything, he'd given her a life lesson and a half. For a brief moment she'd lost her head and forgotten that if it looked like a dream and felt like a dream, then it probably was a dream. Her real world was far more banal and she'd always been destined to return to it. Milo or no Milo.

Punching the pillow beneath her head now, as if she could punch the memories away too, Sam closed her eyes and promised herself that not for a second would she ever betray just how badly that man had hurt her.

'Mummy, the man is still here. He's downstairs in the book room.'

Sam responded to the none-too-gentle shaking of her son and opened her eyes. She'd finally fallen asleep somewhere around dawn. *Again*. Milo's eyes were huge in his face and Sam struggled to sit up, pulling him into her, feeling her stomach clench at the reminder of who was here.

'I told you that he'd be moving in with us for a while, don't you remember?' she prompted sleepily.

Milo nodded and then asked, 'But where's *his* house?'

Sam smiled wryly. Little did her son know that his father had a veritable portfolio of houses around the world.

'He doesn't have a house here in London.'

'Okay.' Milo clambered out of the bed and looked at her winsomely. 'Can we get Cheerios now?'

Sam got out of bed and reached for her robe—and then thought better of it when she imagined Rafaele giving its threadbare appearance a caustic once-over. No doubt he would wonder what on earth he'd ever seen in her.

Hating to be so influenced by what he might think, Sam reached for jeans and a thin sweatshirt and yanked her sleep-mussed hair into a ponytail. No make-up. She cursed herself. She wasn't trying to seduce Rafaele, for crying out loud.

Milo was jumping around now and then stopped. 'Do you...do you think he'll eat Cheerios too?' He looked comically stricken. 'What if he eats *my* Cheerios?'

Sam bent down and tweaked Milo's nose. 'He won't touch your Cheerios while I'm around. Anyway, I happen to know for a fact that he only likes coffee for breakfast.'

Something poignant gripped her as she remembered

lazy mornings when Rafaele would take great pleasure in feeding her but not himself, much to her amusement.

'Ugh,' declared Milo, already setting off out of the room, 'Coffee is *yuck*.'

Sam heard him go downstairs, sounding like a herd of baby elephants, and took a deep breath before following him. The study door was ajar, and as she passed she could hear the low deep tones that had an instant effect on her insides.

Milo was pointing with his finger and saying in a very loud stage whisper, 'He's in there.'

Sam just nodded and put a finger to her lips, then herded Milo towards the kitchen, where he quickly got distracted helping to set the table.

And even though she knew Rafaele was in the house she still wasn't prepared when she turned around and saw him standing in the doorway, looking dark and gorgeous in faded jeans and a thin jumper. It did little to disguise the inherent strength of his very powerful masculine form, akin to that of an athlete. He was so *sexy*. With that unmistakable foreign edge that no English man could ever hope to pull off.

The memory of his initial effect on her four years ago was still raw, but she forced herself to say civilly, 'Good morning. I hope you slept well?'

He smiled faintly but she noticed it barely touched those luminous green eyes. 'Like a log.'

Milo piped up, 'That's silly. *Logs* can't sleep.'

Rafaele looked at his son and again Sam noticed the way something in his face and eyes softened. He came into the kitchen and sat down at the table near Milo. 'Oh, really? What should I say, then?'

Milo was embarrassed now with the attention and started squirming in his chair. 'Aunty Bridie says she sleeps like a baby, and babies sleep all the time.'

'Okay,' Rafaele said. 'I slept like a baby. Is that right?'

Milo was still embarrassed and avoided Rafaele's eyes, but then curiosity got the better of him and he squinted him a look. 'You sound funny.'

Rafaele smiled. 'That's because I come from a place called Italy...so I speak Italian. That's why I sound funny.'

Milo looked at Sam. 'Mummy, how come we don't sound like the man?'

Sam avoided Rafaele's eyes. She put Milo's bowl of cereal down in front of him and chided gently, 'His name is Rafaele.' And then, 'Because we come from England and we speak English. To some people *we* would sound funny.'

But Milo was already engrossed in his food, oblivious to the undercurrents between the two adults in the small kitchen. Sam risked a glance at Rafaele and blanched. His look said it all: *The reason he thinks I sound funny is because you've denied him his heritage.*

Sam turned to the coffee machine as if it was the most interesting thing on the planet and said, too brightly, 'Would you like some coffee?'

She heard a chair scrape and looked around to see Rafaele standing up. 'I had some earlier. I have to go to the factory for a while today but I'll be back later. Don't worry about dinner or anything like that—I have to go out tonight to a function.'

'Oh.' Sam rested her hands on the counter behind her. She hated the sudden deflated feeling in her solar plexus. But hadn't she expected this? So why was she feeling disappointed? And angry?

The words spilled out before she could stop them. 'I forgot that weekends for you are just as important as any other day.' *Except for when he'd spent that whole last weekend in bed with her, and diverted his phone calls.*

Rafaele's eyes flashed. 'We're taking in delivery of some specially manufactured parts today and I need to make sure they're up to spec because we start putting them into new cars next week. Something,' he drawled, with that light of triumph in his eyes, *'you'll* be dealing with next week when you come to work.'

Sam's insides clenched hard even as a treacherous flicker of interest caught her. She'd forgotten for a moment.

Before she could respond, Rafaele had dismissed her and was bending down to Milo's eye level. His ears had inevitably pricked up at the mention of cars. 'I was thinking that maybe tomorrow you'd like to come for a drive in my car?'

Milo's eyes lit up and he immediately looked at Sam with such a pleading expression that she would have had to be made of stone to resist.

'Okay…*if* Rafaele still feels like it tomorrow. He might be tired, though, or—'

He cut her off with ice in his voice. 'I won't be tired.'

'But you're going out tonight,' Sam reminded him.

Immediately her head was filled with visions of Rafaele and some blonde—of him creeping back into the house like a recalcitrant student at dawn, dishevelled and with stubble lining his jaw.

But he was shaking his head and the look in his eye was mocking, as if he could read her shameful thoughts. 'I won't be tired,' he repeated.

He was walking out of the kitchen when Sam thought of something and followed him. He looked back at her as he put on his leather coat and she held out a key. 'The spare front door key.'

He came and reached for it and their fingers touched. A sizzle of electricity shot up Sam's arm and she snatched her hand back as if burnt, causing the key to drop to the ground. Cheeks burning with humiliation, she bent and picked it up before Rafaele could and handed it to him again, avoiding his eye.

And then, to her everlasting relief, he was out of the door. She turned around and breathed in deep, barely aware of Milo running to the reception room window so he could see the car pull away. She had to get a hold of herself around this man or she'd be a quivering wreck by the end of a week.

CHAPTER FIVE

WHEN SAM HEARD the telltale purr of a powerful engine as she lay in bed that night she looked at her clock in disbelief. It was before midnight and Rafaele was home? *Home*. She grimaced at how easily that had slipped into her mind.

Feeling like a teenager, but unable to help herself, she got out of bed and went to her window, pulling back the curtain ever so slightly. Her heart was thumping. Rafaele hadn't got out of the car yet, and even from here she could see his hands gripping the steering wheel tightly.

Sam had the uncanny feeling that he was imagining the wheel was her neck. Then suddenly the door opened and he got out, unfolding his huge frame from the sleek low-slung vehicle. In any other instance Sam would have sighed in sheer awe at the stunningly designed lines.

She stopped breathing as she took in Rafaele, just standing there for a moment. He wore a tuxedo. Sam knew from past experience that he had a dressing room and fully stocked wardrobe at his office. His shirt was open at the throat, his bow tie hanging rakishly undone.

Rafaele shut the car door and then surprised her by leaning back against the car and putting his hands deep in his pockets, crossing his long legs at the ankle. He looked down, and something about him was so intensely *lonely* that Sam felt like a voyeur. She hated the way her heart clenched.

She'd been so stunned to see him again that she hadn't really contemplated how much of a shock it must have been for him discovering he had a son. He would never forgive her.

Sam quickly shut the curtain again and climbed back into bed, feeling cold from the inside. Eventually she heard the opening and closing of the front door, and then heavy footsteps. She held her breath for a moment when she fancied they stopped outside her door, and then, when she heard the faintest sounds of another door closing, let her breath out in a shuddery whoosh.

About an hour later Sam gave up any pretence of trying to sleep. She threw back the covers and padded softly out of her bedroom. All was quiet and still. She looked in on Milo, who was sprawled across his bed fast asleep, and then made her way to the kitchen to get some water. She was halfway into the room before she realised she wasn't alone.

She gave a small yelp of shock when she saw Rafaele in the corner of the kitchen, in low-slung faded jeans, bare feet and a T-shirt, calmly lifting a coffee cup to his lips.

She put a hand to her rapid heart. 'You scared me. I thought you were in bed.'

Rafaele arched a brow mockingly. 'Don't tell me—you couldn't sleep until you knew I was home safe?'

Sam scowled and hated that he'd caught her like this: sleep-mussed, wearing nothing but brief pants and a threadbare V-necked T-shirt.

Anger rushed through her. Anger at the day she'd spent with her thoughts revolving sickeningly around one person—*him*. Anger that she had to face him like this in what she would have once considered her sanctuary. And, worst of all, anger at herself for not having told him about Milo when she should have.

Feeling emotional, and terrified he'd see it, she stalked

to the sink. 'I'm just getting some water. I couldn't sleep and it has nothing to do with you coming home or not.'

Liar.

Sam heard his voice over the gush of water.

'I couldn't sleep either.'

Sam remembered the intensely lonely air about him as he'd waited outside before coming in. Now she felt guilty for having witnessed it. She held the glass of water in both hands and turned, feeling disorientated.

She looked at the coffee cup and remarked dryly, 'Well, that's hardly likely to help matters.'

Rafaele shrugged and drained the coffee, the strong column of his throat working. He put the cup down. 'When I couldn't sleep I came down to do some work.'

His gaze narrowed on her then, and Sam's skin prickled. She gripped the glass tighter.

He drawled, 'But as I'm just a guest in your house perhaps I should ask for permission?'

Sam's anger was back just like that. Anger at herself for thinking she'd seen Rafaele vulnerable even for a moment. 'But you're not really a guest, are you? You're here to punish me, to make me pay for not telling you about your son.'

Feeling agitated, Sam put down the glass, sloshing some water over the side. She clenched her hands and rounded on Rafaele. 'I'm sorry, okay? I'm sorry that I didn't tell you about Milo. I should have, and I didn't. And I'm sorry.'

Rafaele went very still and put his hands in his pockets. The air thickened between them and swirled with electricity. He looked relaxed, but Sam could tell he was as tense as she was.

'Why?'

One word, a simple question, and Sam felt something crumble inside her. He hadn't actually asked her that yet. He'd asked her *how* she could have, but not why.

She looked down and put her arms around herself in an

unconscious gesture of defence, unaware of how it pushed her breasts up and unaware of how Rafaele's eyes dropped there for a moment or the flush that darkened his cheekbones. She was only aware of her own inner turmoil. She would never be brave enough to tell him of her hurt and her own secret suspicion that it had been that weak emotion that had been her main motivator. She was too ashamed.

She steeled herself and looked up. Rafaele's eyes glittered in the gloom. 'It was for all the reasons I've already told you, Rafaele. I was in shock. I'd almost lost my baby only days after finding out that I was pregnant in the first place. It was all…too much. And I truly believed you had no interest—that you would prefer if I just went away and didn't bother you again.'

She almost quailed at the way his jaw tightened but went on. 'My father was not really there for me. Ever. Even though he brought me up and we lived in this house together. He didn't know how to relate to me. What I needed. I think…I thought I was doing the right thing by keeping Milo from a similar experience.'

Rafaele crossed his arms too, making his muscles bunch. It felt as if something was fizzing between them under the words. A subtext that was alive. All she could see was that powerful body. Lean and hard.

'You had no right.'

Sam looked at him, willing down the way her body insisted on being divorced from her mind, becoming aroused as if nothing had happened between them. As if he didn't hate her.

'I know,' she said flatly. 'But it happened, and you're going to have to let it go or Milo will pick up on it—especially now you're living here too.'

Anger surged within Rafaele at her pronouncement. He uncrossed his arms, unable to disguise his frustration. Sam was standing before him, and despite the charged atmosphere and the words between them he was acutely aware that all he wanted to do was rip that flimsy T-shirt over her head and position her on the counter behind her so that he could thrust deep into her and obliterate all the questions and turmoil in his head.

When she'd walked into the room all he'd seen had been the tantalising shape of her firm breasts, their pointed tips visible through the thin fabric. Her sleep-mussed hair had reminded him of when she'd been on top of him, riding him, her head falling back…

Desire was like a wild thing inside him, clawing for fulfilment. It wasn't helped by the fact that in a bid to prove that Sam *didn't* have this unique effect on him, he'd found himself hitting on his friend's mistress at the function earlier. Flirting with her, handing her his card—desperate to provoke some response in his flatlining libido. He'd acted completely out of character, managed to insult his friend Andreas Xenakis, and he'd proved nothing.

Except that he wanted this woman more than ever.

He hated her. But he wanted her. And he wanted his son.

'Let it go?' he asked now with deceptive softness, and something in him exulted when he saw how Sam paled slightly. 'I think I've more than proved myself to be accommodating where my son and your deception are concerned.'

Rafaele knew he was reacting to Sam's almost patronising tone and to his anger at this inconvenient desire.

His lip curled. 'Do you really think I would be here in the suburbs with you if it wasn't in my son's best interests? Do you really think I want you working at the factory for any reason other than because I want to keep you where I can see your every treacherous move?'

She paled even more at that, and Rafaele felt something lance him deep inside, but he couldn't stop.

'You've put us all in this position by choosing the path

that you did. By believing that you knew best. Well, now I know best and you're just going to have to live with it. *You're* going to have to let it go, Samantha.'

The hurt Sam felt at Rafaele's words shamed her. He looked as hard and obdurate as a granite block just feet away. And as unyielding. The thought of them ever reaching some sort of amicable agreement felt like the biggest and most ludicrous fantasy on earth. And yet between her legs her panties chafed uncomfortably against swollen slick folds of flesh. She wanted to scream out her frustration at her wayward body.

Just before he'd fallen asleep earlier Milo had asked, in a small, hesitant voice, 'Will the man…I mean Rafelli… will he remember to take me in the car tomorrow?'

Anger at Rafaele's assertion that he was doing his utmost to think of Milo when all he seemed to be concerned about was needling her made her lash out. 'You might feel like you're sacrificing your glamorous life for your son, Rafaele, but when will you get bored and want out? Milo has been talking about you all day. He's terrified you won't remember to take him out in the car tomorrow. He's fast heading for hero-worship territory and he'll be devastated if you keep leading him on this path only to disappear from his life.'

Sam was breathing heavily. 'This is what I wanted to avoid all along. Milo's vulnerable. He doesn't understand what's going on between us. You can punish me all you want, Rafaele, but it's Milo who matters now. And I can't say sorry again.'

Rafaele was completely unreadable, but Sam sensed his tension spike.

'What makes you think that I am going to disappear from Milo's life?'

The words were softly delivered, but Sam could sense the volcanic anger behind them.

'You know what I mean. You're not going to stay here for ever. You'll leave sooner or later. Milo will be confused. Upset.'

Sam was aware that she could have been talking about herself, about what had happened to her.

Panic at the way Rafaele took a step closer made Sam's breath choppy. Instinctively she moved back. 'I think this was a very bad idea. I think you should move out before he gets too attached. You can visit us. That way he won't be so upset when you leave…we'll have proper boundaries.'

'Boundaries, you say?' His accent sounded thicker. 'Like the kind of boundaries you put around yourself and my son when you decided that it would be a good idea not to inform me of his existence?'

'You're just…not about commitment, Rafaele. You said it yourself to me over and over again. And a child is all about commitment—a lifetime of it.'

Rafaele was so close now that she could see veritable sparks shooting from those green depths.

His voice was low and blistering. 'How dare you patronise me? You have had the experience of giving birth to a baby and all the natural bonding that goes with it—a bonding experience *you* decided to deny me. I now have the task of bonding with my son when his personality is practically formed. He has missed out on the natural bonding between a father and son. You have deprived us both of that.'

He stopped in front of her and Sam found it hard to concentrate when she could smell his musky heat. The anger within her was vying with something far hotter and more dangerous.

'I can give my son a lifetime of commitment. That is not a problem. If and when I do leave this place he will know I am his father. He will be as much a part of me and my life as the very air I breathe.'

His eyes pinned her to the spot.

'Know this, Sam. I am in Milo's life now, and yours, and I'm not going away. I am his father and I am not shirking that responsibility. You and I are going to have to learn to co-exist.'

Sam's arms were so tight now that she felt she might be constricting the bloodflow to her brain. 'I'm willing to try to co-exist, Rafaele. But sooner or later you'll have to forgive me, or we'll never move on.'

Rafaele stood for a long moment after Sam had left, his heart still racing. She had no idea how close he'd come to reaching for her, pulling her into him so that he could taste her again.

Sooner or later you'll have to forgive me.

For the first time Rafaele didn't feel the intense anger surge. Instead he thought of Sam's stricken pale features that day in the clinic. He remembered his own sense of panic, and the awful shameful relief when he could run away, far and fast, and put Sam and the emotions she'd evoked within him behind him.

For the first time he had to ask the question: if he'd been in her position would he have done the same thing? If he'd believed that his baby was unwanted by one parent? It wasn't so black and white any more. Rafaele had to admit to the role he'd played.

Completely unbidden a memory came to him of something Sam had told him one night while they'd been lying in bed. It was something he avoided like the plague—the post-coital intimacy that women seemed engineered to pursue—but this hadn't been like that. Sam had started telling him something and then stopped. He'd urged her on.

It was her mention of her relationship with her father just a short while before that had brought it back to him. She'd told him then of how one night, when she'd been about six, she'd not been able to sleep. She'd come down-stairs and found her father weeping silently over a picture of his late wife—Sam's mother.

Sam had said, 'He was talking to her…the picture…ask-ing her what to do with me, asking her how he could cope because I was a girl. He said, *"If she was a boy I'd know what to do…but I don't know what to do or say to her."*'

Sam had sighed deeply. 'So I went upstairs to the bath-room that night, found a pair of scissors and cut all my hair off. It used to fall to my waist. When our housekeeper saw me in the morning she screamed and dropped a plate.'

Sam's mouth had twisted sadly. 'My father, though, he didn't even notice—too distracted with a problem he was trying to solve. I thought I could try to be a son for him…'

Rafaele could remember a falling sensation. Sam's in-herent lack of self-confidence in her innate sensuality had all made sense. He too had known what it was like to have an absentee father. Even though he'd spent time with his father growing up, the man had been so embittered by his wife leaving him that he'd been no use to Rafaele and had rarely expressed much interest in his son. In some small part Rafaele knew that even resurrecting the family car in-dustry had been a kind of effort to connect with his father.

It had been that weekend that Rafaele had let Sam stay in his *palazzo*. It had been that weekend that he'd post-poned an important business trip because he'd wanted her too much to leave. And it was after that weekend, once he'd gained some distance from her, that he'd realised just how dangerous she was to him.

And he'd just proved that nothing had changed. She was still just as dangerous and he must never forget it.

The following day Milo was practically bursting with ex-citement at being in Rafaele's car. It was the latest model of the Falcone road car—the third to be rolled out since Rafaele had taken control of the bankrupt company.

It was completely impractical as far as children went, but Rafaele had surprised Sam. She'd seen that he'd got a child's car seat from somewhere and had it fitted into the backseat. Every time Sam looked around Milo just grinned at her like a loon. She shook her head ruefully as Rafaele negotiated out of the driveway and onto the main road with confident ease.

Sam tried to ignore his big hands on the wheel and gearstick. But there was something undeniably sexy about a man who handled a car well—and especially one like this, which was more like an art form than a car. Rafaele was a confident driver, and not the kind of person who felt the need for speed just to impress.

Happy sounds were coming from the back of the car—Milo imitating the engine. Sam felt a flutter near her heart and blocked it out. *Dangerous.* She still felt tense after that impassioned exchange the previous evening. Predictably, she hadn't been able to sleep well and she felt fuzzy now. She'd avoided looking directly at Rafaele this morning over breakfast, preferring to let Milo take centre stage, demanding the attention of this new, charismatic person in their midst.

Rafaele had seemed equally keen to be distracted, and Sam could only wonder if he'd taken anything of what she'd said to heart. Was he prepared to forgive her at all?

Sam noticed that Milo had gone silent behind them and looked back to see that he'd fallen asleep. Rafaele glanced her way and Sam quickly looked forward again, saying a little too breathlessly for her liking, 'He was so excited about today… He doesn't really nap any more but sometimes it catches up with him.'

She was babbling, and the thought of increased proximity to Rafaele when she started working with him tomorrow made her feel panicky. She steeled herself and turned to his proud profile. The profile of a great line of aristocratic Italian ancestors.

'Look, Rafaele…about me working at the factory…' She saw his jaw clench and rushed on. 'You said yourself last night that you're only doing it to keep me where you can see me. I can work perfectly well from the university. After last night I can't see how our working together will improve things.'

His hands clenched on the wheel now, and Sam looked at them, so strong and large. She recalled how hot they'd felt exploring her body.

Distracted, she almost missed it when Rafaele said in a low voice, with clear reluctance, 'I shouldn't have said that. It wasn't entirely true.'

Sam gulped and looked back at him. 'It wasn't?' Somewhere a tiny flame lit inside her, and against every atom of self-preservation she couldn't douse it.

'After all,' he reminded her, 'I contacted you about working for me before I knew about Milo and you refused to listen.'

The panic she'd felt then was still vivid. 'Yes,' she said faintly. 'I…it was a shock to hear from you.'

Rafaele slanted her a look and said dryly, 'You don't say.' He looked at the road again. 'But the fact remains that I knew about your research. You were mentioned in an article in *Automotive Monthly* and I realised that you were leading the field in research into kinetic energy recovery systems.'

The little flame inside Sam sputtered. Of *course* he hadn't been motivated by anything other than professional interest. 'I see,' she responded. 'And that's why you wanted to contact me?'

Rafaele shrugged minutely, his broad shoulders moving sinuously under his leather jacket, battered and worn to an almost sensual texture. *Dammit...* Sam cursed herself. Why did everything have to return to all things physical even when he was wounding her with his words? She looked away resolutely.

He continued, 'I knew we were setting up in England, I figured you were still based here... It seemed like a logical choice to ask you to work for us again...'

Out of the corner of Sam's eye she saw Rafaele's hands tighten on the wheel again. His jaw clenched and then released.

'About last night—you were right. I agree that the past is past and we need to move on. I don't want Milo to pick up on the tension between us any more than you do.'

Something dangerous swooped inside Sam at hearing him acknowledge this. She recognised the mammoth effort he must be making to concede this.

'Thank you,' she said huskily. 'And I'll have to trust that you won't do anything to hurt Milo.'

The car was stopped at a red light now and Rafaele looked at her. 'Yes, you will. Hurting my son is the last thing in the world I want to do. It won't happen.'

The fierce light in his eyes awed Sam into silence. Eventually, she nodded, her throat feeling tight. 'Okay.'

A car horn tooted from behind them, and with unhurried nonchalance Rafaele released her from his gaze and moved on.

After a while Rafaele said in a low voice, 'And you *will* be coming to work with me, Sam...because I want you to.'

After a long moment Sam replied again. 'Okay.' In her wayward imagination she fancied that something had finally shifted between them, alleviating the ever-present tension.

They were silent for much of the rest of the journey, but something inside Sam had lessened slightly. And yet conversely she felt more vulnerable than ever.

She noticed that they were pulling into what looked like a stately home and raised a questioning brow at Rafaele, who answered, 'I asked my assistant to look up some things. It's an open house at weekends and they have a working farm. I thought Milo might like to see it.'

Milo had woken up a short while before, and from the backseat came an excited, 'Look, Mummy! Horsies!'

Sam saw Rafaele look to his son in the rearview mirror and the way his mouth curved into a smile. Her chest tightened and she explained, 'It's his other favourite thing in the world apart from cars. You're killing two birds with one stone.'

Rafaele looked at her for a long moment, his eyes lingering on her mouth until it tingled. Sam grew hot and flustered. Why was he teasing her with looks like this when he couldn't be less interested? Was it just something he turned on automatically when any woman with a pulse was nearby? It made her think of that angry kiss—how instantly she'd gone up in flames when he'd only been proving a point.

'Shouldn't you look where you're driving?' She sounded like a prim schoolmistress.

Rafaele eventually looked away, but not before purring with seductive arrogance, '*Cara*, I could drive blindfolded and not crash.'

This was what she remembered. Rafaele's easy and lethal brand of charm. Disgusted with herself, Sam faced forward and crossed her arms.

When he had parked and they'd got out, Milo clearly didn't know what to do first: stand and looking lovingly at the car, or go and see the animals. For a second he looked genuinely upset, overwhelmed with all these exciting choices. It made guilt lance Sam—fresh guilt—because the local park or swimming pool was about as exciting as it had got so far for Milo.

To Sam's surprise, before she could intervene, Rafaele bent down to Milo's level and said, '*Piccolino*, the car will still be here when we get back…so why don't we see the animals first, hmm?'

Milo's face cleared like a cloud passing over the sun and he smiled, showing his white baby teeth. 'Okey-dokey, horsies first.' And then he put his hand in Rafaele's and started pulling him the direction he wanted to go.

Sam caught the unguarded moment of emotion in Rafaele's eyes and her chest tightened at its significance. It was the first time Milo had reached out to touch him.

She followed them, doing up her slimline parka jacket and tried not to be affected by the image of the tall, powerful man, alongside the tiny, sturdy figure with identical dark hair.

Within a few hours Sam could see the beginnings of the hero-worship situation she'd predicted unfolding before her eyes. Milo had barely let go of Rafaele's hand and was now in his arms, pointing at the pigs in a mucky pen.

She was watching Rafaele for signs that this situation was getting old very quickly—she knew how demanding and energetic Milo could be—but she couldn't find any. Again she was stunned at his apparent easing into this whole situation.

Rafaele looked at her then and Sam coloured, more affected by seeing him with Milo in his arms than she cared to admit.

He looked grim and said, 'I think now is a good time.'

Instantly Sam understood. He wanted to tell Milo who he was. Panic flooded Sam. Until Milo knew Rafaele was his father it was as if she still had a way out—the possibility that this wasn't real. It was all a dream. But it wasn't, and she knew she couldn't fight him. He deserved for his son to know. And Milo deserved it too.

Jerkily, feeling clammy, Sam nodded her head. 'Okay.'

So when Milo had finished inspecting all the animals exhaustively they found a quiet spot to eat the food they'd got from the house's café and Sam explained gently to Milo that Rafaele was his father.

She could sense Rafaele's tension and her heart ached for him. Her conscience lambasted her again.

With all the unpredictability of a three-year-old though, Milo just blinked and looked from her to Rafaele before saying, 'Can we look at the horsies again?'

To his credit, Rafaele didn't look too surprised but when Milo had clambered off his chair to go and look at something she said, 'It's probably a lot for him to take in—'

But Rafaele cut her off, saying coolly, 'I know he took it in. I remember how much three-year-olds see and understand.'

He got up to follow Milo before Sam could make sense of his words and what he'd meant by them.

When they were back in the car Milo began chattering incessantly in the back.

'Rafelli, did you see the pigs? Rafelli, did you see the horsies and the goats? And the chickens?'

Sam looked out of the window, overcome with a surge of emotion. It was done. Rafaele truly was his father now. No going back. Tears pricked her eyes as the enormity of everything set in. She'd kept Milo from his own father for so long. Guilt was hot and acrid in her gut.

Suddenly her hand was taken in a much bigger, warmer one and her heart stopped.

'Sam?'

Panicked that he'd see her distress, Sam took her hand from his and rubbed at her eye, avoiding looking at him. Breezily she said, 'I'm fine. It's just some dust or something in my eye.'

CHAPTER SIX

TWO WEEKS LATER Sam was trying to concentrate on test results and threw her pen down in disgust when her brain just refused to work. She got up from her desk in her decent-sized office at the factory and paced, rolling her head to ease out kinks as she did so.

It felt as if an age had passed since that day at the stately home. Within a few days Milo had been tentatively calling Rafaele *Daddy*, much to Bridie's beaming approval, Rafaele's delight and Sam's increasing sense of vulnerability.

Bridie had also paved the way for Sam to go to work with Rafaele every day, assuring her that she had nothing to worry about where Milo's care was concerned. So in the past two weeks a routine had developed where Rafaele took Milo to playschool, either with or without Sam, and then they left for work and returned in time for Milo's supper. Sam had put her foot down, though, and insisted that she still only do a half-day on Wednesdays as that had been her routine with Bridie.

And also she felt the need to establish some control when it felt as if Rafaele had comprehensively taken everything over. They'd even come home one evening to find a chef in the kitchen and Rafaele saying defensively something about it being unfair to expect Bridie to cook for them as well as taking care of Milo.

Needless to say Sam could see that Bridie was not far

behind Milo in the hero-worship stakes. Most evenings now Rafaele tucked Milo into bed and read him a story, making Sam feel redundant for the first time in a long time.

In the middle of all this change and turmoil was the sheer joy Sam felt at being back working on research within an environment where the actual cars and engines were only a short walk away. The scale of Rafaele's English factory had taken her breath away. It proved just how far he'd come even in three and a half years. Professionally she would have given her right arm to be part of this process, and now she was overseeing a group of mechanics and engineers, focusing their expertise on the most exciting developments in automotive technology, thanks to Rafaele's unlimited investment.

But overshadowing everything was the fact that she was working for Rafaele. Back in a place where she'd never expected or wanted to be. She felt as if she was that girl all over again—that naive student, obsessed with her boss. Watching out for him. Aware of him. Blushing when their gazes met. It was galling and humiliating. Especially when Rafaele appeared so cool and seemed to be making every effort to steer well clear of Sam. Only addressing her in groups of people. Never seeking her out alone.

Even on their car rides to the factory and back their conversation centred mainly around Milo or work.

Her hands clenched to fists now, even as her whole body seemed to ache. She was glad. She *was*. She didn't want history to repeat itself. Not in a million years. It had almost been easier when Rafaele had hated her; now that they were in this uneasy truce it was so much more confusing to deal with.

Sam noticed the clock on the wall then, and saw how late it was. Normally Rafaele's assistant would have rung to inform her that he was leaving by now. Giving up any pretence that she could continue to work while waiting,

Sam decided to pack up and find him herself. She would inform him she was going home. He'd offered her one of the cars if she wished, so now perhaps it was time to assert some more independence from him.

Heading for his office, she saw it was quiet all around, most of the other staff and the main engineers and mechanics having left. His own secretary's desk was clear and empty in the plush anteroom of his office.

She hesitated for a second outside his door and then knocked. After a few seconds she heard him call abruptly, 'Come in.'

Rafaele glanced up from his phone call, frowning slightly at the interruption, and then when Sam walked in his whole body reacted, making a complete mockery of any illusion of control over his rogue hormones. She stopped in her tracks and made a motion to leave again, seeing he was on the phone, but everything within him rejected that and he held up his finger, indicating for her to wait.

She closed the door behind her and he couldn't stop the anticipation spiking in his blood. For two weeks now Rafaele had thought he was doing a good job of avoiding her. But it didn't matter how much space he put between them; he saw her everywhere. Worst of all was in the house at night—that cosy, domestic house, with his son sleeping just down the hall—when all he could think about doing was going into Sam's room, stripping her bare and sinking deep between her long legs.

His body was hardening even now, shaming him with his lack of control. The person on the other end of the phone continued talking but they might as well have been talking the language of the Dodo for all Rafaele heard. His gaze travelled down Sam's back and legs hungrily, taking in her slim build and the sweet lush curve of her buttocks as she turned away to look at a model of one of the first cars he'd designed.

When she turned back slightly he could see the profile swell of her breasts and immediately a memory came back, of spilling drops of Prosecco onto one pebbled nipple, making it grow hard— Sweat broke out on Rafaele's upper lip. This was untenable.

Abruptly he terminated the phone conversation, giving up any pretence of control. Sam had turned around to face him and he asked, more curtly than he'd intended, 'What do you want?'

Her face flushed and Rafaele pushed down the lurch of his conscience. Damn her and the way she did that, making him feel like a heel.

'I just…it's after six. We usually leave before now.'

The *we* struck him somewhere forcibly. He stood up and saw how Sam's eyes widened. His body reacted to that look and he cursed her again.

He reacted viscerally. 'I think this is a mistake.'

She frowned. 'What's a mistake?'

'You…here.' Dammit, he couldn't even string a coherent sentence together. The longer she stood there, the more he was imagining her naked, opening up to him, giving him the release he'd only ever found with her. Seeing her here at the factory these past two weeks had been giving him moments of severe *déjà vu*.

She was still frowning, but had gone still. 'Me…here… What exactly do you mean, Rafaele?'

Why was it that the way she said his name in that soft, low voice seemed to curl around his senses, making everything even more heightened?

He gritted out, through the waves of need assailing him, 'I shouldn't have insisted you work here. It was a bad idea.'

The unmistakable flare of hurt made her eyes glow

bright grey for a moment, reminding Rafaele uncomfortably of another day, in another office, four years before.

Stiffly she said, 'I thought I was doing everything you wanted—we set up the research facility here in one week. I know it still needs more work, but it's only been two weeks—'

Rafaele slashed a hand, making her stop. 'It's not that.'

Sounding wounded, she said, 'Well, what, then?'

Rafaele wanted to laugh. Could she not see how ravenous he was for her? He felt like a beast, panting for its prey.

He smiled grimly. 'It's you. Uniquely. I thought I could do this. But I can't. I think you should go back to the university...someone else can take over here.'

Sam straightened before him and her eyes flashed—but with anger and something more indefinable this time.

'You insisted on turning my world upside down, Rafaele, and now, just because you can't abide the sight of me, you think you can cast me out again? It seems as if you rather overestimated your desire for control, doesn't it? Well, if you've quite decided where it is you want me then don't worry. I'll be only too happy to get out of your way.'

Sam was quivering with impotent rage. She wanted to go over and slap Rafaele. Hard. It could be four years ago all over again. With nothing learned in the meantime. She was standing before Rafaele in his office and he was basically rejecting her. Again.

And, like before, Sam was terrified she'd crumple before him, so she fled for the door. But when she tried to open it with clammy hands it slammed shut again, and she squealed with shock when she felt a solid, hard presence behind her.

She whirled around to find her eye level at Rafaele's broad chest and looked up. Emotion was high in her throat. Her eyes were burning. 'Let me out of here, *now*.'

The hurt that had gripped her like a vice in her belly at hearing him say so starkly that he basically couldn't stand to see her every day was still like acid.

'You've got it wrong,' he gritted out, jaw tight, seemingly oblivious to what she'd just said. His hand was snaking around her neck under her hair, making her breath catch. His eyes were like green gems. Glittering.

Sam swallowed the pain, determined he wouldn't see it, but she was acutely aware of how close he was—almost close enough for his chest to touch her breasts. They tightened, growing heavy, the nipples pebbling into hard points.

'Got what wrong?' she spat out.

'I didn't overestimate my desire for control… I overestimated my ability to resist you.'

Sam blinked. But now Rafaele's chest was touching her breasts and she couldn't think straight. His hand tightened on her neck and his face was coming closer. Her lips tingled in anticipation. All the blood in her body was pooling between her legs, making her hot and ready.

Fighting the intense desire not to question this, Sam put her hands on Rafaele's chest. 'Wait…' she got out painfully. 'What are you doing?'

Rafaele's breath feathered over her mouth, making her fingers want to curl into his chest. She couldn't seem to take her eyes away from his, green boring into grey, making reality melt away.

Sam struggled to make sense of this, when only moments ago she'd believed he wanted her out of his sight because something about her repulsed him. 'But you don't… you don't really want me.'

He asked, almost bitterly, 'Don't I?'

Confusion filled Sam—and a very treacherous flame of hope. She fought it desperately, fearing exposure. She pushed against him but he was like steel. 'Let me *go*, Rafaele. I won't be your substitute lover just because you're turned on for five seconds. I don't like to repeat mistakes.'

Rafaele laughed again and it was unbearably harsh, scraping over Sam's sensitised skin like sandpaper.

'Five seconds? Try four years, Sam—four years of an ache that never went away, no matter how much I tried to deny it…no matter how many times I tried to eclipse it…'

His voice had become guttural, thick. Sam couldn't fully process his words, but somewhere deep inside her they did resonate, and she felt something break apart—some resistance she'd been clinging onto.

'I want you, Sam, and I know you want me too.'

And then his mouth was on hers and it was desperate, forceful. Like before, but *not*. Without the intense anger and recrimination behind it. And once again, like a lemming jumping over a cliff to certain death, Sam couldn't help but respond. And she couldn't deny the fierce burst of primal pleasure within her, deep inside where she'd locked it away.

But the kiss didn't stay forceful. Rafaele drew back, breathing harshly, and Sam followed him, too much on fire to be embarrassed by how much she wanted him. He wanted her, and the knowledge sang in her blood. She had nothing to be ashamed of.

Rafaele bent close again, and when he pressed a hot kiss to her neck Sam felt his hand do something behind her. She heard the snick of the lock in the door. It should have made alarm bells ring in her head. It should have reminded her of similar heated moments in the past. But it didn't. Or she wouldn't let it. She was weak and she'd ached for this for too long. Long nights when Milo hadn't wanted to sleep and she'd walked up and down, breasts sore from breast-feeding, but aching, too, for another far more adult touch.

Rafaele straightened and with an enigmatic look took Sam by the hand. For a second she felt absurdly shy and bit her lip. Rafaele stopped and reached out, freeing her lip with his thumb.

He muttered, '*Dio*, I've missed that.' And Sam's insides combusted.

He drew her over towards the desk and then turned to take Sam's bag off her shoulder, along with her jacket. They fell to the floor. Sam felt the back of the desk against her buttocks. Her legs were wobbly.

Rafaele cupped her face and jaw with his hands and then his mouth was on hers again, hot and hard, firm but soft. Demanding and getting a response that she had no control over. Her tongue stroked along his. She was desperate to taste every inch of him, revelling in the spiralling heat inside her. She was vaguely aware of her questing hands going to his chest, exulting in the feel of rock-hard muscle, her fingers finding buttons and opening them so that she could reach in and explore, feel that hair-roughened skin.

Rafaele's hands moved down, coming to her buttocks, kneading them, and then lifting her so that she rested on the desk. He came closer, wedging himself between her legs so that his belt buckle was hard against her belly. Below, the most potent part of his anatomy was also hard, right there between her legs, constrained by their clothes and making her want to strip everything between them away.

One of his hands clasped her head, tilting it so that he had deeper access. His tongue was mimicking another part of his anatomy now, and his hips were moving against her, making her squirm and whimper softly as the fever of desire rose within her.

Suddenly Rafaele pulled away and Sam looked up through a heat haze, aware of her heart pounding and her ragged breath. Rafaele's shirt hung half open.

'I need to see you,' he said thickly, and began to undo the buttons on her shirt.

As the backs of his hands brushed against her breasts she shivered minutely at the exquisite sensation, already imagining him touching them with his hands...his mouth and tongue.

Her shirt was drawn off and her bra dispensed with in an economy of movement, and then he just looked at her for a long moment, with an enigmatic expression that made butterflies erupt in Sam's belly. About to scream with the mounting tension, she felt Rafaele's hand finally cup her breast and shards of sensation rushed through her body. She tensed and arched her back, subconsciously begging him...and he needed no encouragement.

Cupping the full mound of firm flesh, Rafaele bent his head and surrounded that tight peak in moist heat. The feel of his intense hot sucking made Sam cry out.

Blindly, while Rafaele's mouth was on her breast, Sam reached for his belt and undid it, her hands and fingers clumsy. She pulled it free of his trousers and it dropped to the floor, but before she could put her hands to his fly he was standing up again and helping her, pushing his trousers down, leaving him bared to her hungry gaze. *Dear Lord.* He was as magnificent as she remembered. Thick and long and hard. For *her.*

Sam felt hot, as if she was on fire. She moved her numb fingers to Rafaele's shirt buttons, wanting to finish undressing him. Her breath was loud in the quiet of the office. All that mattered to Sam was getting Rafaele bared to her, and when she finally pushed his shirt open and off his shoulders she breathed in deeply, her hands smoothing over hard musculature roughened with dark hair, nipples erect and hard.

Unable to resist the lure, Sam explored with her tongue around those hard pieces of puckered flesh, aware of Rafaele's hand on her head. He sucked in a breath, making his broad chest swell. He was so sensitive there. Sam moved her mouth up now, stretching her whole body, trailing kisses and tasting with her tongue along his throat, discovering the hard resoluteness of his stubbled jaw grazing her delicate skin.

Her hands on his head drew him down. She was searching for his mouth again, like a blind person looking for water in a desert. Sucking him deep into her own mouth, Sam could feel his erection strain against her, and she dropped one hand to put it around him, feeling him jerk with tension.

'Sam...'

She almost didn't recognise his voice. It sounded so tortured. Sam tore her mouth away from his to look up and she was dizzy with need and lust. It was just them and this insane desire. He was so firm in her hand, so strong, and her mouth watered when she remembered how she'd tasted him before, how she'd sucked that head into her mouth, her tongue swirling and exploring around the tip, her hand pumping him the way he'd shown her...

She didn't even realise her hand was moving rythmically until he tipped up her chin with his fingers and said, 'I need to be inside you.'

Sam's sex throbbed. 'Yes,' she breathed, lifting her hips to help Rafaele when he went to pull her trousers and panties off. She was vaguely surprised she still had them on, that they hadn't melted off her before now.

Rafaele took himself in his hand—an unashamed and utterly masculine gesture. Sam was sitting on the desk naked, legs spread like a wanton, but she couldn't drum up any concern. She wanted him inside her so badly. Rafaele ran his hand down over her quivering body, teasing her until she bit her lip. He pushed her legs apart further and looked at her.

He stroked one hand up her inner thigh and let it rest for a moment at the tantalising juncture before his long fingers explored the wetness at her core—and then in one move he thrust them inside her.

Sam gasped and grabbed onto Rafaele's shoulders, unable to look away from that glittering, possessive green gaze. His fingers moved in and out, and her body started to clench around them, the anticipation building to feverpitch.

On some level Sam rejected this. She didn't want to splinter apart while Rafaele looked on. She took his hand away from her and said roughly, 'No—not like this. I'll come when you come.'

Rafaele smiled and it was fierce. The smile of a warrior. He took her mouth in another devastating kiss and her wetness was on the fingers that he wrapped tight around her hips. Rafaele thrust deep inside her in one cataclysmic move and swallowed her scream of pleasure, his hand holding her steady when she went so taut with excitement that she thought she'd splinter apart there and then, despite her brave words.

But slowly, inexorably, expertly, Rafaele drew her back from that brink and then, with slow, measured, devastating thrusts of his body into hers he rewound that tension inside her until it built up higher and higher all over again.

Sam wrapped her legs around Rafaele's waist, her ankles crossed, her feet digging into his hard backside, urging him on, begging without words for him to go deeper, harder. Pushing her away from him slightly, but supporting her with an arm around her, he thrust harder and deeper.

Sam's head went back. Her eyes closed. She couldn't take it—couldn't articulate what she needed. She needed to come so badly, but Rafaele was relentless. She knew she was only seconds from begging. Overwhelmed, she felt tears prick her eyes—and then Rafaele thrust so deep it felt as if he touched her heart.

Eyes flying open, tendons going taut all over her body,

Sam came in a dizzying, blinding crescendo of pleasure so intense she couldn't breathe. She gasped and felt Rafaele thrust deep again, sending her spiralling into an even higher dimension of pleasure. His body jerked between her legs and she felt her endless pulsating orgasm milking him of his essence, which was a warm flood inside her.

In the aftermath of that shattering crescendo Sam barely knew which way was up. Her legs were still locked around his slim hips. Rafaele's head was buried in her neck and she had the strongest urge to reach out and touch his hair, but when she lifted a hand it was trembling too much.

His chest was heaving and damp against hers. Her breasts were tender. Rafaele was still hard inside her, his strength ebbing slowly. And then suddenly he reared back, eyes wild, making Sam wince as he broke the connection between their bodies.

'Protection. We didn't use protection.'

Sam looked at him and went icy, before reason and sanity broke through. Relief was tinged with something bittersweet. 'No,' she breathed, 'It's okay, I'm…safe.'

She bit her lip, suddenly acutely aware of how she was balancing precariously on the desk with Rafaele's eyes on her. She felt raw, as if a layer of skin had been stripped off her body. She clenched her hands.

'Are you sure?' he demanded.

Sam forced herself to look at Rafaele. Her mouth twisted. 'Yes. I'm sure. My period just finished.'

He sighed deeply. 'Okay.'

Sam couldn't keep the bitterness out of her voice. 'You believe me, then?'

He paused in reaching down to grab some clothes and looked at her. 'I believe you. I don't think you'd want to repeat history any more than I would.'

The words shouldn't have hurt her. Much as his earlier

words shouldn't have hurt her. But they did. Sam didn't want to question why.

Grimacing slightly when her muscles protested, she stood shakily from the desk and took her shirt and bra from Rafaele's outstretched hand.

She couldn't look at him. Face burning, she turned away to put on her clothes and castigated herself. She was repeating history right here, right now. Making love with him in his office exactly like she used to. She could remember what it had been like to go back onto the factory floor, feeling exhilarated and shamed all at once, as if a brand on her forehead marked her as some sort of fallen woman. The boss's concubine.

She pulled on her pants and trousers with clumsy fingers, aware of Rafaele just feet away, dressing himself, sheathing that amazing body again.

When she was dressed he said coolly from behind her, 'Shall we go?'

Sam steeled herself and turned around to see Rafaele looking hardly rumpled, his hair only slightly messy. She knew she must look as if she'd just been pulled through a hedge backwards. The tang of sex was in the air and it should have sickened her, but it didn't. It made her crave more.

'Yes,' she said quickly, before he could see how vulnerable she felt.

Rafaele burned with recrimination as he negotiated his car out of the factory in the dark with Sam beside him, tight-lipped. His recrimination was not for what had happened; he'd do that again right now if he could. His recrimination was for the way it had happened. He'd behaved like a teenage boy, drooling over his first lay with finesse the last thing on his mind.

When she'd asked him just now if he believed her, his

reaction had been knee-jerk and not fair. He was already repeating history with bells on, and he knew he wouldn't have the strength to resist her even if he wanted to.

It had been a miracle that he'd had the control to make sure Sam had come first—but then he recalled how ready to explode she'd been when he'd just touched her with his fingers. Just like that he was rewarded with a fresh, raging erection and had to shift to cover it in the gloom of the interior of the car.

He'd taken Sam *on his desk*. He'd only ever let one other woman get to him at work—the same woman. Until he'd met Sam his life had been strictly compartmentalised into work and pleasure. That pleasure had been fleeting and completely within his control. As soon as he'd laid eyes on her, though, the lines had blurred into one.

He could still remember the cold, clammy panic that last weekend four years ago at finding himself waking in his own bed with Sam wrapped around him like a vine. Far from precipitating repugnance, he'd felt curiously at peace. Until he'd realised the significance of that and that peace had been shattered. He'd postponed an important meeting that weekend to spend it with Sam. He'd even turned off his phone. Had not checked e-mails. He'd gone incommunicado. For the first time. For a woman.

It had been that which had made something go cold in his chest. Realising how far off his own strict path he'd gone.

Even now he was aware of that, but also aware of Sam's slim supple thighs in her black trousers next to him. Albeit slanted away, as if she was avoiding coming any closer than she had to in the small, intimate space.

Dio. If she was his he'd make her wear skirts and dresses all the time, so that all he'd have to do would be to slide his hand— *If she was his.* Rafaele let the car swerve momentarily and very uncharacteristically as that thought slid home with all the devastation of a stealth bomb.

He could feel Sam's quick glance of concern and imagine her frowning.

'Sorry,' he muttered, and regained control of himself. He could see from the corner of his eye that Sam had crossed her arms over her breasts. She was so tense he fancied she might crack in two if he touched her.

Her silence was getting to him, making his nerves wind tight inside him. He wanted to provoke her—get her to acknowledge what had just happened. What it possibly meant to her. Was the same round of unwelcome memories dominating *her* head?

Injecting his voice with an insouciance he didn't feel, Rafaele asked, 'Don't tell me you're already regretting what happened, *cara*.'

She snapped at him, 'Is it that obvious?'

Rafaele's mouth tightened in rejection of that, despite his recent thoughts. 'It was inevitable and you know it. It's been building between us from the moment we saw each other again.'

He glanced at Sam and their eyes met. A jolt of electricity shot straight to Rafaele's groin.

She hissed at him, 'It was *not* inevitable. It was a momentary piece of very bad judgment. You were obviously feeling frustrated—maybe it's because you've been forced to move to the suburbs so you can't entertain your mistress.'

Rage was building inside Rafaele and he responded with a snarl, 'I don't have a mistress at the moment.'

Sam sniffed. 'Maybe not, but I'm sure there's been a number in the last four years.'

And not one of them Rafaele could remember right now. But if he was a painter he could paint Sam's naked body with his eyes closed. He recalled seeing Sam bite her lip and how he'd let slip *'I've missed this.'* He'd also told her that no one had come close to her in four years. Then he'd all but admitted that he'd used other women to try and forget her. His belly curdled.

He ground out, 'Are you expecting me to believe that you've been celibate for four years?' He glanced at her and saw her go pale in the gloom. 'Well? Have you?'

Sam stared straight ahead. Stonily. 'Of course not. There was someone…a while ago.'

For a second Rafaele only heard a roaring in his ears. He saw red. He almost gave in to the impulse to swerve the car to the kerb. He'd fully expected her to say *of course not*, and his own hypocrisy mocked him. But, he told himself savagely, *he* hadn't given birth to a baby.

He was aware that irrational emotions were clouding his normally perfectly liberal views and it was not something Rafaele welcomed.

'Who was he?' he bit out, knuckles white under the skin of his fingers on the wheel. Just the thought of Sam even kissing someone else was making him incandescent.

'He was a colleague. He's a single parent too…we bonded over that.'

Rafaele felt as if a red-hot poker had been stabbed into his belly. In a calm voice, belying the strength of his emotions, Rafaele said, 'You were a single parent by choice, Samantha. You are *not* a single parent any more.'

Rafaele struggled to control himself. He wanted to demand Sam tell him more—how many times? Where? When?

As if sensing his intense interest, Sam blurted out, 'It didn't amount to anything. It was just one time. We went to a hotel for an afternoon and to be perfectly honest it was horrible. It felt…sordid.'

She clamped her mouth shut again and Rafaele realised he was holding his breath. He let it out in one long shuddery breath. His hands relaxed. Even though he still wanted to find this faceless, nameless person and throw him up against a wall.

From the moment Sam had stepped into his office earlier he'd been on fire. The culmination of weeks of build-up. The inferno inside him had been too strong to ignore. Feeling Sam in his arms, her mouth under his, opening up to him, pressing herself against him... He'd been thrusting into the tight, slick heat that he'd never forgotten right there on his desk before he'd even really acknowledged what was happening. He'd been in the grip of something more powerful than his rational mind.

They hadn't even used protection. Sam was the only woman that had ever happened with, and the result of that was probably being put to bed right now. He looked at Sam again and saw that she was still pale, a pulse throbbing at the base of her neck. She'd uncrossed her arms finally and her breasts rose and fell a little too quickly, giving her away. They were stopped in traffic and he reached over and took her hand, gripping it when she would have pulled away.

He forced her to look at him and her eyes were huge. Rafaele saw something unguarded in their depths for a split second, but then it was gone and he crushed down the feeling of something resonating deep inside him. The jealousy he felt still burned in his gut.

He wanted to hate Sam for ever appearing in his life to disrupt his ordered and well-run world. A world where nothing had mattered except rebuilding Falcone Industries and ensuring that he would never be ruined like his father. Sam had jeopardised that for a brief moment in time and now it was happening all over again. But he found that he couldn't hate her for that any more because Milo existed. And because he wanted her.

'Let me go, Rafaele,' Sam breathed.

Never resounded in his head before he could stop it. He kept his gaze on hers, slightly discomfited that it wasn't harder to do so. Usually he avoided women's probing looks. But not this one. Something solidified within him. He couldn't *not* have Sam again after that passionate interlude. It was an impossible prospect.

'No, Sam.'

He lifted her resisting hand and brought it to his mouth, pressed his lips to her palm. Her scent made him harder. His tongue flicked out and he tasted her skin, fancying he could distinguish her musky heat—or was that just her arousal he could smell?

Frustration at the prospect of the weekend ahead gripped him. He couldn't make love to her in the house. Not while his son lay sleeping. The thought of Milo waking and witnessing how feral Rafaele felt around Sam was anathema after his own experience of being that small and witnessing his father's breakdown.

Sam's eyes grew wide. Glittering. Pupils dilating. They were distracting him. Making him regret that he couldn't make love with her again for at least a few days. It would not happen in his office again. Never again. But they weren't done—not by a long shot.

'I'm not letting you go. Not until this is well and truly burnt out between us. I let you go too soon once before and I won't make that mistake again.'

The lights went green and Rafaele let Sam's hand go. He turned his attention to the road again and the car moved smoothly forward.

Sam clasped her tingling hand and turned her head, staring straight in front of her. Her whole body was still deeply sensitised after what had happened and yet she already felt ravenous for more. His words sank in: *I let you go too soon.*

He'd said something earlier about trying to eclipse her memory... His admission made her heart race pathetically.

And why on earth had she spilled her guts about her one very sad attempt at another relationship? To score points? To try and convince Rafaele that he hadn't dominated her life so totally?

But that was what she *had* attempted to do with the perfectly nice and normal Max. He'd caught her at a particularly vulnerable moment one day. Sam had seen a random newspaper report documenting the launch of a new Falcone car and there had been a picture of Rafaele with his arm around some gorgeous blonde model.

More than upset, and disturbed that she was still affected by him and the memories which would not abate after so much time, Sam had recklessly taken Max up on his offer of dinner. After a few weeks of pleasant but not earth-shattering dating Sam had felt a need to try and prove to herself that her memory of Rafaele was a mirage. That surely any other man could match him in bed and then she would not feel such a sense of loss, that she'd never experience such heights again.

It had been her suggestion to meet in a hotel one afternoon. As if they were both married and having an affair. But she'd thought it practical, considering their children were in their own homes, being minded. And Sam hadn't felt at all comfortable with introducing Max to Milo...even though he'd been hinting that the time to do so had come.

The afternoon had been awkward and horrendous from the first moment. Completely underwhelming. Disgusted with herself, because she had known that she'd acted out of weakness, Sam had called it off there and then.

Something very dangerous and fragile fluttered in the vicinity of her heart, where she'd blocked off any emotions for Rafaele a long time ago. Sam had fancied for a second that he had appeared jealous when she'd mentioned Max…which was ridiculous. What right had he to be jealous? He'd given up that right when he'd been with a woman less than a week after letting her go.

Sam took a deep breath and tried to crush the nebulous and very dangerous feeling growing within her. She would be the biggest fool on this planet if she was to read anything into Rafaele's possessive gesture and demeanour just now. As he'd said himself, he was only interested in whatever this was between them until it burnt out.

As Sam knew to her cost it was far more likely to burn out for him than for her, and she'd be left picking up the pieces again—except this time it would be so much worse because they were forever bound together now through Milo, and she had a very sick feeling that she was in danger of falling for him all over again. Or, more accurately, that she'd never stopped.

She went cold inside to think that perhaps part of her reluctance to tell him about Milo had been to avoid this very selfish scenario.

Rafaele smoothly drove the car into the space outside her front door and Sam blinked. She hadn't even been aware of the journey. Just then a curtain moved and Sam saw Milo's small face appear, wearing a huge grin. Her heart clenched hard. She could imagine him declaring excitedly, *'Daddy's home!'* as he'd been doing for the past few days according to an approving Bridie, who seemed to see nothing but good in Rafaele's appearance in their lives.

It was Friday. They had a weekend to get through now, and Sam had no expectation that Rafaele would be sneaking in through her bedroom door at night to pick up where they'd left off. She knew from experience that he liked to keep her a secret, on the periphery of his world.

Sam took a deep breath and schooled her features, hoping that Rafaele would never guess the extent of her turbulence around him, or that even now she ached between her legs for one of his hands to press against her and alleviate her mounting frustration.

The fact that she was back in a place she'd clawed her way out of four years before was not a welcome revelation. At all.

CHAPTER SEVEN

ON SUNDAY SAM was folding laundry in the little utility room off the kitchen. Rafaele had taken Milo swimming on his own earlier, and since they'd come home they'd played with Milo's cars in the sitting room. Now he was putting him to bed.

She'd felt like a cat on a hot tin roof all weekend. Lying in bed at night, *aching* with frustration. Locking her muscles to avoid walking down the hall to Rafaele's room to beg him to make love to her. She refused to give herself away so spectacularly. And she'd been right. He'd treated her coolly all weekend, clearly reluctant to draw what had happened in his office into the domestic sphere.

Sam was only good enough within an environment which suited him. Nothing had changed. The bitterness that scored her shocked her with its intensity. Her emotions were see-sawing all over the place.

What *hadn't* helped was the little surprise Rafaele had had lined up when they'd woken that morning. The sleek supercar Rafaele had been using since he'd appeared in their lives had been replaced, probably by some hardworking minion, with a far more sedate *family* car.

'What's this?' Sam had asked faintly from the front door as Rafaele had deftly strapped Milo into his car seat to take him swimming.

He'd cast her a quick dry glance. 'It's a car, Sam. A more practical car, I think you'll agree, for a child…'

Sam had felt as if she'd just tipped over the edge of a precipice. All she'd been able to think about after they'd left, with an ecstatic Milo in the back, was of how Rafaele—one of the most Alpha male men she'd ever met, if not *the* most—had segued from playboy with a fast car into man with a child and a safety-conscious car without turning a hair. And somehow that had made Sam more nervous than anything else. She was too scared to look at all the implications and what they might mean…

She heard a noise then and tensed as she sensed Rafaele's presence behind her in the kitchen. She felt far too vulnerable to face him right now.

'I want you and Milo to come to Milan with me.'

Sam went very still for a moment, and then proceeded to fold a sheet as if he *hadn't* just dropped a bomb from a great height. Irritation with herself, with him, at the sexual frustration clawing at her insides, laced her voice. 'What are you talking about, Rafaele? We can't just go to Milan with you.'

Sounding impatient, Rafaele said, 'Sam, I can't talk to your back.' His voice changed and grew rougher. 'As delectable as it is. And your bottom in those jeans… *Dio*, do you know how hard it's been not to touch you all weekend?'

That made Sam whirl around, her blood heating instantaneously and rushing to every erogenous zone she had. She dropped the sheet from nerveless hands.

Despite her own craving need all weekend she hissed, 'Stop it. You can't talk to me like that. Not here, with Milo in the house.'

Rafaele was leaning against the doorjamb, far too close. His eyes narrowed on her, taking in her jeans and shirt. Grimly he admitted, 'I know. That's precisely why I restrained myself.'

Something gave way inside Sam at hearing him admit that his concern for Milo had been uppermost. It made her feel exposed, vulnerable. Between her legs she throbbed almost painfully.

Sam picked up the sheet and thrust it at Rafaele's chest. 'Here's some fresh linen for your bed.'

Rafaele caught the linen when it would have dropped to the ground again. His mouth had gone flat and tight.

'Well? Did you hear what I said about Milan? I want you and Milo to come with me this week.'

The thought of going back to the scene of the crime made Sam's emotions seesaw even more. She turned around again and blurted out, 'It's not practical, Rafaele. You can't just announce—'

'*Dio*, Sam.'

Sam let out a small squeak of surprise at Rafaele's guttural voice and saw the linen she'd just shoved at him sail over her head to land back on the pile haphazardly. Then she felt big hands swing her round until she was looking up in his grim face.

'Sam, I—' He stopped. His eyes went to her mouth and then he just said, *'Dio!'* again, before muttering something else in Italian and then pulling her into him.

His mouth was on hers, branding her, and she was up in flames in an instant, every point of her body straining to be closer to his hard form.

With a moan of helpless need and self-derision Sam submitted to the practised and expert ministrations of Rafaele's wicked mouth and tongue. Some tiny morsel of self-preservation eventually impinged on the heat and gave Sam the strength to pull free. She looked up into Rafaele's face and almost melted there and then at the sight of the feral look in his eyes. She put a hand to his chest, but that was worse when she felt his heart pounding.

'We can't. Not here...'

Rafaele smiled, but it was humourless. 'Maybe we'll have to book a hotel as you're partial to that kind of thing.'

That gave Sam the impetus to move, and she scooted out of the small space and rounded on Rafaele, arms crossed over the betraying throb of her breasts. Her voice was low with anger. 'You have no right to judge me when you were jumping into bed with someone new barely a week after I left Italy.'

Rafaele frowned. He looked volcanic. 'What the hell are you talking about? I wasn't with anyone.'

Sam emitted a curt laugh and tried to hide the flare of something pathetic within her. *Hope.* 'Well, that's not what it looked like—you were photographed all over the place with some Italian TV personality.'

Rafaele opened his mouth to speak but Sam put up a hand, stopping him.

Fiercely, she said, 'I don't care, Rafaele.' *Liar.*

Irrational guilt over her own liaison made her even angrier.

'Even if I had told you about Milo, it wasn't as if we were going to become some happy family. You told me what you thought of marriage and how you never wanted it in your life.'

Sam stopped, breathing heavily, and saw how Rafaele's face had become shuttered. Clearly he didn't like to be reminded of that.

'I seem to recall you agreeing fervently, Sam. Something about how seeing your father weep over your mother's picture had made you dread ever investing so much in one person only to lose them and be lonely for the rest of your life?'

Sam's insides contracted. She felt dizzy for a second and then mortification rushed through her like a shameful tide. She'd been so *open* with him. Had told him every little thing. As if he'd even been interested! Wasn't that exactly what she'd done, though? After a mere month in this man's bed she'd been ready to invest everything in him, only to realise how far off-base she'd been.

Panicking, she said the first thing she could think of to try and get them off this topic. 'What did you mean… about Milan?'

Rafaele's jaw clenched, but to her intense relief he appeared prepared to let it go.

'I want to take Milo to meet his grandfather—my father. It's going to come out sooner or later in the press that I have a son and I'd like Umberto to meet him before that happens. Also, he is old and frail…I'm conscious of his mortality.'

The words were delivered dispassionately enough to shock Sam slightly. Rafaele had never spoken of his father much before, except to say that he lived in a place called Bergamo, not far from Milan, and that he'd moved away after the family business had disintegrated and they'd lost everything. Sam knew that one of the first things Rafaele had done was to buy back the Falcone *palazzo* just outside Milan, as that was where he'd lived four years ago.

She hadn't met Umberto Falcone during the time she'd been with Rafaele, and against her better judgment her interest was piqued at the thought of seeing this tantalising glimpse of another aspect of Rafaele's life. And also to acknowledge that Milo had one grandparent still alive.

Rafaele continued, 'He's coming to Milan next week for a routine medical check-up and he's staying at the family *palazzo* just outside the city. I have to go back for a few days to attend a board meeting and drop in on the factory there. It would be a perfect opportunity to do this.'

She still resisted, despite being intrigued. 'Perfect for you, maybe… Milo has playschool, a routine. And what about my work?'

Rafaele's lip curled. 'Please—do you really expect me

to believe that Milo will be irreparably damaged by missing a few days of playschool? And…' those laser-like eyes narrowed on her '…I think that your boss would be very amenable to you taking the time off.'

Looking smug, Rafaele delivered the final nail in the coffin of Sam's hopes to escape.

'I spoke with Bridie about it when we met her outside just a while ago and she said she'd be only too happy to come to Italy with us and help watch Milo. She confided that as a devout Catholic she's always wanted to visit Rome, and I promised her we could make a stop there on the way back…'

Sam clenched her hands into fists at her sides. 'That's low-down and dirty manipulation, Rafaele.'

He shrugged lightly. 'Call it what you want, Sam, but I believe I'm entitled to a little "manipulation". You, Milo and Bridie are coming to Italy with me in two days' time so you'd better get prepared.'

Sam watched Rafaele turn and walk out and welcomed the rush of anger. No doubt he'd been planning this all along, lulling her into a false sense of security by moving into the house, demonstrating his capacity to compromise for his son's sake. Rafaele was just showing his true colours now: his desire to dominate.

But worse, much worse than that, was the prospect of how hard it would be to return to the place where it had all started. If she was barely holding it together here, how would she manage when she was face to face with the past?

Two days later, in accordance with Rafaele's autocratic decree, they were on a private plane belonging to Rafaele's younger half-brother, the Greek aviation and travel billionaire Alexio Christakos.

Bridie was in silent raptures over the plush luxuriousness of it all and Milo was like a bottle of shaken-up lemonade—about to fizz over at any moment. Every day for him at the moment seemed to bring nothing but untold treasures, and Sam looked at him kneeling on the seat beside her now, watching the world get smaller and smaller beneath them.

It was his first time on a plane and Milo automatically looked for his new favourite person on the planet: Rafaele. Pointing with a chubby finger, he said, 'Look, Daddy, *look!*'

Sam's heart squeezed so tight she had to put a hand there, as if that could assuage the bittersweet pain and the anxiety. How could she trust that Rafaele wouldn't grow bored and disappear from their lives, leaving Milo bereft? *And her...* Sam didn't even want to go there.

They were cruising now, and Rafaele stood up and managed to dwarf the very comfortable ten-seater plane. He held out a hand to Milo. 'Do you want to see the cockpit?'

He'd barely stopped talking before Milo had leapt off the seat and run to him. Rafaele picked him up. Milo didn't even look to Sam for reassurance.

Sam felt silly tears prick her eyes and turned away, but she heard Bridie saying quietly from across the small aisle, 'He's a good man. He'll take care of you both.'

Sam fought valiantly for control and looked at Bridie, gave her a watery smile. She couldn't hide anything from this woman who had seen her devastation when she'd come home from Italy. Her father hadn't even noticed, and had barely acknowledged her pregnancy in his sheer self-absorption. When Milo had appeared her father had merely raised an eyebrow and proceeded to behave as if he'd always been there.

Sam reached out and took Bridie's hand, squeezing it. 'I'm glad you're here.'

'So am I, love,' Bridie said, and then with obvious glee, 'I'm going to meet the Pope!'

Sam laughed, 'I know Rafaele can do most things, but I'm not sure his influence extends to that.'

'Not sure my influence extends to what?'

Sam tensed and looked up to catch Rafaele's green gaze. She blushed and said, 'Nothing… Milo should eat now. He'll be hungry.'

Bridie stood up and took Milo from Rafaele. 'I'll have a word with the stewardess and we'll get him sorted.'

Rafaele sat down in Bridie's vacant seat when they were gone and extended his long legs into the aisle. He was the epitome of Italian masculine elegance today, in a dark grey suit, white shirt and tie. But all Sam could think of was the raw magnetism lurking under the surface of that urbanity.

'It's rude to talk about people behind their backs, you know,' he observed without rancour.

Sam was immediately suspicious of this more civil Rafaele. He was undoubtedly happy to be returning to his own milieu.

She smiled tightly and avoided his gaze. 'Don't worry. Your number two fan only has good things to say about you.'

'Unlike you…'

In a bid to break the sudden tension Sam asked quickly, 'Your father…he knows about us coming?'

Rafaele sat back a little further. Milo could be heard chattering happily further up the plane.

The reserve that came over Rafaele's features at the mention of his father didn't go unnoticed by Sam.

'I spoke to him on the phone and explained.'

'How did he take the news of…of a grandson?'

Rafaele's mouth thinned. 'He's looking forward to meeting the next generation.'

'You're not close to him, are you?'

Rafaele looked at her and asked almost accusingly, 'How do you know?'

She shrugged minutely. 'You never spoke about him much…and I know you didn't grow up with him.'

'No,' he conceded. His mouth was even thinner, making Sam want to reach out and touch him. She curled her hands into fists in her lap.

With evident reluctance he said, 'My mother left him when I was three and took me with her. He was in no state to care for me even if she'd wanted to leave me behind.'

In an instant Sam remembered the day they'd told Milo who Rafaele was and Rafaele had made that enigmatic comment about being three years old. He must have been referring to this.

'Your mother wouldn't have done that, surely…?'

Rafaele arched a dark brow. 'No? So why did she abandon my older half-brother? Her firstborn son?'

Sam's mouth opened and closed. 'You have another brother?'

As if regretting saying anything, Rafaele said briskly, 'He turned up out of the blue at my mother's funeral. Alexio and I had no idea he even existed… Well, I had a memory of meeting him briefly when I was small but I thought it had been a dream.'

Half to herself, Sam said, 'So Milo has two uncles…'

Rafaele emitted a curt laugh. 'Don't worry, it's not likely we'll be getting together as one big happy family any time soon. Alexio is busy running his empire and Cesar wants nothing to do with us.'

Just then Milo came running down the aisle and grabbed Rafaele's hand, pulling him out of the seat. 'Lunch is ready!'

Rafaele let himself be pulled up and held out a hand to Sam.

She felt unsettled and a little vulnerable after their conversation. It was another snippet Rafaele hadn't revealed before. She put her hand into his and let him pull her out of the seat. He held it tightly all the way to the other end of the plane but Sam didn't feel as if the gesture was meant to be romantic. On the contrary—it was meant to remind her that they had unfinished business.

Rafaele's *palazzo* was as she remembered it: imposing, beautiful and impressive. The lush green gardens were stunningly landscaped. Its faintly crumbling grandeur hid opulent luxury inside. Four years ago Rafaele had still been in the process of doing it up and now it was finished.

As they approached up the grand steps Sam didn't even notice how tense she'd become until Milo said plaintively, 'Ow Mummy, too *tight*.' She immediately relaxed her grip on his hand.

A different housekeeper from the one Sam remembered met them at the door and Rafaele introduced her as Luisa. She was soon busy directing the driver with their bags. Bridie was open-mouthed with shock and awe, and Sam felt a semi-hysterical giggle rise up, but it faded fast when she saw the stooped figure of a man with a cane approach them.

He barked out something in Italian and Sam saw Rafaele tense just a few feet ahead of her. She had that disturbing urge again to touch him, to offer some comfort.

He said curtly, 'In English, Papa. They don't speak Italian.'

The old man snorted and came into view. His eyes were deep set and so dark they looked black, staring out from a strong face lined with age and disappointment.

Milo was clutching Sam now and she lifted him up.

'Well?' Umberto growled. 'Where is my grandson?'

Hesitantly Sam moved forward to stand beside Rafaele. She felt him snake an arm around her waist and didn't like the way something within her immediately welcomed and gravitated towards the support.

'Papa, this is Samantha Rourke, our son Milo, and Sam's friend Bridie.'

Our son.

Sam nodded in the man's direction. His black gaze seemed to be devouring them. He said nothing. Then, to Sam's complete surprise, Milo squirmed to be set free and she had to put him down.

Holding her breath, Sam watched as Milo started to walk towards his grandfather. She wanted to snatch him back, as if from the jaws of danger, and even moved. But Rafaele's hand stopped her, gripping her waist, making her *über*-aware of his hard body alongside hers. Even now...

Milo stopped in front of the man and asked with all the innocence of a child, 'Why do you have a stick?'

The man just looked at him for a long moment and then barked out a laugh. '*Dio*, Rafaele, it's like looking at you when you were that age. He's a Falcone—no doubt about it.'

Rafaele's hand gripped her waist so tightly now that Sam looked at him, but she could only see his hard jaw, a muscle twitching. Before she could do or say anything Rafaele had let her go and strode over to crouch down near Milo, who curled into him trustingly.

Huskily he was saying, 'This is your grandpapa, *piccolino*.'

Umberto Falcone held out a hand to his grandson. 'I am pleased to meet you.'

Milo grinned and took his hand, shaking it forcefully, making Umberto wince comically. Milo giggled and looked at Rafaele. 'Can we play now?'

Rafaele stood up, still holding onto Milo's hand, and something tense seemed to pass from him to his father. He said to Milo, 'Why don't we settle in first, hmm? We can play later.'

'Okey-dokey.' Milo took his hand from Rafaele's and came back to Sam, who picked him up again.

Rafaele was now drawing her and Bridie forward to introduce them to Umberto, but gone was the joking man of moments ago. He seemed to have retreated again.

Bridie was saying politely, 'You have a beautiful home here, Mr Falcone.'

The old man glanced at his son and said stiffly, 'It's not mine…it's Rafaele's. He bought it back after—'

'Papa,' Rafaele said warningly, and the man's mouth shut.

He looked at Bridie then and said, 'Come, let us take some refreshments and leave these young ones to settle in.'

Bridie looked at Sam, and Sam noticed that she was a bit pink in the cheeks. Sam pushed her gently in the direction where Umberto was setting off, surprisingly agile despite his cane and stooped figure. 'Go on—sit down and have a rest. We'll be fine.'

The housekeeper was despatching a younger woman in the direction of Umberto and Bridie with rapid Italian before leading them up the stairs herself. Sam was clinging onto Milo, afraid of the onslaught of memories lurking around each corner. She and Rafaele had made love all over this *palazzo*. He'd used to bring her here after work, apart from a couple of times when he'd taken her to her apartment, too impatient to wait, but she'd never spent a weekend here with him until that last weekend…

They were walking down a familiar corridor now, and Sam's heart thumped hard when she recognised Rafaele's bedroom door to the left. Thankfully they stopped at another door, just opposite.

'This is your room. Milo is in an adjoining one.'

Sam walked into the room indicated by Rafaele. The housekeeper disappeared. Milo wriggled to be free and she put him down so he could explore. The room was sumptuous without being over the top. Understated luxury. Lots of discreet flower designs and soft greys. Sam heard a squeal of excitement from Milo and followed him into his room.

It was a small boy's paradise. His bed was made in the shape of a car. The walls were bright. Books and toys covered almost every available surface. Sam looked at Rafaele helplessly as Milo found a toy train set.

He grabbed it up and went to Sam, 'Is this mine, Mummy?'

Sam shot Rafaele a censorious look. She bent down. 'Yes, it is, sweetie. But this is Rafaele's house. You'll have to leave it behind when we go home.'

Milo looked perturbed and turned to Rafaele. 'Will you mind it for me when we go home?'

Rafaele sounded gruff. 'Of course, *piccolino*.'

Milo's lip quivered. Sam could see that it was all too much.

'But…but what if another little boy comes and wants to play with it?'

Rafaele bent down and looked Milo in the eye. 'That won't happen. You are the only little boy who is allowed to play here, I promise.'

Instantly reassured, Milo spun away to start playing again.

Sam hissed at Rafaele. 'This is too much for him. You can't *buy* his affection, Rafaele.'

Rafaele stood up and took Sam's arm, leading her out of earshot. 'Damn you, Sam, I'm not trying to buy him… I want to spoil him—is that so bad?'

Sam looked into Rafaele's eyes and felt herself drowning. She knew instinctively that Rafaele had done this out of the generous good of his heart, *not* out of any manipulative desire. He might do that with her, but all along he'd been ultra-careful to take her lead on how to deal with Milo.

She crossed her arms and felt like a heel. She looked down. 'I'm sorry...that wasn't entirely fair.'

Rafaele tipped her chin up. 'No, it wasn't.'

All Rafaele could see were those swirling grey depths, sucking him down and down to a place he didn't want to investigate. Like Milo feeling overwhelmed, he suddenly felt the same. Letting go of Sam's chin, he stepped back. He needed space. Now.

'I'll have Luisa bring you up some refreshments. You and Milo should settle in and rest. We'll eat at seven.'

When he reached his study on the ground floor he closed the door and took a deep breath. He headed straight for his drinks cabinet and poured himself a shot of whisky, downing it in one. To his chagrin it wasn't even Milo and the fact that he had his son in this house that seemed to be featuring prominently in his head. It was Sam. Having Sam back here. Reminding him of the heated insanity he'd felt around her before. Of how badly he'd needed her, how insatiably.

How sweet she'd been—so innocent. So bright. So unlike any other woman he'd known, seducing him effortlessly into a tangled web of need from which he'd only extricated himself with great effort. And he had been relieved to do so, no matter what the dull ache he'd felt for four years might have told him.

The ache had disappeared as soon as he'd decided that he'd contact her in England. He'd told himself that it would be different, that he wouldn't still desire her. That he would be able to demonstrate how he'd moved on... But even at the first sound of her voice on the end of the phone his body had convulsed with need...

And then...*Milo.*

Rafaele felt pain lance his hand and looked down stupidly to see that he'd crushed the delicate glass. Cursing himself, he got a tissue and told himself he was being ridiculous. Seeing Sam here again, with his father too, in this *palazzo*…it was something he'd never expected to have to deal with. That was all.

The following morning when Sam woke up she was disorientated for a few long seconds, until the opulent surroundings and softer-than-soft bed registered. She sat up in a panic.

Milo.

Quickly she got out of bed and went to the open adjoining door. Milo's bed was tossed, his pyjamas were on the ground and he was nowhere to be seen.

Bridie must have taken him for breakfast. The previous evening had seen them all seated for dinner—Milo sitting on big books on a chair to elevate him, insisting on feeding himself like a big boy, wanting to impress his new grandpapa, who had looked on approvingly.

To Sam's relief, after dinner Rafaele, far too disturbing in jeans and a black top, had made his excuses and disappeared to his study. And then Bridie had insisted on taking Milo up to bed, as he'd been barely able to keep awake long enough to feed himself his new favourite dessert: *gelato*.

Sam had felt awkward, sitting with Umberto on her own, but the man had stood up and indicated for her to follow him and have some coffee, so she had. He'd led her to a small room off the dining room—comfortable, cosy.

Luisa had come and poured them coffee and Sam had felt she needed to break the ice. 'I'm sorry…that you didn't know about Milo before now.'

The old man had waved her words aside and admitted gruffly, 'I gave up any right to pry into Rafaele's life a long time ago.'

Not knowing how to respond, Sam had just taken a sip of coffee. She'd always loved the strength and potency of well-made Italian coffee.

'Milo is the same age as Rafaele was when he left here with his mother.'

Sam had looked at Umberto.

'He was very young.' The old man's face had darkened. 'Too young to witness what he did.'

Sam had frowned. 'I'm sorry… I don't know…'

Umberto had looked at her, his gaze shrewd. 'When my wife left me, Samantha, I was a broken man. I'd already lost everything. My house, the family legacy, the factory. My dignity. I begged her on my knees not to leave me but she did anyway. Rafaele witnessed my lowest moment and I don't think he's ever forgiven me for it.'

Sam had tried to take it in. She'd known Rafaele's mother had left, but not the extent of it. She wondered how traumatic it must have been for a child to see his mother turn her back on his father and it was as if something slid home inside her—she could see now where Rafaele's intensely commitment-phobic issues might stem from.

'It was a long time ago…' Umberto had said. 'It's good that you are here with Milo. This will be a challenge for my proud son, and perhaps that's not a bad thing.'

Sam blinked in the morning light of her bedroom, the memory fading. She remembered now that she'd had disjointed dreams all night of a man on his knees, begging, pleading, with Milo looking on, crying in distress… She pursed her lips. One thing she could guarantee pretty categorically was that Rafaele would never be reduced to begging on his knees to *anyone*.

Trying not to think of that vulnerable three-year-old Rafaele, when all she could see was Milo in her mind's eye, Sam washed and dressed and went to search for Milo and Bridie. She found them in the dining room with the sun pouring in.

Sam bent to kiss her son, aware of a cool green gaze on her from the head of the table. Umberto and Bridie broke off from their conversation to greet Sam and Rafaele stood up. Sam had to quell a dart of hurt. She felt as if the minute she entered a room he wanted to leave it.

'I've got to go to the factory this morning for my meeting… I've arranged for a driver to come and pick you all up in an hour. He will drop Umberto off at the doctor's and take you into Milan to sightsee. I'll join you there this afternoon for a late lunch.'

Umberto muttered something rude about doctors and Sam saw Bridie smile.

Milo was asking Sam, 'What's *sightsee?*'

Rafaele had pinned Sam with that unreadable gaze and instantly she felt breathless. 'I have to go to a function this evening. I'd like it if you accompanied me.'

Sam opened her mouth. 'I…'

Bridie chipped in quickly. 'Of course she will. You could do with a night out, Sam, love. I'll be here, and Milo can sleep with me so you won't have to worry about disturbing him.'

Sam glared at Bridie, who looked back at her with an innocence she didn't trust for a second. Umberto was unhelpfully silent.

Sam looked at Rafaele and was loath to let him see that she might not want to go for very personal reasons.

She shrugged a shoulder. 'Sure—why not?'

CHAPTER EIGHT

THAT EVENING SAM realised a fundamental flaw in her plan to join Rafaele for his function. She had no dress. She hadn't even thought about it earlier, while in Milan, too caught up in the whistlestop sightseeing tour Rafaele had arranged for Bridie and Milo, who obviously hadn't been there before. Then they'd picked Umberto up from the doctor's and met Rafaele for lunch.

Biting her lip and wondering what to do, Sam went to the wardrobe, fully expecting it to be empty. When she opened the door, though, she gasped and her heart stopped cold in her chest. There was a dress hanging up inside, and it was the dress Rafaele had bought her four years before. She remembered the big white box it had come in, along with the matching underwear, shoes and jewels. She'd left it all behind at the *palazzo* because she'd felt as if it had never really belonged to her.

About two months after Sam had returned to England the box containing the dress, shoes, underwear and jewellery had arrived via a courier company. As soon as she'd realised what it was and had read the accompanying note— *I bought this for you. Rafaele*—Sam had sent it back with the note torn in two pieces.

And now it was here.

Sam felt short of breath. She took the dress out of the wardrobe, its material heavy and slinky, and stalked out of her bedroom and across the hall to Rafaele's, not bothering to knock on the door.

Her eyes widened when she took in a naked Rafaele, strolling out of his bathroom and rubbing his hair with a towel. For a long moment he just stood there, and Sam's eyes were glued to that broad, magnificent chest. Instant heat bloomed in her belly.

With a strangled sound she lifted her eyes and held the dress out. 'What is the meaning of this?'

With supreme nonchalance Rafaele secured the towel around his waist and quirked his mouth sexily on one side. 'It's amazing how you can still blush, *cara*.'

Sam gritted out, 'Don't call me that. I'm not your *cara*. Why do you still have this dress?'

Rafaele's face was inscrutable. He shrugged. 'It seemed a shame to throw it away just because you didn't want it.'

Bile rose inside Sam. 'And how many lucky women have worn it since me?'

A muscle popped in Rafaele's jaw. 'None. I thought you'd appreciate blending in with the crowd tonight instead of appearing in your habitual tomboy uniform.'

To Sam's disgust she felt tears prick her eyes. 'I'll try not to disappoint you, Rafaele. After all, I know what an honour it is to be taken out in public with you, because you never deemed it appropriate before.'

She whirled around and left the room, slamming the door behind her.

Rafaele winced and put his hands on his hips. His chest was a tight ball of blackness. He cursed himself. He should have followed his head and thrown that dress out as soon as he'd realised she'd left it behind—instead of sending it to her, almost intrigued as to how she might respond when even then he'd known that he couldn't have anything more to do with her.

When it had arrived back with the torn note, *then* he

should have thrown it out. But instead he'd instructed his housekeeper to hang it up and had refused to analyse why he'd done such a thing.

It was just a dress.

Thoroughly disgruntled now, and regretting the impulse he'd had earlier to ask Sam to accompany him this evening, Rafaele got dressed.

Sam was still tight-lipped in the back of one of Rafaele's chauffeur-driven cars about an hour later. She was as far away from him as she could get without falling out of the door, and she hated the electric awareness that pulsed between them.

As they'd been leaving Milo had been holding Umberto's hand in the grand hallway of the *palazzo* and he'd gasped. 'Mummy, you look like a princess.'

Sam had gone red, and then grown even hotter when Rafaele had appeared, looking stupendously gorgeous in a classic tuxedo. Suddenly she'd been glad of the effort she'd made. She needed all the armour she could muster.

Her hair was up in a topknot, held in place with a jewelled pin loaned to her by Bridie. She'd put on more make-up than she'd normally wear, outlining her eyes and thickening her lashes. And wearing the vertiginous heels that had come with the dress Sam reached to Rafaele's shoulder.

He hadn't touched her while they were leaving. He'd merely indicated that she should precede him and, feeling horribly exposed under his cool gaze, Sam had walked out, praying she wouldn't fall over.

Now they were pulling up outside the glittering façade of a building with men in uniforms waiting to assist all the guests in their finery. Butterflies swarmed into Sam's belly.

She felt her arm being taken in a warm grip and showers of electric shocks seemed to spread through her body. Reluctantly she looked at Rafaele, and the momentarily unguarded look on his face took her by surprise.

'I should have told you earlier… You look beautiful.'

'I…' Sam's voice failed. 'Thank you.'

And just like that she felt the animosity drain away. She realised that as soon as she'd seen the dress hanging up she'd harboured a very treacherous wish that Rafaele had kept it for sentimental reasons, and that was the basis for her lashing out at him. It had been anger at herself for her own pathetic weakness.

Rafaele had let her go. Sam's door was being opened and someone was waiting for her to step out. When she did so, Rafaele was standing there, his face unreadable again. She wondered if she had imagined what he'd just said…

He took her arm and led her inside and Sam was glad he was supporting her, because nothing could have prepared her for the dazzling display of wealth and beauty as soon as they walked in.

She felt instantly gauche: both underdressed and over-dressed. Rafaele got them drinks and almost immediately was surrounded by gushing acolytes—a mixture of men and women. As they stood there the number of women seemed to increase. They shot Sam glances ranging from the curious to the downright angry—as if he had no right to come here with a woman.

Clearly Rafaele was a prize to be fought over, and Sam really didn't like the way her own hackles rose and her blood started to boil in response. She felt a very disturbing primal urge rise up within her to claim him in some way. The fact that she had borne his child seemed to resonate deep within her, and she wanted to snarl at the women to back off.

With a lazy insouciance that did nothing to help cool her blood, Rafaele reached out and drew her to his side. The level of malevolence coming from the women increased exponentially.

He said to the people surrounding them, 'I'd like to introduce you to Samantha Rourke.'

Something in Sam went cold at this very bare introduction, which left her in some kind of limbo land—what exactly *was* she to him?

But what had she expected him to say? *Meet the mother of my child, who is such a pushover that she lets me sleep with her even though she knows I hate her...?*

Sam caught one or two smug looks from a couple of the women. As if to say, *She's no competition.* Her blood boiled over.

She managed to keep it together until they were alone again and then she rounded on him. 'If you brought me here just to deflect the attention from those man-eaters then I think I've done my bit. I'd prefer to be at home with Milo than to witness your simpering fan club line up to tell you how marvellous you are.'

Furious at herself for feeling so emotional, Sam stabbed Rafaele's chest with a finger. 'I'm the mother of your child—tell *that* to your next prospective mistress.'

Rafaele looked at Sam and felt something pierce his chest. Her words were lost to him for a second in the glare from those grey eyes. She looked so young, so stunning. Her neck was long and graceful, her skin so pale he could see the delicate veins underneath. The dress hugged and emphasised every curve, fitting her better now than it had four years ago. His eyes dropped down over the swell of her breasts and her words resounded within him: *I'm the mother of your child.*

Moments ago, when he'd reached out to pull her to him and introduce her, he'd felt a second of blind panic. The realisation had been immediate and stark: he'd just introduced his peers to Sam and when the news emerged of his son, and that she was his mother, they would assume that they were together. And that thought wasn't making him want to flee.

Rafaele had not even considered this prospect when he'd asked Sam to the function. He'd just looked at her that morning and the words had spilled out... Proving once again how she scrambled his thought processes. How she effortlessly tapped into something deep and instinctive within him that led to choices and decisions that his head might normally balk at.

He couldn't even blame her. It wasn't as if she'd inveigled her way to an invitation—if anything she'd looked horrified at the suggestion. Rafaele's blood simmered. He felt the imprint of Sam's finger in his chest. The rest of the room died away and he saw only her. Need and desire rose up to strangle him and magnified his feeling of exposure.

Reaching out a hand, he snaked it around her neck and brought her closer. Something triumphant moved through him when he saw those eyes flare with awareness. But the realisation of how comfortable he was with people knowing who Sam was, assuming they were together, was too raw, too new. He needed to push it back. Push *her* back.

'I have the only mistress I need right here, Sam. Why would I go looking when you've already proved yourself so amenable?'

Her cheeks went white and Rafaele felt the punch of something dirty and dark down low.

'You bastard.'

She pulled away from him and spun around, moving through the crowd. It was a long second before Rafaele could function again, and then he set off after her, a dense darkness expanding in his chest when he thought of those huge eyes and the pain in their depths that he'd just witnessed. That he'd just caused. Wilfully. From weakness.

* * *

Sam could barely drag enough oxygen into her lungs. She was seething. Hurt and angry with herself for letting Rafaele get to her. For feeling so possessive and jealous around those other women. For ever hoping even for a second that his bringing her here tonight had meant something...

She raised a hand to get the doorman's attention, to ask him to call her a cab, but just then it was caught by a firm grip and she was whirled around.

'Where do you think you're going?'

Rafaele looked as livid as she felt, and he had no right to be. Sam pulled her arm free. 'I'm going home, Rafaele. I don't need to be reminded publicly how little you like to acknowledge me in your life.'

She turned around again, but gave a gasp of dismay when she saw Rafaele's chauffeur-driven car stopping at the foot of the steps. He was marching her down to the open door before she could do anything. The door was quickly shut and he was sliding in the other side. Sam had a perverse urge to open the door and jump out but she curbed the childish desire. And also she realised she didn't have enough money for a cab. She scowled at herself. Being with Rafaele was eroding her very independence.

Rafaele issued a terse instruction to the driver and the privacy window slid up noiselessly. His eyes glittered at her in the gloom of the backseat but even now Sam's muscles clenched in her pelvis, and she felt the betraying heat of desire getting her body ready for this man. *Her man.* The stupid assertion flashed again. She could have growled with frustration.

Eventually he bit out, 'I shouldn't have said what I did back there. You didn't deserve that.'

It was the last thing Sam had expected to hear, and she said faintly, 'No, I didn't.' And then, 'Why did you bring me with you, Rafaele? People will only ask questions...

when they find out about Milo… We shouldn't be seen together. It doesn't help matters.'

Rafaele's face looked as if it was carved out of stone. 'You're the mother of my child, Samantha. It's inevitable that we'll be seen together, no matter what happens in the future.'

Sam had an image then of Rafaele, married to some cool blonde beauty, and of an older Milo heading off on a plane on his own to stay with his father and his new family. The image made her suck in a breath of pain and she scooted as far away from him in the back of the car as she could.

Mixed in with the pain she was feeling was the ever-present and building sexual frustration. She felt as if she was going mad. Heat burned her insides and made her skin prickle. All she could see in her peripheral vision was the huge dark shape of Rafaele and imagined that powerful body, naked and surging into hers, thrusting so deep that she'd finally feel some measure of peace.

She had to hold back a groan, and was aware of Rafaele's quick glance at her through the thick tension between them.

Lord. It had been a long time since Sam had had to pleasure herself, but if this need wasn't assuaged soon she'd go mad.

'Sam.'

Rafaele's voice was thick and Sam's heart palpitated. Reluctantly she looked at him and a pulse throbbed between her legs. She clamped her thighs together desperately.

He reached over and took her hand and Sam almost cried out at the sensation. She tried to pull back but he wouldn't release her.

'I want you.'

His face was in shadow but she could sense his desperation. It was little comfort. Inevitability rose up inside her. She could resist anything but this declaration. This promise that soon, if she allowed it, he would ease this ache that was inside her, tearing her apart. It transcended even what had just happened.

Helplessly, in a whisper of supplication that she hated, Sam just replied, 'Yes...'

Yes.

Rafaele felt primal satisfaction rush through him, hardening his body. He wanted to devour Sam, consume her, brand her. He wanted her *for ever.*

No!

Rafaele rejected that rogue assertion, which had slid into his mind before he'd even acknowledged it.

He couldn't let her hand go, though, even when she turned her head away to look out of the window. The rapid rise and fall of her breasts beneath the dress made him curl his other hand to a fist, just to stop himself reaching out to cup their heavy weight.

Sam was clearly aware of the same ramifications as he, of being seen together and how that might be construed. But the thought of her rejecting that suddenly made him want to claim her. In any way that he could. Publicly *and* in private.

But right now he couldn't really focus on what that meant. Right now he wanted the physical.

As the car swept gracefully through the *palazzo* gates anticipation spiked like a fever in his blood. When the car came to a halt he got out and strode around to Sam's door, helping her out himself. She looked up at him with those huge expressive eyes and desire was hot and urgent inside him—part of the tangled mess of emotions this woman inspired in him on a regular basis.

With one smooth move he picked her up into his arms. Her mouth was tight with a need that resonated within him.

He felt like a beast. He couldn't speak. What he needed right now was not something he could even articulate. It was visceral, physical. Urgent.

Sam was in Rafaele's arms and he was striding through the front door of the *palazzo*. All she could feel was her breasts crushed to the solid wall of his chest and the pulse of awareness between them, like a tangible forcefield of energy.

The house was quiet. He was striding up the stairs now and Sam bit her lip. Rafaele carried her straight into his bedroom. She tensed against the leap of her blood at the promise of satisfaction. A moment of sanity intruded, reminding her of the certain self-recrimination she would face in the aftermath and all the uncertainty about how he felt about her.

Weakly she seized on the first thing she thought of. 'Wait… Milo…'

Rafaele was putting her down, sliding her along the length of his hard body, one part of which in particular was very hard. He was already pulling down the strap of her dress and her skin tingled.

His voice was rough. 'Milo is with Bridie, as you well know.'

That sliver of sanity compelled her to try again, even though every part of her protested. 'Rafaele…'

'Stop talking, Sam. I want you. You want me. It's very simple.'

It *wasn't* that simple, though, and Sam opened her mouth to protest again. But then Rafaele was kissing her, and pulling the strap of her dress down further, and she felt the rising lust suck her under and weakly…she gave in. She wanted to forget sanity and take *this*.

Between her legs she was slick and throbbing. She didn't have a hope of resisting when Rafaele bared one breast and cupped it in his hand, squeezing the plump flesh, his thumb grazing her nipple.

Letting out a soft moan halfway between frustration at her own weakness and excitement at her building desire, Sam wound her arms around Rafaele's neck and pressed herself against him, trapping his hand on her breast.

Rafaele's other hand came down and cupped her buttocks, kneading the flesh, making Sam's hips roll against him impatiently. She could feel the thick length of his erection between them and fresh heat pulsed to her core.

Rafaele pulled back for a moment, breathing harshly, his eyes glittering fiercely. It was hard for Sam to open her eyes. She felt dazed. He'd always had this effect on her—one touch and she felt drugged.

He was dragging off his jacket, tie and shirt, dropping them to the ground, unbuckling his belt, undoing his trousers.

His voice was guttural. 'I want you naked *now*.'

Sam's flesh prickled with anticipation. Her hands felt stupid as she tried to pull down her strap and, issuing something that sounded like a curse, Rafaele took over, turning her around and finding the zip, pulling it down and peeling the heavy fabric from her body.

Sam kicked off her shoes. Now she wore only black lace panties. Rafaele turned her around again and that hot green gaze swept down her body, lingering on her breasts, which seemed to swell and tighten under his look.

'You're so beautiful.'

Sam ducked her head. 'No, I'm not.'

Rafaele tipped up her chin, forcing her to look at him. 'Yes, you are.'

He'd done this before—made her feel buoyant. Feminine. And it had all been ripped to pieces when he'd rejected her. But Sam couldn't focus on that now.

He pulled her into him again and Sam swayed towards

him like a magnet. He kissed her, tongue thrusting deep, fanning the flames of lust within her. He was naked now, and her hand instinctively sought to touch him, finding and encircling his erection, moving up and down, feeling the slip and slide of satin skin over all that steely strength.

His mouth not leaving hers, Rafaele skimmed his hand down from her breast over her belly, down to her panties and underneath, his fingers seeking and finding that sweet molten spot, making her legs part so that he could have more access.

As he stroked and explored Sam broke off the kiss. And then one of Rafaele's fingers thrust inside her and Sam's legs went weak with the sharp, spasming pleasure that gripped her.

With dextrous hands Rafaele pushed her panties down and lifted her, to deposit her on the bed. Sam could only look up at Rafaele and marvel at his sheer masculine magnificence. He was so broad and powerful. Narrow waist and hard-muscled thighs and between them... Her mouth watered.

She sat up and looked up at Rafaele. He was watching her almost warily and she felt a heady rush of power. She moved to the edge of the bed and reached for him, her hands going to his hips, pulling him towards her.

'Sam...'

She ignored him and drew his length into her hand, and then she took him into her mouth. The remembered taste and feel of him was like an explosion on her senses. She barely heard his deep moan of satisfaction as she swirled her tongue around the bulbous tip, relearning his shape and what made him tense. His hands were in her hair, gripping her head.

Her hand encircled him and her mouth and tongue licked and sucked. *He'd* taught her how to do this.

'*Dio*, Sam...'

Sam felt him tensing, the instinctive thrusting of his hips towards her, as if he couldn't help himself. His hands were trying to pull her back, but she knew it was against his will. He'd never let her go this far before but stubbornly Sam wanted to see him lose control because of *her* and she kept going, ignoring his rough entreaties, until finally she felt the heat of his climax gush into her mouth and throat, felt his hips jerking.

Sam kept her mouth on him for a long moment and then finally pulled back. She couldn't help a smile when she saw Rafaele's dazed-looking expression. Slowly that expression cleared and his eyes narrowed on her. She felt a shiver of trepidation mixed with anticipation go through her and recognised that he wasn't happy with the way she'd made him lose it like that. She felt more powerful in that moment than she'd ever felt…

Rafaele bent down and loomed over her on his hands, forcing her to move back onto the bed. She collapsed onto it.

'I think I'm going to have to restrain you…'

Sam looked at Rafaele blankly for a second, and then watched him stand up and go to a nearby cabinet. He pulled out two long slivers of silk and she realised they were ties. Something deep inside her quivered—but it wasn't with fear, it was excitement. She didn't know what he intended but secretly wanted to find out…

He took each hand and quietly wound a tie around each wrist, knotting it. Sam looked at him and bit her lip. Then Rafaele stretched her hands over her head, and Sam only realised what he'd done when she couldn't bring her hands down again…he'd tied them to one of the bed's four posts.

'Rafaele… What…?'

He came back down and over her. Not touching her, but letting her feel his body heat. 'I want you to know what it feels like to lose control…'

Sam could have laughed. She lost control every time she looked at this man! And there was something that felt so wickedly decadent about being restrained it overshadowed the sliver of discomfort. She trusted Rafaele above anything else, and that deep-seated knowledge shook her now. She hadn't realised just how much she trusted him till this moment.

He bent his head then, and his mouth was a hot brand on hers, opening her up to him, demanding a response which she gave unerringly. Already she felt the frustration of being bound. She wanted to touch him but couldn't. She moaned softly with it, and could have sworn she heard Rafaele chuckle darkly.

His mouth moved down, trailing over her jaw and neck. His hands were smoothing over her body, touching her but staying away from erogenous zones, making her grit her jaw to stop herself from begging. Her hands pulled ineffectually at the silken ties.

And then Rafaele's mouth was on her breast and her back arched. *Yes.* He lavished both taut peaks with attention until they were tingling and stinging. His hand had moved down to her belly and, like a wanton, Sam felt her legs part in mute appeal. Rafaele reared back for a moment and looked at her body. Sam gazed down to see his arousal already hard again, still glistening wetly from her mouth and tongue. She ached inside.

Rafaele's hand went to the juncture at her legs and then he was moving down, his mouth leaving little trails of fire as he pressed kisses under her breasts, to her abdomen and down. Sam's breath stopped when she felt him pull her legs wide apart. Her hands pulled at the ties. She'd never been so bared or so vulnerable.

Rafaele's mouth settled *there*, between her legs, and Sam's breath came back, choppy. She felt too hot, too tight, too…sensitive.

'Rafaele...'

But his tongue was on her now, exploring her sex, finding where she was so wet for him, opening her up, stabbing deep, making her moan uncontrollably, making her hips twitch. And then his tongue was replaced by his fingers, thrusting deep, and his other hand had found her breast, his thumb and forefinger pinching a nipple.

A broken scream emerged from Sam's mouth—a feral sound. Her hips were lifting off the bed, begging Rafaele for more, for him to drink from her as she came...as she'd done to him. And then the pleasure was peaking and spiralling out of all control, wresting her sane mind from her brain and leaving behind nothing but heat and deep, boneless satisfaction, with his mouth on her right to the end.

Rafaele slowly came up and over her body. He pressed a kiss to her mouth and Sam could taste the essence of her desire on him. Could he taste himself on her? The thought ignited new fires deep down, diminishing her need to curl up and cling onto the boneless feeling. Sam was barely aware of being restrained now. She didn't think she could have lifted her arms even if she'd wanted to.

And then Rafaele was sliding into her...deeply. Sam sucked in a breath, her eyes going wide. He looked down at her and all she could see was green. And heat. And broad shoulders damp with sweat. He moved back out... slowly. One arm came around her back, arching her into him, making one breast pout up towards him, so he bent his head and took it into his mouth, suckling fiercely as he thrust, going a little deeper, harder.

Sam gasped. It was too much. And now she *did* feel the restraints and she pulled against them. She needed to anchor herself to something. She felt as if Rafaele was going to drive her over the edge completely and she'd have nothing at all to hang onto.

But she couldn't articulate any words. Rafaele's chest against her breasts was delicious torture. The ruthless rhythm of his body in and out of hers drove her higher and higher. She could only look deep into his eyes, as if that alone could hold her to this earth.

Just at that moment something pierced her—*anger* at Rafaele, for reducing her to this mindless wanton, gasping and mute being. His powerful body was going so hard and deep now that Sam had to close her eyes, feeling as if a very secret part of herself was being bared to him in a way that she wasn't ready for.

Rafaele's voice was guttural. 'Sam, look at me.'

But she couldn't. He'd see it if she did. She'd never been laid so bare, made so vulnerable, and if she looked at him now he'd see how much she loved him—because she'd never stopped loving him. Even after all that had happened and the million reasons he'd given her for not loving him.

'No,' she said, equally guttural.

Sam heard his rough shout as he made his frustration clear, but both their bodies were locked in a primal dance now and they were equally unable to stop. They could only go on, until the tight grip of tension was shattered and they orgasmed moments after each other, Sam's body convulsing around Rafaele's thick length so hard that she could feel it. She was milking him, taking his very essence into her, and the feeling was so intense and powerful on top of this awful, excoriating vulnerability that tears pricked her eyes.

She turned her head away. Rafaele's body was still within her, pulsing, slowly diminishing. She felt a tear slip down one cheek and finally managed to find the words she hadn't been able to till now.

'Untie me Rafaele.'

She was trembling from an overload of pleasure and the revelation of just how deep her feelings for him were, still.

'Sam…'

'Just untie me.' Her voice sounded harsh to her own ears.

His hands reached up. She felt his arms and chest brush her body and she shivered convulsively against him. Even now. Deftly he undid the knots and Sam's arms were free again, her wrists sore after pulling against the restriction. Terrified that Rafaele would see her emotions bared, Sam scooted out from under him and off the bed. She grabbed the nearest covering she could find, which was his shirt, and pulled it on and walked to the door.

She heard Rafaele curse behind her and say, 'Sam, wait… Where are you—?'

But she was gone, walking blindly, on very wobbly legs, going anywhere that was away from his presence and his ability to reduce her to a melting mass of sensations and turbulent emotions. He'd wanted to dominate her and show her who was in control and he had done that beyond doubt. The eroticism of what she'd just been through felt tawdry now, as she imagined Rafaele coolly and clinically deciding how he would best show her who was boss. She had to get a grip before she faced him again.

Rafaele felt poleaxed. Self-recrimination rose upwards like bile. He would have an image burnt onto his retina for ever of Sam, with her hands bound above her head, her face turned away and a tear slipping down one cheek. He could still feel the strength of the pulsations of her body around his, and knew that it wasn't pain or discomfort that had made her turn away.

His last moment of semi-rational thought, he remembered, had been just before he'd come into Sam's mouth, his body thrusting against her, his hands holding her head so that he could— He cursed and got up off the bed, a restless jagged energy filling his body.

She'd always pushed him further than any other woman. He'd looked down at her when she'd taken her mouth from him—that wicked device of a torture more pleasurable than he could ever remember. She'd smiled at him and it had been full of something inherently feminine and mysterious... Rafaele's first insidious thought had been...Did she do that with *him?* The lover she'd taken? Had *he* been the first to experience her mouth around him, taking him in so deep that he'd not been able to pull back but had gone to the brink and over it... Had she milked him the same way?

The thought had made him see red. He'd felt exposed—far more exposed than just being naked in front of her. Vulnerable in a way he hadn't felt in a long time. It had had echoes of the past, when he recalled his mother looking at his father so dispassionately, even though he was broken, at her feet.

And suddenly Rafaele had wanted to regain control of a situation that was careening out of all control. He'd been losing it. So he'd bound her...so she couldn't touch him and make him forget again...but he'd still lost it anyway. Tying her up had only heightened the experience, making it even more erotic, compelling...and it had done nothing but highlight the fact that even while restrained she exerted a power over him that he couldn't deny.

He grabbed some clothes and pulled them on perfunctorily. Rafaele's gut felt sick as he left his room. She'd been crying. He looked in her room first, but it was dark and the bed was untouched. Then he went downstairs.

He found her in the drawing room, standing at the window through which he could see a full moon hanging low in the sky. On Sam his shirt reached down to the backs of her thighs. Her legs were long and slim underneath. She looked incredibly fragile in the voluminous white material.

'Sam...'

CHAPTER NINE

SAM'S SHOULDERS TENSED. Rafaele padded silently towards her on bare feet and she turned around, as if afraid he'd come too close. He saw a tumbler in her hand with a dark golden liquid.

She smiled and it was tight, lifted the glass towards him. 'Chin-chin.' And then she took a deep gulp, draining the glass.

He saw her cheeks flush but she made no sound. The evidence of tears was gone but her eyes looked huge, bruised.

'Sam…' He spoke through a sudden constriction in his throat. 'I'm sorry. I didn't mean to hurt you…'

'You didn't hurt me, Rafaele, I enjoyed it. You've obviously developed a kinkier side since I knew you… Was it any mistress in particular? Or is it just a sign of the times—routine sex is too boring?'

Rafaele gritted his jaw. He knew that Sam had been with him all the way because he'd felt the excitement in her body pushing him on…her distress had come afterwards…

'I've never done that with another woman,' he admitted reluctantly. He'd never felt the need to.

Sam emitted a curt laugh and raised a dark brow. 'So it's just me? I should feel flattered that I made you so angry you felt you had to restrain me…?'

Rafaele frowned, losing the thread. 'Angry?' Had it been that obvious? His fit of jealousy and vulnerability?

But Sam was continuing. 'I know you're angry about Milo, Rafaele, but you can't take it out on me like this.'

Half without thinking, Rafaele said, 'But I'm not angry about Milo.'

He realised in that moment that he truly didn't feel angry about that—not any more. It had faded and been replaced by a much darker anger...stemming from this woman's unique ability to make him lose his self-control and lose sight of what was important to him. Anger that he felt so vulnerable around her.

But Sam seemed not to have heard him. She came closer to put the empty glass down and Rafaele could see the tantalising curve of her breast through the haphazardly tied shirt. Instantly his lower body was on fire, reacting. He had a momentary revelation: *he was never going to get enough of this woman, not even in a lifetime. It would never burn out between them, only grow brighter.*

Rafaele was stunned, his head expanding with the terrifying knowledge that he would never be free of this insatiable need. He was barely aware of Sam walking out of the room. His brain was working overtime, trying to take in the knowledge that had come to him earlier, before he'd really been ready to deal with it, that he couldn't let her go. And now it was the most obvious thing in the world.

Sam gripped the bannister as she went up the stairs. Rafaele might have just said that he wasn't angry about Milo... but he *was* still angry with her. It was as clear as day. Maybe it was because he wanted her and resented himself for it?

Any control she'd clawed back before Rafaele had appeared and during that brief conversation had drained away again, leaving her feeling shaky. Somehow she got to her room, closed the door behind her and sagged against it. Tears pricked her eyes. Again. More tears for the man downstairs whom she would probably never be able to read.

Sam was too drained to deal with buttons. Her body was made weak from pleasure and sensation. She ripped Rafaele's shirt, making buttons pop and fall silently to the ground, and crawled into bed. In the morning she would shower and wash the scent of sex off her skin, but right now—treacherously—she didn't want to. In spite of what had happened.

'Rafaele said that we'll be leaving in an hour for Rome.'

Sam looked up with a studied air of nonchalance at Bridie, who had just come into the dining room. 'Oh?'

Bridie had Milo by the hand and he ran over to Sam, who picked him up and hugged him close, revelling in his sturdy body and sweet baby scent.

Bridie helped herself to some coffee and asked, 'How was the function last night?'

When Sam had woken that morning and come downstairs Bridie, Milo and Umberto had evidently already eaten, because the detritus of breakfast had been at the table but they had not. To her intense relief it appeared as if Rafaele had eaten also, as his place at the head of the table had already been used.

'It was…very swish,' Sam replied, knowing Bridie would love to hear about all the gowns and luxury. She took the cowardly way out and detailed to Bridie all of those things, while trying to ignore the disturbing memories threatening to spill into her mind at any given moment.

It took less than an hour to get from Milan to Rome and they arrived by lunchtime. Rafaele had arranged for one of his assistants to meet them at the airport with a car, and Bridie was whisked off in it to the Vatican, for the private tour Rafaele had arranged for her—much to her delight.

Another car was waiting for them, and Sam saw that Rafaele was going to drive them himself as he deftly secured Milo into the child's car seat installed in the back. It made Sam think once again of how seamlessly Rafaele had incorporated Milo into his life and her heart ached to think of what might have happened if she had told Rafaele from the start about her pregnancy.

Sam got into the car and her heart thudded heavily when Rafaele settled his powerful body behind the wheel. So far this morning she'd managed to avoid saying anything more than yes or no.

He glanced at her now and she had to acknowledge him. She turned and his gaze on her was intent. Her face grew hot as lurid images from the previous night came back.

'Okay?' he asked, disconcerting her because there was a quality to his voice she hadn't heard before. It sounded intimate. Concerned.

Sam was sure she'd imagined it so nodded quickly and looked back at Milo, who smiled, showing his small teeth. He was clutching a floppy teddy bear that Umberto had gifted him on their departure. Sam had been surprised to see what had looked suspiciously like tears in the old man's eyes as they'd left, and also a lingering glance or two at Bridie, who had looked a bit more flustered than she usually did.

As Rafaele negotiated their way out of the private airfield Sam said, 'Your father...was not what I expected.'

Rafaele's mouth tightened, but he said, 'No...I was surprised at how he welcomed Milo so instantaneously.'

'It was nice,' Sam admitted. 'After all, he's his only living grandparent now. My father was only alive to see Milo as a baby, so they didn't really connect and Milo won't remember him. Bridie is like a granny to Milo, but it's different when it's blood...'

Rafaele looked at her, his face inscrutable. 'Yes,' he agreed. 'It is.'

For the first time Sam didn't feel that Rafaele was getting in a dig. He was sounding almost as if he was realising the same thing himself.

'We should...' Sam blushed and stopped. 'That is, I should make sure to try and let Milo see Umberto as much as possible. Do you think he'd come to England?'

Rafaele's mouth quirked and he slid another glance to Sam. 'I think he could be persuaded—especially if Bridie is going to be there.'

Sam smiled, rare lightness filling her chest. 'You noticed it too, then?'

Rafaele looked at her and grew serious. He took her hand from her lap and held it. Immediately Sam's body reacted. She tried to pull away but he wouldn't let her. Memories of the bondage of last night came back. Arousing her. Disturbing her.

He said something crude in Italian and had to let Sam's hand go to navigate some hairy traffic. When it was clear again he said, 'Sam, we need to talk...'

'No,' Sam said fiercely, panicked at the thought of dissecting what had happened last night. She looked back at Milo, who was still happily playing with the toy, and then back to Rafaele. 'There's nothing to discuss.'

'Yes, there is, Sam,' he asserted, 'whether you like it or not. Tonight we'll go out for dinner.'

'Rafaele—'

But he cut her off with a stern look.

Sam shut her mouth and sat back, feeling mutinous. But deep down she knew Rafaele was right. They had to talk, but she would make sure that it would centre around the future and what would happen with Milo and also on the fact that she didn't want to sleep with him again. *Liar*, a voice mocked her. But she quashed it. Last night had almost broken her. She'd nearly revealed just how much Rafaele made her feel. And if they slept together again... she wouldn't be able to keep it in.

'I'll drop you and Milo off at the apartment and show you around, and then I'm afraid I have to go into the office for a couple of hours.'

'Okay,' Sam said, too quickly, seizing on the fact that she'd have a few hours' respite from Rafaele's disturbing presence. Maybe then these memories would abate and give her some peace.

Rafaele's Rome apartment was situated in a beautiful crumbling building just streets away from the famous Piazza Barberini, right in the heart of Rome's bustling centre. A smiling housekeeper met them and conversed easily in English for Sam's benefit. Rafaele showed Sam to her room, which was stunning, with parquet floors and delicate Rococo furnishings. There was another door which Milo was already reaching up to try and open, but the handle was too high.

He turned around, comically frustrated, and Rafaele scooped him up. 'First you have to grow a little more, *piccolino*.'

Rafaele opened the door and walked through, leaving Sam to follow them. It was a room for Milo, and once again Rafaele had obviously given instructions for it to be decked out for a three-year-old. It was a kiddie's paradise, and Milo was already jumping out of Rafaele's arms to explore all the treasures.

Rafaele looked at Sam, as if expecting another diatribe, but she could only smile ruefully and shrug her shoulders as if to say, *What can I do?*

He came closer then, blocking out Milo behind him, and cupped her jaw with a hand, his thumb rubbing her lower lip, tugging at it. Instantly Sam craved his mouth there, kissing her hard, pressing his body against hers.

Heat flooded her and she had to pull away with an effort. She shook her head, warning him off.

He said silkily, 'Tonight, Sam. We'll talk then.' He turned back to Milo. '*Ciao, piccolino*. I have to go to work now.'

Milo stopped what he was doing and for the first time since Rafaele had entered their lives, ran to him and gave him a kiss when Rafaele bent down to hug him.

'Bye, Daddy.'

Milo's easy and rapid acceptance of this whole situation made Sam's chest ache, and that emotion threatened to bubble over. She'd never in a million years envisaged that it could be this easy…or this cataclysmic.

Rafaele left and a long, shuddering breath emerged from her mouth. In truth, she'd not known what to expect if she'd ever plucked up the courage to tell Rafaele about Milo, but it had ranged from complete uninterest to his storming into their lives to take over, demand to take control.

It had definitely veered towards the latter end of the scale, but also *not*. For one thing she hadn't expected Rafaele still to want her. Or to admit that he had thought about her—that he'd never *stopped* wanting her.

Questions made her head hurt… So why had he let her go, then? If he'd wanted her…? She knew instinctively that she'd got too close. Was that why he'd pushed her away?

'Mummy, play with me!' came the imperious demand that sounded suspiciously like someone else.

Sam looked at her son and smiled. She got down on the floor beside him and devoted herself to the fantastical world of a bright, inquisitive three-year-old and welcomed the distraction.

That evening Bridie was still brimming over after her trip to St Peter's and the Vatican. 'I was the only one looking at the Sistine Chapel—the only one! And I think I saw the Pope walking in a private garden, but I couldn't be sure… A lovely priest said Mass in Latin. Oh, Sam, it was gorgeous.'

Sam smiled indulgently as she went to pick up her bag. Rafaele had called to say he was sending a car to pick her up and he'd meet her directly at the restaurant.

Suddenly Bridie broke off from her raptures and said in a shocked voice, 'You're not going out like *that?*'

Sam looked down at her outfit of jeans and a plaid shirt. Trainers. Suddenly she felt gauche. Of course Rafaele would have probably booked somewhere extremely fancy and expensive. She should have realised.

Bridie was bustling off. 'I know you packed that black dress, Sam. You have to change.'

Sam followed Bridie, knowing that she couldn't leave without changing now. Bridie seemed determined to throw her and Rafaele together, clearly believing that a fairytale ending was in the making.

When Sam walked into the bedroom Bridie was shaking out the plain black dress that Sam had packed just in case.

'Now, put this on and do your make-up. I'll let you know when the car gets here.'

Milo came barrelling down the hallway. Bridie caught him and said, 'Right, dinnertime for you, young man, and then an early night. We have to go home tomorrow so you need to be fresh.'

Sam quickly changed clothes and grimaced at her reflection, finally putting on some foundation to take away the pallor of her cheeks and then some mascara.

Home tomorrow. No wonder Rafaele wanted to talk now. He would have strong ideas about how they would proceed from here, she didn't doubt it, and she felt a shiver of trepidation that he would want to change their routine utterly.

This was all an exciting holiday to Milo now, but it couldn't continue like this. He needed routine and stability, and his life—*their* lives—were in England.

Sam heard Bridie call out, 'Sam, the car is here!'

Taking a deep breath and slipping on the one pair of low-heeled shoes she'd brought, Sam went to meet her fate.

The restaurant was nothing like Sam had expected. The car had taken her across the river to the very hip and bustling Trastevere area and the building looked small and rustic, with tables outside despite the cool early February air. Golden light spilled onto the pavement and the smells coming out of the door were mouth-watering.

Sam went in and immediately her eye was drawn to the tall man who'd stood up. Her heart kicked betrayingly, as if she hadn't seen him just hours ago. She felt ridiculously shy all of a sudden too—which was crazy, considering what had taken place in Rafaele's bedroom last night.

By the time a solicitous waiter had taken her coat and she'd made her way through the small tables to Rafaele her face was burning.

He held a chair out for her and Sam felt self-conscious in her dress, hoping that Rafaele wouldn't think she'd gone to any extra-special effort.

In a bid to deflect his attention she said quickly, 'Bridie thought I should dress up a bit...' She looked around the restaurant. 'But I don't think I needed to. I thought you might choose somewhere more upmarket.'

'Disappointed?' Rafaele's voice sounded tight.

Sam looked at him quickly and felt her hair slide over her shoulder. 'Oh, no! I love it. It's just...I never expected you to like a place like this.'

Something relaxed in Rafaele's face and seeing the faint stubbling on his jaw made Sam feel hot for a second as she imagined the abrasive rub of it between her legs. She pressed them together tightly under the table, disgusted with herself.

'This is my favourite restaurant. They specialise in cuisine from the north and they're world renowned. But they've remained humble and haven't sold out...'

Just then a man with a huge barrel chest came over and greeted Rafaele effusively, before taking Sam's hand in his and lifting it to his mouth to kiss. She couldn't help smiling, even though she couldn't understand a word he was saying. She caught *'bellissima'* and blushed, which only made him gush some more.

Eventually he left, and Rafaele indicated after him with his head. 'That's Francisco—the manager... I've known him since my student days when I used to work here.'

Sam's eyes widened as she recalled Rafaele telling her about his working three jobs to get through college. 'You worked *here?*'

He nodded and broke some bread to dip into oil and balsamic vinegar. Sam took some bread too, a little blindsided at imagining a younger, driven Rafaele working here, with women drooling over him in his waiter's uniform of white shirt and black trousers.

She admitted wryly, 'That's a little hard to believe.'

Rafaele arched a brow, mock affronted. 'You don't think I'm capable of taking orders and clearing tables?'

Sam felt a flutter near her heart and looked away, embarrassed. This was so reminiscent of before, when Rafaele had been intent on wooing her.

She looked at him. 'You never...talked about this stuff before...'

Immediately his expression closed in and Sam wanted to reach out and touch him. Her hands curled to fists.

'Before was different...'

Sam's mouth twisted and old bitterness rose up. 'I know. You didn't want to be seen in public with me.'

Rafaele looked at her, his jaw tense. 'It wasn't like that—'

A waiter interrupted them then and asked for their orders.

Another couple entered the restaurant, hand in hand, and Sam felt a bittersweet yearning rise up within her. Damn Bridie for making her wish for something that would never exist. She'd been foolish enough to hope for it in the past. She wouldn't make the same mistake again.

When the waiter had left with their menus Sam sat back and looked at Rafaele. 'What *was* it like, then?'

For a second he looked so like Milo did when he was reluctant to do something that he took her breath away and she felt tenderness fill her.

'I didn't want to share you…that's the truth. I wanted to lock you away in my *palazzo*. It used to drive me crazy that you worked all day surrounded by men who would look at you and want you.'

Sam had to bite back a strangled laugh and ignore a very treacherous swooping of her belly to hear the evident jealousy in Rafaele's voice. 'No, they didn't!'

'They did,' Rafaele growled. 'You didn't notice, though—oblivious to your effect on them. I'd never met another woman like you, and certainly not one who could match any man around her for knowledge and expertise. One who managed to turn me on more than I'd thought was possible.'

The swooping sensation intensified and Sam felt increasingly out of her depth—as if the rules had changed and she wasn't sure where she stood any more. Their starter arrived and Sam concentrated on it as if it was the most interesting thing in the world. She was in uncharted waters with Rafaele, and not sure where this conversation was headed.

After the starter was cleared Rafaele sat back and took his wineglass in his hand. Sam sensed the interest coming from a couple of women who had come in a few minutes before and, like last night, felt the rush of jealousy in her blood.

Slowly he said, 'Sam…last night at the function…'

She tensed. She really didn't want to talk about it. That acrid jealousy was all too recent and current.

'I didn't mean what I said…about you becoming my mistress. I know you're not that kind of woman.'

Sam emitted a small laugh and felt a dart of hurt. 'You can say that again.'

He leant forward and put his wine down, '*Dio*, Sam, stop putting words in my mouth. I meant that you're worth more than any other woman who was there last night.'

She looked at him and her heart jumped into her throat. His eyes were intense on hers.

With imperfect timing the waiter appeared again with their food, and Sam looked at the fish she'd evidently ordered but couldn't remember selecting now. *You're worth more than any other woman who was there.*

She looked at Rafaele and whispered, 'What do you mean?'

'Eat…then we'll talk.'

Sam felt as if she could no more eat than walk over hot coals, but she forced some of the succulent food down her throat and wished she could enjoy it more. She was sure it was delicious.

When the dishes were cleared away Sam felt very on edge. Rafaele regarded her steadily and her nerves felt as if they were being stretched taut.

Finally he clarified, 'I should have thought more about it before taking you with me last night.'

He obviously saw something Sam was unaware of on her expressive face because he put up a hand and went on, '*Not* because I don't want to be seen with you in public but because you were right. We need to know what…we are.'

Sam frowned. 'What *we* are?'

Rafaele reached out and took her hand. Sam looked at her much smaller pale hand in his dark one and her insides liquefied.

'Sam…I think we should get married.'

Sam raised her eyes to his. Shocked. 'What did you just say?'

'I said, I think we should get married.'

Sam was barely aware of Rafaele letting her hand go so that the waiter could put down coffee and dessert in front of them. She was stunned. Blindsided.

She shook her head, as if that might rearrange her brain cells into some order so that she could understand what Rafaele had just said. She had to be sure. 'Did you just say that you think we should get married?'

He nodded, looking at her carefully, as if she was made of something explosive and volatile.

'I… Why on earth would you say that?'

Now that the words were sinking in, a reaction was moving up through Sam's body, making her skin prickle. Four years ago, in the time between finding out she was pregnant and seeing Rafaele again, she'd daydreamed of such a moment—except in her dream Rafaele had been on one knee before her, not sitting across a table looking as if he'd just commented on the weather.

The most galling thing of all was that she had grown up vowing never to marry, terrified of the way her father had effectively gone to pieces after losing her mother. But she'd forgotten all about that when she'd met Rafaele, weaving dreams and fantasies around him that had had no place in reality.

'Why?' she repeated again, stronger now. Almost angry. Definitely angry, in fact. 'Do you think that I'm some kind of charity case and I'll be only too delighted to say yes because you can take care of me and Milo?'

She couldn't stop now.

'Decorating a few bedrooms doesn't a father and husband make, Rafaele. So I don't know where you're getting this notion from. It's just another way to control us, isn't it?'

His eyes flashed at her outburst. 'No, Sam. Think about it. Why *shouldn't* we get married? I've been thinking about buying a home in London. We could live there. Bridie could come too… We could look for a good school for Milo. A lot of my work for the foreseeable future will be in England, and my commutes to Europe shouldn't take me away too much…'

He had it all figured out. Square Sam and Milo away in a convenient box and tick them off the list. On the one hand the image he presented tugged at a very deep and secret part of her—a fantasy she'd once had. She only had to think of last night and how close she'd come to baring herself utterly. She didn't doubt that he hadn't factored in the reality that she would want to be a wife for *real*.

Terrified at the strength of emotion she was feeling, Sam stood up and walked quickly out of the restaurant.

Rafaele watched Sam leave. Not the first time he'd provoked her into walking away from him. She'd looked horrified. Not the reaction a man wanted when he proposed. He grimaced and acknowledged that he hadn't exactly *proposed*. But since when had Sam wanted hearts and flowers? *Did* she want that? What he was suggesting was eminently practical. Logical. Unfortunately Sam plus any attempt on his part to apply logic always ended up in disaster.

Rafaele stood up. His friend Francisco was waving him

out of the restaurant to go after his lover. The old romantic. Rafaele just smiled tightly.

When he emerged into the street it was quiet. This time of year it was mainly locals. But in a few months the place would be warm and sultry and heaving. Sam was stalking away, and when he called her she only seemed to speed up.

Cursing softly, Rafaele followed her and caught up. 'Your coat and bag, Sam.'

She stopped and turned around, arms crossed mutinously across her breasts. She reached out and grabbed for them, pulling the coat on, hitching her bag over her shoulder.

She looked at him and her eyes were huge in the gloom. 'I don't know why you would even suggest such a thing.'

Rafaele curbed his irritation. Did she really have to sound so repulsed at the idea?

He dug his hands into his pockets to stop himself from reaching for her—he didn't know if he wanted to shake her right now or kiss her. Actually, that was a lie. He'd always want to kiss her, no matter what. That thought sent shards of panic into his bloodstream.

'I happen to think it's a very good idea. There are far more reasons why you should consider this than not. We have a history. We get on well. We have a child together... And there's the physical chemistry. You can't deny that, *cara*.'

'The chemistry will burn out.'

That was said with a desperately hopeful edge that resonated within Rafaele.

He had to make her see what he'd realised last night— that marriage was the solution... *To this tangled mess of emotions you don't want to deal with*, his conscience sneered. He ignored his conscience. Surely by marrying her he would no longer experience this wildness around her? This need to devour, consume? This loss of all reason? It would negate this completely alien need to possess her... It would publicly brand her as *his*, and maybe then he'd feel some equanimity again.

'We have a child. Is that not enough of a reason? I want Milo to have my name. He is heir to a vast industry and fortune.'

'No, Rafaele,' she said in a small voice. 'It's not enough. I might have thought it would be at one time, but not any more. I want more for me and Milo. He deserves to have two parents who love each other.'

Rafaele responded with a sneering edge to his voice. 'You and I both know that fairytale doesn't exist. What we have is better than that, Sam. We can depend on each other. We respect each other.'

She lifted her chin. 'How do I know you've forgiven me for keeping Milo from you? That you won't use it in the future? That it won't be a reason for resentment when you think about it?'

Rafaele slashed a hand through the air. 'Sam, it's not about that any more. I appreciate that you had your reasons, and I admit that I didn't give you any indication to believe that I would welcome a child into my life. We can't change the past, but we can make sure we go into the future right.'

For a long moment Sam just looked at him, and then she said, 'I won't marry you. Not just to make things nice and tidy. To make things easier for you. I want more...' She shrugged her shoulder in a gesture of apology.

Rafaele felt the red mist of rage rising when he thought of some other man moving into that cosy house in the quiet suburbs, waking up next to Sam, having lazy early-morning sex...

'Do you really think someone like your ex-lover can give you a happy-ever-after? When it doesn't even exist?'

Sam started to back away. 'I'm not talking about this

any more, Rafaele. I don't want to marry you. It's plain and simple.'

Rafaele felt his chest tighten and an awful cold feeling seeped into his veins. 'Well, then…' He almost didn't recognise his own voice. 'It would appear that you're giving me no option but to take the legal route to establish custody of my son.'

Sam stopped and crossed her arms. She whispered, 'It doesn't have to come to that, Rafaele. We can come to an arrangement.'

Rafaele felt as hard inside as granite. 'I want my son, Sam, and I want him to have my name.'

'I can't fight you in a court, Rafaele. I don't have those kinds of resources.'

Rafaele pushed down his conscience. He was full of darkness—a darkness that had clung to him all his life. He was standing in front of this woman and for one second, when she'd said she didn't want to marry him, he'd been tempted to go down on one knee to convince her. It had been fleeting, but there. And it had been like a slap in the face. Had he learnt *nothing?*

Sam would not reduce him to that. No woman would. All that mattered was his son. He would not walk away from him and leave him to fend for himself as his own father had done with him.

Rafaele's voice was as cold as he felt inside. 'You're the one who started this, Samantha.'

Sam's arms tightened and Rafaele could see her knuckles turn white against the skin of her fingers.

'You were stringing us along all this time, lulling me into a false sense of security. We're leaving here tomorrow to go home. Do your worst—see if I care.'

Rafaele felt impervious to anything in that moment. He was numb. He saw Sam spot a taxi driving slowly alongside them. A very rare Rome taxi. She hailed it and jumped in. When she passed him, her profile was stony through the window. Rafaele felt something trying to break through, to pierce this numbness that had settled over him, but he pushed it down ruthlessly and tried to ignore the feeling that something very precious had just shattered into pieces.

CHAPTER TEN

THE FOLLOWING DAY Rafaele saw them off at the airport. They had been booked onto a scheduled flight home, albeit first class.

Milo was confused and kept saying, 'Why is Daddy not coming too, Mummy?'

Sam repeated for the umpteenth time, praying that she wouldn't start crying, 'Because he has to work. We'll see him again soon.' *Probably in a courtroom!* she thought half hysterically.

She'd gone straight to her bedroom last night when she'd got in, and locked the door. Not that Rafaele would be banging it down to get in. Rafaele's cold proposal had shown her that nothing had changed. He wanted Milo and he merely saw her as a way to get to him.

Once she'd said no to him he'd revealed his true colours. She felt sick to think that perhaps even the physical side of things had been a monumental act for him. Going through the motions so that he could use that as one more thing to bind them together.

Sam caught a worried glance from Bridie and forced a smile. She couldn't take Bridie's maternal inquisitiveness now. Better that she think nothing was wrong and everything was as per schedule—Rafaele had told them on the flight over that he would be staying on in Rome for work. Sam's head hurt when she thought of what would happen in the immediate future, with regard to Rafaele staying in her house.

Rafaele had Milo in his arms and was saying in a low, husky voice that managed to pluck at Sam's weak and treacherous heartstrings, '*Ciao, piccolino*. I'll see you very soon.'

Milo threw his small chubby arms around Rafaele's neck and Rafaele's eyes met Sam's over Milo's shoulder. His green gaze was as cold as ice and it flayed Sam. Their flight was called and she put her hands out for Milo. After a long moment he handed him over.

Then Bridie was saying goodbye to Rafaele, and gushing again over her trip to the Vatican, and Sam was walking away towards the gate, feeling as if her heart was being ripped to pieces.

'I thought I might stay on here for a while, if you don't mind?'

Rafaele curbed the urge to snarl at his father. It had been a week since Sam and Milo had returned home and an aching chasm of emptiness seemed to have taken up residence in his chest.

'Of course,' he said curtly. 'This is your home as much as mine.'

The old man smiled wryly. 'If it hadn't been for you it would have remained in ruins, owned by the bank.'

Rafaele said gruffly, 'That's not important. Everything is different now.'

'Yes,' Umberto said. 'Milo is…a gift. And Sam is a good woman. She is a good woman for *you*, Rafaele. Real. Honest.'

Rafaele emitted a curt laugh and said, 'Don't speak of what you don't know, Papa. She kept my son from me for nearly four years.'

Rafaele stood up from the dining table then and paced

to the window. He'd only come back to Milan to check on the factory and now he felt rootless. He wanted to go back to England to see Milo but was reluctant because... *Sam*. She brought up so many things for him.

'She must have had good reason to do so.'

Yes, she did. You gave her every reason to believe you couldn't wait to see the back of her.

Rafaele's conscience slapped him. It slapped him even harder when he thought of the resolve that had sat so heavily in his belly when he'd decided that he would have to let her go. Of her face when he'd confirmed that he didn't want to see her any more. It was the same feeling he'd had in his chest the other night in the street.

His jaw was tight as he answered his father. 'Once again, it's none of your business.'

He heard his father's chair move behind him but stayed looking out the window, feeling rigid. Feeling that old, old anger rise up even now.

'I'm sorry, Rafaele...'

Rafaele tensed all over and turned around slowly. 'Sorry for what?'

Umberto was looking at him, his dark gaze sad. 'For everything. For being so stupid as to lose control of myself, for gambling away our fortune, for losing the business. For begging your mother not to leave in front of you... I know seeing that must have had an effect...'

Rafaele smiled and it was grim, mirthless. It hid the awful tightening in his chest, which made him feel as if he couldn't draw enough breath in. 'Why did you do it? Why didn't you just let her go? Why did you have to beg like that?'

His father shrugged one shoulder. 'Because I thought I loved her. But I didn't really love her. I just didn't know it then. I wanted her because she was beautiful and emotionally aloof. By then I'd lost it all. She was the one thing left and I felt that if she went too then I'd become vapour. Nothing.'

Rafaele recalled his words as if it was yesterday. *'How can you leave me? If you leave I'm nothing. I have nothing.'*

'I wanted you, you know,' he said now in a low voice. 'I wanted to take you back when I got a job and was making a modest living. But your mother wouldn't let me near you. I was only allowed to see you on those visits to Athens.'

Rafaele remembered those painfully tense and stilted meetings. His mother had been vitriolic in her disgust at the man who had once had a fortune and had lost it, compounding Rafaele's sense of his father as a failure and compounding his own ambition to succeed at all costs.

'Why are you telling me this now?' Rafaele demanded, suddenly angry that his father was bringing this up.

'Because I can see the fear in you, Rafaele. I know that it's driven you to become successful, to build Falcone Industries from the ground up again. But you don't have to be afraid. You're not like me. You're far stronger than I ever was. And you won't do to Milo what I did to you. He will never see you weak and humiliated.'

Rafaele felt dizzy now, because he knew that he did have the capacity to repeat exactly what his father had done. He'd almost done it the other evening, albeit not in front of his son. *Thank God.*

Umberto wasn't finished, though. 'Don't let fear ruin your chance of happiness, Rafaele. I lived with bitterness for a long time and it makes a cold bedfellow. You have proved yourself. You will never be destitute... Don't be afraid to want more.'

Rafaele saw his father then, slightly hunched, his face lined with a sadness he'd never truly appreciated before.

'I'm not afraid,' he said, half defiantly. But he knew it was a lie. He realised he was terrified.

* * *

'Come on, you, it's time for bed.'

'No. Don't want to go to bed.'

Sam sighed. Milo had been acting up ever since they'd got home, and every single day he asked for Rafaele.

'Where's my daddy? When is he coming back in the car? Why can't we have a car? Where is Grandpapa?'

Sam shared a look with Bridie, who was helping to clear up Milo's things, just as the doorbell rang. They looked at each other and immediately Milo ran for the door, shrieking, *'Daddy, Daddy!'*

Sam went after him, her heart twisting. 'Milo, it won't be him…'

She pulled him back from the door and opened it, fully expecting to see just a neighbour or a door-to-door religious tout. But it wasn't either of those.

'Daddy!' Milo's small clear voice declared exactly who it was.

He was jumping up and down, endearingly still too shy to throw himself at the man who had only so recently come into his life. But when Rafaele bent down and opened his arms Milo ran straight into them and Sam's heart squeezed so tight it hurt. She heard Bridie behind her exclaim and usher Rafaele in.

Sam could see that he was holding something in his hand, and when he put Milo down he handed it to him. It was a mechanical car.

Milo seized it with inelegant haste. 'Wow!'

Sam chided him automatically through a fog of shock. 'Milo, what do you say?'

'Thank you!'

Sam was so tense she could crack. She avoided looking at Rafaele, dreading seeing that ice-cold green again.

Bridie was taking Milo by the hand and saying, 'Come

on, you promised you'd help me to find my spectacles in my flat earlier—'

Milo started protesting, and Sam felt like doing the same, but Bridie had lifted Milo up and was quelling his protests by promising him a DVD. And then they were gone before Sam could get a word out, and she was alone in the hall with Rafaele.

She still hadn't really looked him in the eye as he reached out and pushed the front door closed. Finally she looked at him and her eyes widened. He looked terrible. Well, as terrible as a gorgeous Italian alpha male *could* look—which was not terrible at all. But Rafaele looked tired, drawn, pale. Older. Somehow diminished.

Immediately Sam was concerned and said, 'What is it? Your father?'

Rafaele shook his head. 'No, it's not my father. He is fine. Asking after you all.'

'Well…what is it, then? You look…' *As bad as I feel.*

Rafaele smiled, but it was tight, and then it faded again and he'd never looked more serious.

Sam crossed her arms and started babbling out of nervousness. 'Are you here ahead of your team of lawyers? Because if you are you could have saved yourself the bother, Rafaele…'

He shook his head and looked pained. For an awful moment Sam thought there might be something wrong with *him* and she felt weak.

'No. I should never have said that to you. I'm sorry. Of course there won't be a team of lawyers…'

Sam wanted to sit down. Relief swept through her like a cleansing balm. 'But why did you say it then?'

Rafaele gave out a curt laugh. 'Because you threaten me on so many levels and I thought I could control it… control *you*.'

His words sank in. *You threaten me.* And then, as if

feeling constricted, Rafaele took off his battered leather jacket and draped it over the bottom of the stairs. He was wearing a light sweater and worn jeans and Sam could feel her blood heating. Already.

Suddenly Rafaele asked, 'Do you mind if I have a drink?'

Sam shook her head and stood back. He walked into the front room and, bemused, she uncrossed her arms and followed him. Rafaele was at the sideboard, pouring himself a shot of her father's whisky. He looked around and held up a glass in a question but she shook her head. She stood tensely inside the door. Half ready to flee.

Her voice felt rusty, unused. 'Rafaele, why are you here?'

He turned around to face her. 'Because we need to talk. Properly talk.'

Sam tensed even more, and as if sensing she was about to say something Rafaele put up a hand to quell her.

'I told you that I was about Milo's age when my mother left my father and took me with her?' he began.

Sam nodded carefully.

Rafaele's mouth became a thin line. 'Unfortunately that day I was subjected to a vision of my father prostrating himself at my mother's feet...begging her not to go. Crying, snivelling. I saw a broken man that day...and I believed for a long time—erroneously—that it had been my mother's fault, that she had done it to him. When, of course, it was much more complicated than that... It didn't help that he blamed her for most of his life, refusing to acknowledge his own part in his downfall.'

Sam took a breath. 'Your father told me a bit...'

Even now her heart ached, because she thought of Milo's pain and distress if he were to witness something like that. How would a scene like that affect a vulnerable, impressionable three-year-old?

But Rafaele didn't seem to hear her. He was looking at the liquid in the glass, swirling it gently. 'And then my stepfather... He was another piece of work. I'd gone from the example of a broken man who had lost everything to living with a man who *had* everything. What they had in common was my mother. They were both obsessed with her, wanted her above all. And she...?' Rafaele smiled grimly. 'She was aloof with them both, but she chose my stepfather over my father because he could provide her with the status and security she'd come to enjoy...'

Rafaele looked at her and his smile became bleak.

'For a long time I never wanted to think about why she did those things...but since I've discovered my older brother and learned she abandoned him I have to realise that perhaps for her, security had become the thing she needed most—above warmth and emotion. Above anything. God knows what happened with her first husband to make her do such a drastic thing as to leave her son, leave his father...'

His mouth twisted.

'From an early age I believed instinctively that women could ruin you *even* if you had money and success. I believed that to succeed *I* had to hold women at the same distance my mother had always done with the men around her. I wouldn't ever be weak like my father or stepfather, and never lose control.'

Rafaele smiled again but it was impossibly bleak.

'And then you came along and slid so deeply under my skin that I didn't realise I'd lost all that precious control until it was too late.'

Sam's heart was beating like a drum now. She felt light-headed. 'I don't... What are you saying, Rafaele?'

He looked at her and his gaze seemed to bore into her. 'I still want us to get married, Sam...'

Something cold settled into her belly. He wasn't going

to let this go. He'd basically just told her how he viewed the women in his life and that only the fact that she'd proved herself to be completely different had merited her this place in his life. She backed away to the door and saw him put down his glass and frown...

'Sam?'

Sam walked out through the door and went to the front door and opened it. Rafaele appeared in the hallway, still frowning.

She shook her head. 'Rafaele, I'm really sorry that you had to see so much at a young age, and that it skewed your views of women... And I can see how Milo is at an age where he must have pushed your buttons... But I can't marry you.'

She forced herself to keep looking at him even though she felt as if a knife was lacerating her insides. 'I want more, Rafaele... Despite what I told you about my views on marriage I've always secretly hoped I'd meet someone and fall in love. I thought I could protect myself too, but I can't...none of us can.'

Rafaele saw Sam backlit in her porch and even in such a domestic banal setting she'd never looked more beautiful. His heart splintered apart into pieces and he knew that he had no choice now but to step out and into the chasm of nothing—*and possibly everything.*

He walked into the middle of the hall and looked at Sam. And then very deliberately he got down on his knees in front of her. For a terrifying moment Rafaele felt the surge of the past threatening to rise up and strangle him, heard voices about to hound him, tell him he was no better than his father... But it didn't happen. What he did feel was a heady feeling of *peace* for the first time in a long time.

Sam was looking at him, horrified. She quickly shut the

door again and leant against it. 'Rafaele, get up... What are you doing?'

Somehow Rafaele found the ability to speak. 'This has been my nightmare scenario for so long, Sam, and I'm tired of it. The truth is that I want more too. I want it all. And I am willing to beg for it—just like my father. Except I know that this is different. I'm not him.'

Sam shook her head and Rafaele could see her eyes grow suspiciously bright.

Her voice sounded thick. 'You don't have to do this just to prove a point. Get *up*, Rafaele...'

He shook his head. The view from down here wasn't bad at all, Rafaele realised. Prostrating himself in front of the woman he loved was something he'd do over and over again if he had to.

Almost gently now, he said, 'Sam...don't you realise it yet?'

She shook her head faintly. 'Realise what?'

Rafaele took a deep breath. 'That I am so madly and deeply and crazily in love with you that I've made a complete mess of everything...'

He looked down for a moment and then back up, steeling himself.

'I know you don't feel the same way...how could you when I've treated you so badly in the past? But... I truly hope that we might have enough to work with...and in time you might feel something. We have Milo...'

Sam just looked at him for a long moment, and then she whispered, 'Did you just say you love me?'

Rafaele nodded, sensing her shock, feeling icicles of pain start to settle around his heart despite his brave words. Humiliation started to make his skin prickle. The demons weren't so far away after all.

Sam closed her eyes and he heard her long, shuddering breath. When she opened them again they overflowed with tears.

'Sam…' he said hoarsely, and went to stand up.

But before he could move she'd launched herself at him and they landed in a tangle of limbs on the floor. The breath was knocked out of Rafaele's chest for a second, and then he saw Sam's face above his own, felt her tears splash onto his cheeks. And he couldn't resist pulling her head down so that he could kiss her. Even in the midst of not knowing, he had to touch her.

The kiss was desperate and salty and wet, and then Sam drew back, breathing hard. She put her hands around his face and said again, 'You love me?'

She was lying on his body, they touched at every point, and Rafaele could feel himself stirring to life. He nodded. 'Yes. I love you, Sam. I want you in my life for ever…you and Milo. I want us to be a family. I can't live without you. When you left last week…I died inside.'

A sob escaped Sam's mouth and Rafaele felt her chest heaving against his.

Finally she managed to get out, 'I love you, Rafaele. I fell for you four years ago, and when you let me go I thought I'd die…but then there was Milo…and I thought I'd stopped loving you and started hating you. But I hadn't. I've always loved you and I will always love you.'

Rafaele sat up and Sam spread her legs around his hips so they faced each other. She sat in the cradle of his lap, where his erection was distractingly full, but he forced himself to look at her, sinking willingly into those grey depths and wondering how on earth he'd not let himself do this before now. It was the easiest thing.

His chest expanded as her words sank in and he felt a very fledgling burgeoning sense of trust take root within him and hold…

'I fell for you too…but it was so terrifying that I ran.

You got too close, Sam—closer than I'd ever let anyone get—and when I realised it I couldn't handle it. Like a coward I left you alone to deal with your trauma...'

Sam smoothed his jaw with a tender hand. She looked at him, her eyes wounded. 'I punished you...in the most heinous way. You were right. I was hurt and upset, heartbroken that you didn't want me... I kept Milo from you, and you didn't deserve that.'

Rafaele tucked some hair behind Sam's ear. He was very serious. 'I understand why you did it. You sensed my reluctance, Sam, my need to escape. But it wasn't from you, it was from myself... You never really left me. You haunted me.'

Sam's eyes flashed. 'Not enough to stop you going to bed with another woman almost immediately.'

Rafaele struggled to comprehend, and then he recalled her accusing him of being with another woman a week after he'd left. He shook his head and smiled wryly, knowing that she was going to demand every inch of him for the rest of his life and not wanting it any other way.

'Would it help you to know that, despite appearances to the contrary I didn't sleep with anyone for a year after you left?' He grimaced. 'I couldn't...perform.'

Sam's eyes widened with obvious feminine satisfaction. 'You were impotent?'

Rafaele scowled. 'I'm not impotent.'

Sam wriggled on his lap, feeling for herself just how potent he was. 'You're not impotent with me.'

Rafaele groaned softly, his hands touching her face, thumb pressing her lower lip. 'I could never be impotent with you. I just have to look at you and I'm turned on.'

Sounding serious, Sam said, 'Me too...'

'Sam...that night when I tied you up...'

A dark flush highlighted those cheekbones and something inside Sam melted anew at seeing him so unlike his usual confident, cocky self. He was avoiding her eye and she tipped his chin towards her.

'I liked it…' she whispered, blushing.

'But you cried afterwards…'

Her eyes softened. 'Because I had just realised how much I still loved you. I felt so vulnerable, and I thought you were still punishing me for Milo.'

Rafaele groaned. 'I *was* angry, but it was because you were under my skin again and I didn't want you there. You brought up too many feelings, made me feel out of control…so I needed to control *you*.'

A wicked glint came into Sam's eyes. 'We can call it quits if you let me tie you up next time.'

Sam felt Rafaele's body jerk underneath hers.

He quirked a brow at her. 'Bridie has Milo…'

Needing no further encouragement, Sam scrambled inelegantly off Rafaele's lap and stood up. She looked down at him and held out a hand. Rafaele felt his heart squeeze so much that it hurt. The symbolism of the moment was huge as he put his hand in Sam's to let her help him up, but just before he came up all the way, he stopped on one knee.

'Wait…there's one more thing.'

Rafaele's heart beat fast at the way Sam bit her lip. He gripped her hand like a lifeline and with his other hand pulled out the small but precious cargo from his pocket.

He held up the vintage diamond ring and looked at her. 'Samantha, will you marry me? Because I love you more than life itself—you and Milo.'

She looked at the ring and her eyes glittered again with the onset of fresh tears. 'It's beautiful…'

He could see the final struggle in her face, the fear of believing that this was *real*…but then she smiled and it bathed him in a warmth he'd never known before.

'Yes, I'll marry you, Rafaele.'

She held out her hand and it trembled.

With a none too steady hand himself, Rafaele pushed the sparkling ring onto her finger. And then, with his other hand still in her firm grip, she pulled him up out of the painful past and into a brighter future.

A month later...

Sam took a deep breath and started her walk down the aisle of the small church in the grounds of Rafaele's Milan *palazzo*. Umberto was giving her away and he wasn't even using his cane. He was walking taller and stronger almost every day...especially on the days when Bridie was around...

Milo walked ahead of them in a suit, throwing rose petals with chaotic random abandon. He'd look back every now and then with a huge smile and Sam would have to prompt him to keep going. The small church was filled with people, but Sam was oblivious. She saw only the tall figure of the man waiting for her at the top of the aisle. And then he turned around, as if unable to help himself, and he smiled. Sam smiled back.

Umberto handed her over with due deference and then Rafaele was claiming her, pulling her into him. The priest's words washed over and through Sam. She would never have said she was a religious person, but something in the ritual seemed to complete the process she and Rafaele had embarked on a month before, cleansing away any vague residual painful pieces of the past.

There was only now and the future, and the heavy weight of the wedding band on her finger, and Rafaele bending to kiss her with such a look of reverence on his face that she could have wept. In fact she did weep, and he wiped her tears away with his fingers.

Later, as they danced at their reception, which had been

set up in a marquee in the grounds of the *palazzo*, Rafaele said, 'Have I told you yet how beautiful you look?'

Sam smiled. 'About a hundred times, but I don't mind.'

And Sam *felt* beautiful, truly, for the first time in her life. Even though her dress was simple and her hair hadn't been styled by a professional and she'd done her own make-up. She felt confident, and sexy, and most importantly *loved*.

Milo appeared at their feet and Rafaele lifted him up and that was how they finished their wedding dance—in a circle of love, the three of them.

Over in a corner of the marquee stood Alexio Christakos, Rafaele's half-brother. He'd been best man, done his duty and given his speech, made everyone laugh. Made the women giggle and look at him covetously. Even now they surrounded him, waiting for their moment to strike, for the slightest gesture of encouragement.

Alexio grimaced. He was starting to feel claustrophobic. *Hell*. Who was he kidding? He'd been feeling claustrophobic on his brother's behalf ever since Rafaele had told him that he was getting married and had a *son!*

He shook his head again and grimaced when he saw Rafaele kiss his bride for the umpteenth time. Alexio looked at her. He guessed she was pretty enough, in a subtle and unassuming way, but he couldn't see how she made Rafaele turn almost feral whenever another man came close. Even Alexio had been sent none too subtle hands-off signals from the moment he'd met her.

Alexio wondered how it was possible that Rafaele couldn't see that she *must* be marrying him only for his security and wealth. Had he become so duped by good sex that he'd forgotten one of the most important lessons they'd learnt from their dear departed mother? That a woman's main aim in life was to feather her nest and seek the security of a rich man?

Alexio mentally saluted his brother and wished him well. He told himself he'd try not to say *I told you so* when it all fell apart. Mind you, he had to concede the kid was cute. *His nephew.* He'd actually had quite an entertaining time with him earlier, when he'd looked after him for a bit between the wedding and the reception. Still… He shuddered lightly. He had no intention of embarking on that path any time soon, if ever…

Alexio stopped focusing on his brother and his new wife and son for a minute and took in the crowd around him. From nearby, a gorgeous brunette caught his eye. She was tall and lissom, with curves in all the right places. She looked at him with sexy confidence and smiled the smile of a practised seductress.

Alexio felt his body stir, his blood move southwards. It wasn't the most compelling spark of attraction he'd ever felt…*but when was the last time that had happened…?* Alexio ignored that voice and smiled back. When he saw the light of triumph in her eyes at catching the attention of the most eligible bachelor in the room, Alexio forced down the feeling of emptiness inside him and moved towards her.

* * * * *

A sneaky peek at next month...

MODERN™

POWER, PASSION AND IRRESISTIBLE TEMPTATION

My wish list for next month's titles...

In stores from 21st February 2014:

- ☐ A Prize Beyond Jewels — Carole Mortimer
- ☐ Pretender to the Throne — Maisey Yates
- ☐ The Sheikh's Last Seduction — Jennie Lucas
- ☐ The Woman Sent to Tame Him — Victoria Parker

In stores from 7th March 2014:

- ☐ A Queen for the Taking? — Kate Hewitt
- ☐ An Exception to His Rule — Lindsay Armstrong
- ☐ Enthralled by Moretti — Cathy Williams
- ☐ What a Sicilian Husband Wants — Michelle Smart

Available at WHSmith, Tesco, Asda, Eason, Amazon and Apple

Just can't wait?

Visit us Online

You can buy our books online a month before they hit the shops! **www.millsandboon.co.uk**

0214/01

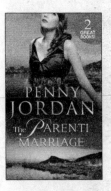

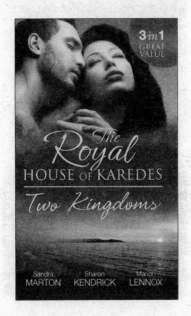

MEET THE
AUSTRALIAN ALPHAS!

Pick up the first title of this sizzling new *Australia* collection by the wonderful

Emma Darcy

**Available at
millsandboon.co.uk**

Join the Mills & Boon Book Club

Want to read more **Modern™** books?
We're offering you **2 more** absolutely **FREE!**

We'll also treat you to these fabulous extras:

- 🌹 **Exclusive offers and much more!**
- 🌹 **FREE home delivery**
- 🌹 **FREE books and gifts with our special rewards scheme**

Get your free books now!

**visit www.millsandboon.co.uk/bookclub
or call Customer Relations on 020 8288 2888**

The World of Mills & Boon®

There's a Mills & Boon® series that's perfect for you. We publish ten series and, with new titles every month, you never have to wait long for your favourite to come along.

By Request
Relive the romance with the best of the best
12 stories every month

Cherish™
Experience the ultimate rush of falling in love
12 new stories every month

Desire™
Passionate and dramatic love stories
6 new stories every month

nocturne™
An exhilarating underworld of dark desires
Up to 3 new stories every month

M&B/WORLD4a

Discover more romance at

www.millsandboon.co.uk

- ❤ WIN great prizes in our exclusive competitions
- ❤ BUY new titles before they hit the shops
- ❤ BROWSE new books and REVIEW your favourites
- ❤ SAVE on new books with the Mills & Boon® Bookclub™
- ❤ DISCOVER new authors

PLUS, to chat about your favourite reads, get the latest news and find special offers:

- ⓕ Find us on facebook.com/millsandboon
- 🐦 Follow us on twitter.com/millsandboonuk
- ❤ Sign up to our newsletter at millsandboon.co.uk